D1265169

ORAGENITALISM

Other works by G. Legman

LOVE & DEATH: A STUDY IN CENSORSHIP (1949)
THE HORN BOOK: STUDIES IN EROTIC FOLKLORE (1964)
THE GUILT OF THE TEMPLARS (1966)
THE FAKE REVOLT (1967)
RATIONALE OF THE DIRTY JOKE (1968)

Edited works:

NEUROTICA (1948–1951)
THE LIMERICK: 1700 EXAMPLES (Paris, 1953)
(*enlarged edition*, New York, 1969)
BURNS' MERRY MUSES OF CALEDONIA (1965)
THE BALLAD: UNEXPURGATED FOLKSONGS
(*in preparation*)
KRYPTÁDIA: THE JOURNAL OF EROTIC FOLKLORE

ORAGENITALISM

ORAL TECHNIQUES IN GENITAL EXCITATION

By G. LEGMAN

NEW YORK · THE JULIAN PRESS, INC
1969

© COPYRIGHT 1969 BY G. LEGMAN

Library of Congress Catalog Card Number 74-92325
Published by The Julian Press, Inc.
150 Fifth Avenue, New York, N.Y. 10011
Manufactured in the United States of America

CONTENTS

I

CUNNILINCTUS

ORAGENITALISM

THE EROTIC use of the mouth in caressing and exciting the genitalia of the sexual partner is, after the use of the hands and the sexual parts themselves, the most valuable erotic technique, and the most efficacious. It is also the most misunderstood and the most maligned.

I do not propose to analyse this misprisal of a caress which can as easily be immensely useful and immensely delicate, as it can be beastly and unæsthetic. Nor will I attempt to trace the history and development of the peculiar modern attitude of contempt – actual or pretended – toward oragenitalism. I will remark simply – after pointing out that religious and olfactory prejudices probably have some bearing in the matter – that it is precisely that subservience of the mouth, which has made the oragenital caress the focus of jest and insult in modern civilization, which also makes it the most intimate and the most fervent gesture of love and adoration possible between a man and a woman. For the mouth is to most people the most *personal* part of the body, being the organ of speech, and therefore the most obvious seat of the actual and projected personality or "soul" (the eyes and the rest of the face, then the hands, being next in personalness); and both the misprisal of oragenitalism and its peculiar value stem from this fact.

The ultimate taboo in sex technique, in the Anglo-Saxon world and the English-language literature certainly, is that concerning the oragenital acts that are a primary routine in the sexual approach of most mammals, particularly the quadrumanes and quadrupeds in whom the sense of smell is predominant in sexual selection. The lay and even medical disapprobation of oragenital acts has been largely toned by the moral condemnation actually intended for the male homosexuality and Lesbianism with which they are often connected. The legal prohibitions against oragenitalism show this very clearly, lumping it with "sodomy," with punishments up to twenty years in prison, even though taking place between persons of the opposite sex, whether or not they are married to each other!

How it is intended to enforce sexually intrusive laws of this type is not stated; and where public avowals of oragenital acts are thought necessary – as in divorce cases – the euphemism "mental cruelty" has been invented to avoid criminal liability. As there are neither religious nor logical grounds for the prejudice, recourse is usually attempted to a vague "æsthetic" objection against acting "like animals." To this the didactic modern literature of sex technique counterposes an equally vague romantic defense, stressing the presumable similarity to the kiss, as in Van de Velde's term "the kiss of genital stimulation, or genital kiss." (*Ideal Marriage*, Leiden, 1926; English translation, 1930.) And in the title itself of the first, and still the best, of the recent popular works on oragenital acts, *The Love Kiss* (Los Angeles, 1965), signed "David Davidson," actually the work of Dale Koby and Dr. Leonard Lowag.

Oragenitalism is a term which I have coined, as the title of the first edition of the present work in 1940 – the author's first book – to include both the oral excitation of the male genitalia, *fellation;* and of the female genitalia, *cunnilinctus*. The term has since been popularized by Prof. Kinsey and others in the clumsy, hyphenated form, "oral-genital," but the original is retained here. The work is accordingly divided into two main sections, on cunnilinctus and fellation; the latter being further divided into fellation proper, and *irrumation*, which is identical with fellation so far as the oral insertion or acceptance of the penis is concerned, but in positions or situations in which it is the genital partner, the man, who is dominant, and not the oral partner. A brief final section is also included on mutual, simultaneous oragenitalism, often referred to in English under the polite disguise of the French numerical term, *soixante-neuf*, to which the colloquial English term, "sixty-nine," is preferred.

The frequent use, throughout this monograph, of such modifiers and qualifiers as "generally," "possibly," "usually," "perhaps," *et cætera*, may be irritating to the reader, or at least seem over-cautious. But the literature of oragenitalism is so very scant, and what there is of it – especially in the last few years, capitalizing on the New Freedom – is so sketchy, so timid, and so gruellingly unscientific, impractical, and inadequate, that much of the material here presented derives from personal experience, and from evidence and inspirations which may be exceptional or untrustworthy or both. I have therefore qualified to the hilt, so that any generalizations which I may make or imply will be fairly reliable.

In the section on "Fellation," owing to a total lack of personal experience in the oral-active sense, I have trusted particularly to the existing literature, especially in French, and have also included a hitherto-unpublished "Practical Treatise" on fellation, translated from that language, as well as discussions of technique by avowedly homosexual authors. I hope, in this way, to have redeemed myself for the very long delay since the private publication of the first edition of this work (comprising only the section on "Cunnilinctus") exactly thirty years ago. The announced Part II: "Fellation & the Sixty-Nine," was not at that time written, the author not having the courage to do the research.

I. CUNNILINCTUS

THE MODERN literature of sexual technique "in marriage" — always in marriage, and always notably heavy-handed — is nowhere more lacking in psychological penetration than in its persistent discussion of sexual acts in terms of what they may be expected to do for the *other* person. The moral intention here is of course laudable, but almost nowhere in this literature is there any recognition of the underlying ego-drive, and the need for it, in sexual acts. Oragenitalism in particular, when it has been treated at all — whether in English or French — has almost always been discussed as a specially valuable technique for exciting or satisfying orgastically the genital partner. The oral drives (nursing substitutes) almost certainly motivating the oral partner are entirely overlooked. This is true of Van de Velde's short passage, mentioned above . . . and similar works. It should be noted very positively, however, that in spite of all statements to the contrary, oragenitalism is generally engaged in at the request of and to give pleasure primarily *to the oral partner* and not to the genital partner, unless it is the genital partner who has suggested or initiated the act. A most striking proof of this is the fact that, when enacted simultaneously in the "sixty-nine," the usual complaint is that "what is being done to one distracts one from what one is doing."

Sexual folklore offers the unspoken and rather naïve explanation that this overlooking of the oral motivation stems from men's desire to be the recipients of oragenital caresses, in fellation, for their own (genital) pleasure. And that in the arguing with, and persuading of inexperienced young women to comply with this desire, the whole matter of the woman's own possible oral drives and oral pleasure in fellation is lost sight of. Even the widespread recognition that male homosexuals may engage pleasurably in thousands of oragenital acts with men, without their own genitals entering at all into the sexual concurrence (although, of course, erection and auto-masturbatory or spontaneous orgasm generally take place), has not cast any broad light on the obvious and almost invariable relationship between orality and oragenitalism.

Another even more striking demonstration is the fact that all authentic cases of auto-fellation, or self-fellation, that have been studied — auto-cunnilinctus is apparently impossible — have proved to be those of homosexual men looking to satisfy specifically *oral* desires, and not trying to attain some special phallic pleasure, which could of course be achieved in less contortionistic ways. (The two usual methods for auto-fellation are either by simply bending very far forward in a sitting position, or by lying on the back and throwing the legs back over the head. The head of the penis can be reached orally in these positions only by rather slender and supple persons.)

For the basic fact concerning oragenital acts is that these are NOT essentially a special type of sex technique, intended to satisfy the erotic needs of the genital partner, but are the expression of a profound psychological urge, and intended to satisfy the erotic needs of the oral partner — unless, to be sure, it is the genital partner who has initiated or requested the act. This is made desperately clear in the absolutely frank public advertisements for oragenital partners — actually for genital partners, since the advertiser is almost invariably the oral partner — both in the folkloristic form of wall-scrawls or *graffiti*, and in the "classified" columns of the "underground" newspapers or New Freedom press, in recent years, which are the printed media equivalent of the outhouse *graffiti*.

In the case of cunnilinctus, as sexual folklore also shows in the most unmistakable way, the element of orality is well understood to be paramount, with, for instance, jocular tales of dying men asking the nurse to let them perform cunnilinctus – which they have sworn to try once before they die (*n.b.*) – and invariably being revived by it . . . even made immortal, as though they had drunk, in this way, at the maternal Fountain of Life. Much evidence of this kind, from various cultures, is gathered in the present writer's *Rationale of the Dirty Joke: An Analysis of Sexual Humor* (New York, 1968) First Series, pages 549–584, in the sections on "Fellation," "Cunnilinctus," and "Cunnilinctus and Masochism," to which the interested reader is referred. The extraordinary folk-materials and evidences there presented cannot be given in full here.

Cunnilinctus, usually spelled "*cunnilingus*," is a subject of great psychological complexity. The most important point that can usefully be made concerning it (as with fellation) is the much greater importance in its motivation shown by oral and even masochistic strivings – the desire to return to the mother's breast, or frankly to her womb, and certainly to infant dependence – than by any desire to excite the other (genital) partner by this "technique." In the case of the less taboo oral caressing of the woman's breasts, men are quite frank about admitting that this is done by them as much or more for their own pleasure as for the woman's. This is not to suggest, of course, that the woman does not enjoy it, but that it is really done more for the man's fore-pleasure and sexual excitement than for hers.

One must not, as the proverb has it, reckon without one's host. The woman is not actually being either nursed at or eaten. There are sexual and maternal satisfactions to the woman herself in oral caresses of both her breasts and genitals. There is also the peculiarity, as to the ego-drives involved, that where fellation is often thought of as a domination of the genital partner by the oral partner (though admittedly for the genital partner's pleasure, in some or major part), in cunnilinctus this is reversed. There the oral partner — in the present frame of reference, the man — is considered to be dominated by, and subservient to, the woman (the genital partner), however willingly he may be engaging in cunnilinctus, and, in fact, *because* of this willingness. Just how universal this point of view is, can be seen from the anthropological materials concerning cunnilinctus performed publicly by numerous men upon one woman, in cultures as disparate as the matrilocal Pacific islands and present-day California, quoted in full in *Rationale of the Dirty Joke*, pages 571–77 and 778–85, which also cover the related question of the ingestion during cunnilinctus of such substances as menstrual blood or male semen, specifically as a masochistic act.

But it must also not be lost sight of, in considering the oragenital relations between normal lovers, that the masochistic element in cunnilinctus, which bulks so large and even perversely in the anthropological materials just cited, is essentially an encapturing for neurotic purposes of a perfectly normal mammalian erotic preliminary. To this, the male throughout our species may properly be expected to be attracted for his own pleasure, and attracted specifically by the genital odor of the female.

Finally, though no one seems ever to have mentioned it before, it should never be overlooked, as to the normality of cunnilinctus, that every human life begins — except for those rare and unfortunate Cæsarean sections and breech-presentations — with the act of cunnilinctus performed by the infant at birth, over the whole length of the mother's vagina, from the inside out! As such, cunnilinctus is surely as much the Freudian return to the womb, as to the maternal breast, with all the emotional power of these symbols and these realities.

II

To consider, now, the matter of physical technique. Kissing the vulva or external female genitals, whether on the pubic mound of the mons veneris or on the unspread vulvar lips or nymphæ, is the most usual preliminary to active cunnilinctus. Such kissing may be done spontaneously and affectionately by the man, or else deliberately, as a part of the erotic ritual necessary or customary either to himself or the woman, or both. To avoid suddenness, a very common progression from ordinary embracing to cunnilinctus is that in which the man, from a position in which he has been lying facing the woman – or lying over her between her thighs – and kissing her mouth, slides or bends his body downward, or kneels back until he can kiss and suck her nipples. Then, curling his body further downward, he can tongue her navel playfully and kiss her mons veneris.

In order, at this point, actually to approach the vulva with his mouth – especially the vulva of a grown woman, in whom the pelvis is usually so tilted that the vulva is directed downward and rather backward between the thighs, and not forward as in young girls – it is necessary for the man to slide his knees down toward and past the woman's feet, supporting himself on his hands or elbows as he does so, and then to embrace her hips with his arms from underneath, and lift her legs and thighs over his shoulders. He can also lift the woman's thighs in this manner while kneeling between them, without sliding downward to a prone position, but it is necessary for him to lift the woman's hips somewhat higher when he is kneeling than when he is prone, in order to bring her vulva directly before his mouth, accessible for further caresses.

A pillow or cushion stuffed under the woman's hips is very useful at this point to relieve the man's shoulders of any oppressive weight, and to allow his shoulders, neck and head freedom of movement in cunnilinctus. If a pillow is used and not a stiff cushion, it will usually be found to raise the woman's hips higher and more firmly if it is folded in half. It should then be pushed under her buttocks with the folded edge – that being the thinner edge of a folded pillow – toward her head, and the two free ends forming the higher side closer to the man. Thus, if the woman's body slides on the pillow at all, it will slide down the pillow, away from the man, and will not slide toward him and tend to imprison his head between her thighs. The folded pillow should also be pushed up under the woman's hips – folded edge first – by the man, and the woman should not attempt to place it herself from above, with the free edges first, as it is likely to unfold when its upper half scrapes against her lifted hips as she presses it beneath them. However, when the pillow is not folded, the woman can then place it under her hips, or help the man to do so, at least by handing it to him (especially if it is taken from the head of the bed, where it may be hard for him to reach), and by lifting her hips. This all takes far longer to describe than to do!

All such preparations should be made as unceremoniously and as easily and nonchalantly as possible, in order not to seem to be cold-bloodedly going about matters and making a business of things, an appearance which is usually very repugnant to both partners: to the woman who is lying and waiting for the touch of the man's mouth, as well as to the man who is fumbling about – probably in the dark and in a state of excited haste and passionate urgency – trying to get everything conveniently and properly arranged. However, it is difficult to generalize, for some women and men are very excited by slow and deliberate preparations, which allow time for, and give impetus to, erotic anticipation and imagination. People of this type or in this mood are also likely to engage in sex-play during the early morning or late afternoon, or, if at night, in the presence of some subdued lighting. The light afforded them is likely to make their deliberate preparations just so much more effective, both in stirring the imagination and in arranging matters properly.

Once in a suitable position for cunnilinctus, the man will find it simple to progress from kissing the mons veneris and vulva to spreading the pubic hair and the outer and inner lips, and to pressing his mouth full against the vulva. He then can engage without difficulty in the mouthing, licking, and sucking of the vulvar groove, the clitoris, and the nymphæ or labia minora. The various forms and combinations of such oral maneuvres will be discussed more fully below, as also their various useful combinations with excitement of the woman's genitals by means of the hands at the same time.

It is important that the vulva be spread open preliminary to extended and serious cunnilinctus for two principal reasons. First, the excitation to the woman is greater when a greater surface of her vulva is available to the caresses of the man's lips and tongue, and when his tongue does not have to pry between the closed or fallen-together nymphæ (which often protrude during excitement between the outer lips, and may each be anywhere from an inch to three-and-a-half, or even four-and-a-half inches from the vulvar groove to the tip of the nympha), nor have to press its way through the pubic hair, which may be irritatingly wiry, especially in brunette women. Second, this hair, unless it is carefully and completely spread back on both sides of the vulva, by the man's hands or otherwise, is very likely to get into the man's mouth during the action. Only a few hairs caught on the tongue, or swallowed, will usually occasion the man rather unpleasant choking or gagging sensations, and must be coughed up with inappropriate sounds and facial expressions of revulsion, which may hurt the woman's feelings as she is likely to feel these to be directed somehow at her.

The pubic hair and labia need not be spread exclusively by the man's hands, as this is sometimes difficult for him to do, particularly when his arms are holding up the woman's thighs. Of course, by supporting her thighs close to the buttocks with his hands, it will be found that his thumbs, which are facing inward, can usually contrive to spread the vulva open. But this is clumsy, and the vulva can be spread almost as effectively by pressing it open with the man's lips, turning the head first to one side to press one vulvar lip and its hair outward by holding the mouth firmly against it while turning the head; then releasing the pressure of the mouth and turning the head to press the other vulvar lip and its hair outward to the other side.

Or, which is both more effective and more pleasant, the woman can spread her vulva open with her own hands, to assist the man. Her participation will often serve to excite her the more, since it will place the image and idea of cunnilinctus forcibly, graphically, and excitingly before her imagination, instead of having it be something delicious but extraneous happening to her from outside, as it were, without her coöperation. When a woman enjoys this sort of erotic participation, she will usually prepare herself for cunnilinctus by spreading her legs eagerly, and often her vulva as well, without being asked or urged to – unless she is one of the many women who like to be re-seduced at every encounter, and more or less forced. She will perhaps also originate certain auto-excitational maneuvres, such as keeping her hands on her inner thighs or her labia majora, with her forefingers or thumbs alongside her clitoris, rubbing her labia alternately up and down against each other, against her clitoris, and against the man's mouth during cunnilinctus. Her imagination may even be so inflamed by the *idea* of cunnilinctus, as she spreads her vulva with her hands, awaiting the caress of the man's mouth, that she may lie alternately opening and closing her vulva – possibly even rubbing her clitoris meanwhile – as she waits for the man to get in place. These remarks, incidentally, apply equally to the similar participation of the woman in preparing for coitus.

However, some women are by no means excited by having to participate in the preparation for cunnilinctus (or coitus) by spreading open their own vulvæ; and though she may enjoy cunnilinctus immensely – almost all women do – the woman may be distressed and even disgusted by this forcible participation of her own hands and imagination. What many women want, in this way, is for something to *happen* to them, something for which they are not really responsible, and of which they do not take the direction: a sort of glorious but friendly rape. This is perfectly in keeping with what is psychologically believed to be a certain natural passivity in women, as in all mammalian females where the male has an intromittent genital organ and they an ensheathing vagina. The woman should not be argued or shamed into taking a more active part than she really wishes. Encouraged, yes.

Unless, therefore, the idea of spreading her vulva with her own hands preparatory to cunnilinctus (or coitus) occurs spontaneously to the woman, or unless she does it willingly when it is suggested, and repeats it without being reminded or requiring undue urging on subsequent occasions – an important sign – and unless, finally, she seems thoroughly to enjoy this sort of participation, it is wise for the man not to insist upon it. He should do his unaided best, which may also make him feel more like a man, and the woman more like a woman. Sometimes, too, the slightest note of querulous insistence or moral constraint can effectively inhibit the woman's pleasure or orgasm, especially in cunnilinctus or in strained positions for vaginal intercourse.

Observe that cunnilinctus is not necessarily or even usually taken to the point of the woman's orgasm. It is principally used as the most exciting possible preliminary for the woman, to be completed by vaginal intercourse — an important point. As to auto-excitational maneuvres by the woman during cunnilinctus, one very sincere young woman recently, extremely anxious to feel and to experience sexually only what she truly and authentically felt, and *not to fake anything*, as she put it, told me that she had been very upset and angered by a man's asking her to rub her own clitoris in her favorite rhythm while he engaged in cunnilinctus upon her. He was of course undiplomatic, in referring in this way to her masturbatory life preceding, and also in implying verbally that she was perhaps frigid or impotent, that is to say sexually inadequate in the real man-&-woman relationship, without falling back to the presumably adolescent assist of auto-masturbatory tricks and traits. But the really important point was the profound self-unveiling of her angry response: "*No, I won't do it! What I want is for* YOU *to do it to me!*" Meaning, anyone but herself.

If cunnilinctus is being used as a preliminary to coitus, which is probably its most common occurrence, the man should wait and continue with cunnilinctus until the woman is sufficiently aroused by it, and her pre-coital vaginal secretion has manifested itself abundantly, making unnecessary the messy and cold-blooded application of oils, creams, or lubricant jellies. At that point he can easily and far more satisfactorily lie forward on the woman from his kneeling position between her thighs, or slide upward from a similar prone position, to lie upon her belly and breast, and engage her in coitus. He can also *come back* to cunnilinctus, after a period of coitus, then return again to coitus, several times consecutively.

The man can also take the opportunity afforded by cunnilinctus preparatory to coition, to reach down with one hand and roll onto his penis a condom which has been rolled beforehand and discreetly placed in some convenient spot, under the pillow or at the bedside. Discreetly, to avoid the appearance of cold and calculating preparation. The convenience of this method of contraceptive preparation during preparatory cunnilinctus makes the condom the favorite contraceptive of many men who are much given to oragenitalism, when the woman does not use the oral-contraceptive Pill or other non-vaginal method. The use of the condom actually as a prophylactic against disease is now again becoming its main use, owing to newer and less intrusive non-genital methods of birth control, but occasions do arise. On the other hand, its use as an actual prophylactic against venereal disease need hardly be mentioned here, since obviously no one will engage in oragenital acts when there is the slightest suspicion that the partner's genitalia (or mouth) may be infected, and there are no tongue-condoms — at any rate, not yet.

The condom is also favored by cunnilinctors or cunnilinguists (both terms are used) by a process of elimination of the other practical and effective genital methods of contraception. Cunnilinctus in the presence of the spermicidal jelly used with the vaginal diaphragm or cervical pessary is very likely to be unpleasant to the man because of the taste and viscosity of this jelly. Vaginal foams are even worse! Such jellies or foams are usually inserted vaginally well before the erotic session is begun, which is a very sensible practice indeed, since it avoids the necessity of disrupting the erotic rhythm of the couple by the woman's pausing to run to the bathroom (in France: the bidet) to insert the diaphragm and jelly or other intra-vaginal contraceptive device or substance. This necessity is also avoided, between cunnilinctus and immediately-following coitus, by using a condom instead, in the way described above.

Some twenty years ago, in connection with my invention of the ovulation thermometer, for use in pinpointing the impregnable days of the woman's menstrual cycle, in the "rhythm" method of birth control – which is otherwise indeterminable and unreliable – I made the serious suggestion to the most important American manufacturer of vaginal diaphragms and spermicidal jellies, that these jellies should be made in the usual six delicious flavors: cherry, peppermint, and so forth. His reaction was shocked surprise at what he considered to be levity, in alluding in this way to cunnilinctus as a pre-coital technique. Or perhaps he really thought of it as a competitive *encroaching on his company's medium.* In any case, the flavor of most spermicidal jellies has been much improved since that time: they are at least tasteless now. Meanwhile, jocular "Raspberry Douches" and similarly flavored vaginal jellies and confections for use in cunnilinctus are nowadays offered at the folk-level, in advertisements in the modern Underground Press, where allusions to cunnilinctus are now considered standard and "in" – especially in the classified ads, looking for sexual partners sight-unseen. Actually, anyone who has to *advertise* for human sexual contacts of any kind, even for presumed specialties under the code-names of "French culture" (oragenitalism), "Greek culture" (anal intercourse), "Roman culture" (orgies), and the like, is not really "in" anything. Rather is he showing himself, by such pitiful shifts and subterfuges, to be a human failure and a sexual washout, sedulously to be avoided as only one step — if that — above the authors of the equally wholesale and undiscriminating anonymous obscene telephone calls.

III

THE PROGRESSION from cunnilinctus to coitus is possible from most cunnilingual postures, with a certain amount of changing of position, and sometimes of milieu. As, from the chair in which the woman has been sitting during cunnilinctus, her hips far forward at the edge, she might simply slide down to the floor where the man has been kneeling before her, to join in coitus with him. However, several cunnilingual postures are particularly suited to this progression to coitus, and they are therefore mentioned specially here, rather than later in the section devoted to postures. Note in particular that, in sliding his body upward from a cunnilingual to a coital posture, it is not necessary for the man to withdraw his arms or shoulders if these are under the woman's thighs. Instead, he can press her thighs upward toward her hips as he rises to lie forward and over her, meanwhile catching the hollows or hocks of her knees in the hollows of his elbows, or even lifting her calves up along and over his shoulders. The man is afforded the deepest possible penetration into the vagina in this posture, with the woman's legs so lifted. Where his penis is quite long and the woman's vagina relatively short, the posture should be used with care: that is to say, the thrusting forward of the man's hips as he begins coitus, and during its reciprocating movements, should not be allowed to drive his penis too deep.

Progressions of this type, from cunnilinctus to coitus, and from one posture of coitus to another, without withdrawing the penis from the vagina to re-arrange the new posture, are a very important and effective sexual technique, but one which is never mentioned or taken cognizance of in any way in the usual manuals on "How To Be Sexually Happy Though Married." Such progressions should be done easily and flowingly — that is their whole art — and without too much grunting and straining, or evident effort. Of particularly useful progressions from cunnilinctus to coitus, the first is from that type of cunnilinctus in which the woman lies on her back or sits up slightly, leaning back on her elbows, while the man lies *on his side* between her thighs. Instead of the man's legs being stretched out behind him, flat on the upper surfaces of his thighs, as would be natural in the male-prone posture for cunnilinctus; in this side-lying posture his legs are curled backwards under him, and his body leans on the side and in the direction opposite to his legs. In this position, the woman's leg on the side opposite his head can be lifted over the man's waist, instead of being held between his upper shoulders and neck, as he holds the leg nearest the side in which his head faces. Or this former leg — the woman's far leg — may be held by the man at its calf, and lifted directly upward and outward into the air, while the woman supports it with one hand hooked under her knee. This will have the effect of opening and spreading the vulva appreciably, and of allowing the man both free play for his head, and room (and air) to breathe.

The woman's free hand may press the man's head passionately to her vulva, a gesture of encouragement and appreciation which is always pleasant to the man during cunnilinctus in any position, so long, that is, as the pressure does not become excessive and does not prevent him from breathing or from withdrawing his head, for a moment of pause, when he seriously wishes to withdraw it. Women have a way of seizing a man's head passionately, as much during cunnilinctus as during mouth-to-mouth kissing, very violently and with both hands, sometimes tangling the hands in the man's back hair, or gripping his ears (the middle- or little-fingers are sometimes hooked into the ear-holes, which is particularly unbearable, or into the hollows deep behind and under the lobes of the ears), and absolutely dragging the man's head to them in an excess of passion. One is glad to see a woman that hot, and yet . . .

There are reports of teeth being broken during a thoughtlessly violent kiss or embrace of this sort, and of false teeth and dentures being started loose. There is also a folk-belief (I am assured it is true) about adolescent couples – both of them wearing braces on their teeth for orthodontic purposes – becoming inextricably locked at their jaws, like dogs in copulation, during too-violent kissing! Eyeglasses also do sometimes, quite authentically, become tangled in this way, though obviously the man would not wear eyeglasses during cunnilinctus, owing to the danger of breakage and of scratching the woman's thighs. A man in cunnilinctus is not really in a position to shout up to the woman, clutching him too strongly at the sides or back of his head with her hands or thighs, "*Let go my ears – I know my business!*" (as the folk-phrase would have it), but the temptation to do so is sometimes very strong.

The progression described above, in which the man moves from cunnilinctus in a side-lying position, to coitus, may be varied by the man's bringing his body around, still lying on his side, till his torso is at right angles to the woman's, or even further till his legs are directed upward along the bed or rug and almost parallel to her side, in the direction of her head. In these variant postures, the man's penis approaches within reach of the woman's hand on the side where his legs lie, and she can excite his penis manually while he cunnilingues her. Most men *very much* desire this reciprocity, though the usual positions for cunnilinctus do not allow it.

Actually, in manually exciting the man during cunnilinctus, the woman need only wet her palm with the pre-coital flow that will appear at the tip of the penis when the man becomes erect and excited – the so-called distillation – or with her own saliva, if his pre-coital distillation is tardy, scant, or absent. She then, with her moistened palm, presses back his foreskin – if he has one and if it has not already retracted by itself during his erection – and holds his naked glans penis warmly and tightly in her wetted hand. As the man becomes more and more excited during the course of cunnilinguing her, he will probably make coital movements into her gripping hand. He may thus be excited to the extreme point for subsequent coitus. This should not, of course, be done in the case of those many men who are likely to ejaculate too quickly during coitus anyhow, and who are engaging in cunnilinctus to bring the woman to that state of high excitement where even the few coital strokes the man will be capable of will suffice to bring her to orgasm. The man may occasionally be brought, or rather may bring himself, to the point of orgasm in this way, by simili-coital motions in the grip of the woman's moistened hand, if cunnilinctus is intended to bring the woman to her climax too, and if coitus is not contemplated.

In these side-lying postures of the man, it will be found that he can lift his head higher and more freely up and down in all directions than was possible to him in prone cunnilingual postures. The variant side-lying positions of the man, just described, up under one of the woman's thighs and along her side, in which the woman can reach the man's penis with her hand, can also be achieved through the original side-lying posture between her thighs, or, almost as easily, from the following more primary position: with the man lying at the woman's side or somewhat over her, facing and embracing her, and kissing her mouth. He then sits up at her side, and twists his upper torso to face her. Then, pulling his legs upward and behind him, he finds that he is kneeling facing her side. He then sits down again, but leaning sideways toward her feet, and resting on his elbow. In this position his legs extend backwards toward the woman's head, or are curled under his own body on that side. He then lifts her near thigh, as the woman lies supine on her back, and presses his head and shoulders *beneath* her lifted thigh to approach her vulva with his mouth.

If the woman is sufficiently tall, or if her torso is very long (as, for instance, among the Japanese, though combined with rather short lower legs in this case), she can twist to one side, in the position just described, and fellate the man while he is engaged in cunnilinctus upon her. Their position then becomes that of the unusual twisted or "cross-back" sixty-nine, to be discussed further in the final section of this monograph. The original position can be varied further by the man's remaining in a kneeling posture facing the woman's side, while he progresses from embracing her to cunnilinctus, as described above, and by his pressing his head and shoulders under her near thigh, twisting his upper torso so that he faces her vulva, while his lower torso and his kneeling legs remain extended backwards, somewhat between being at angles to, and being parallel to the woman's torso, in the general direction of her head. Again, this requires many words to describe understandably, and the reader may even need to reduce it to a little drawing or stick-figure to "see" the progression of motions; but it can be done — and should be done — in an easy and flowing sequence of movements, without any apparent effort and especially without jolting re-arrangements of the body while moving from stage to stage. *Like every kind of love-making, the progression of sexual postures should be done like a beautiful dance.*

It has already been observed that in side-lying postures of this kind, the man's penis is within reach of the woman's nearer hand, and she is able to masturbate him while he cunnilingues her, and to press or lightly claw with her fingertips under his testicles ("spider-clawing"), to titillate his perinæum, or insert her finger or thumb into his anus — the so-called "postillioning" — to massage his prostate gland, or in any other way to excite his genitals, to the point of his orgasm or not, as may be desired. The man, meanwhile, aside from cunnilinguing the woman, which should in general be done without long pauses, is able at the same time to lift her near thigh over his arm or shoulder, and to reach up around it to caress her closest breast and nipple while he rests his weight on his other forearm. Of this, the hand will simultaneously fall in perfect position to titillate the woman both vaginally or rectally, while his tongue and mouth press against the upper part of her vulva; or to reach past his own face, or all the way around the woman's far thigh, to excite her clitoris. It is not hard to understand that the simultaneity of all these approaches to, and titillations of the woman's erotic body by the man, bring her to a great deal higher pitch of excitement, or *quality of orgasm* ultimately, than simple and uncombined cunnilinctus can do.

Because of the many oral and manual excitations possible to each of the partners simultaneously in these kneeling and side-lying cunnilingual postures, they are favorites of many men and women who are much given to cunnilinctus. They have also the advantage — and it is for this reason that they have been described at this point and at such length — of being very easy to move or progress from, into the ordinary posture of coitus with the woman supine and the man prone upon her. Also into the extremely useful posture for coitus called variously "The Scissors" (Spanish, "*las tijeras*"), the "Horizontal Cross," and "T-upside-down," *which is probably the best of all coital postures* for many reasons, and particularly for the ease of manually exciting the woman's clitoris meanwhile. In this extraordinarily valuable "scissors" position, the man lies on his side, at right angle to the woman's torso and underneath her uplifted thighs, which rest on or hang over his upper hip. The legs of the partners are often crossed with each other, after the man's penis is fully entered vaginally, in such a way that both his legs are gripping her farther leg – the under leg if she is slightly on her side – while her nearer leg lies over his upper thigh. The position of the four legs is then not unlike the capital letter *W*, or rather two *V*'s crossing and combining with each other, the partners' genitals being at the bottom apex of the combined *V*'s. The man can also lift the woman's near leg high, entirely up onto his upper shoulder (even up over his head and onto his lower shoulder), to facilitate his manual excitation of her clitoris; but the woman often feels spread-eagled and imprisoned, with one leg stretched so high while the other is gripped flat to the bed, and cannot take her mind off her legs to enjoy the sensations at her clitoris. Expressed simply, the "scissors" position is really just the woman *sitting on the man's lap*, as though on a chair, facing either way. The couple then, as it were, tip the chair over sideways, so that the woman ends up lying on her back, the man on his side.

The "scissors" posture can also easily be reached from the side-lying and kneeling postures for cunnilinctus, already described above. In the side-lying posture the man pulls his body up along under the woman's thighs, meanwhile pushing her hips downward along his body, till their genitals are together. In the kneeling posture of cunnilinctus mentioned above, the "scissors" position can be reached by the kneeling man's dropping his hips away from the woman onto their side, and pressing her hips downward along his body as he pulls her to him. Again, these motions are to be done by both partners in unison, and in silent accord, smoothly and flowingly, and without any absurd hoisting and pullyhawlying of one's own or the other's body – like a dance. As the late Havelock Ellis wished to say, but was dissuaded or prevented from saying, as the motto of one of his most famous books: *Sex is the dance of life.*

Among the many other advantages of the "scissors" position for intercourse is the ease – perhaps irrelevant here – with which it can be assumed from positions where the man and woman are originally sitting or lying side-by-side. The woman simply leans somewhat away from the man, and lies back, lifting her thighs over the man's hip. The man meanwhile turns to lie on his side facing her, and pivots down and around on his hip till his body is at right angles to hers. (Or he may pivot first, and then turn to lie on his side.) The couple are now in the "scissors" posture, as described in the second paragraph preceding. As stated already, this posture is remarkable for the ease and thoroughness with which the woman's clitoris may be simultaneously excited by the man's fingers or thumb during complete vaginal coitus, his hand approaching either from above or below her thighs. For it should not be lost sight of that, with her legs lifted and together while she lies in any way – whether supine on her back, or prone forward, or lying on her side, or kneeling – *a woman's vulva is much more accessible from behind than from in front.* This is only to be expected, considering the mammalian heritage of the human being, since all other mammals without exception approach the female sexually from behind, and it may be assumed that human beings also did so at the beginning of their pre-history.

In addition, there is the ease with which, in the "scissors" position, by stretching his torso just a little, a man of average height can simultaneously suck the woman's closer breast and nipple during complete vaginal intercourse. Also the added advantage of requiring neither partner to bear much of the other's weight at any time. It is therefore possible, and quite usual, for both partners to fall asleep after or during coitus in this posture, both without discomfort during the first hours of sleep and without withdrawing the penis or re-arranging their bodies. There are very few postures in which this is possible, the only other practical one being coitus from behind with both partners lying on their sides, "making spoons" together.

The only real disadvantage of the "scissors" position is psychological, in that it is practically impossible for the partners to kiss each other's mouth in it. But this disadvantage is perhaps offset by the fact that, in this posture and by the same token, it is not necessary for the two to breathe each other's breath, both during intercourse and in falling asleep afterward while remaining sexually joined. In postures where kissing *is* possible, it is generally necessary either to breathe the other partner's breath at all times, or to bury one's own face at one or the other side of the partner's face, so that kissing is *not* possible. The necessary drawing of the partners' faces apart in the "scissors" position, which makes kissing almost impossible in it, also makes it the position of choice in erotic trios or minor orgies of one man and two women, since the man is able to engage vaginally with one woman in the "scissors" while performing cunnilinctus on the other, his head being disengaged and free.

This is typical of the neurotic isolation of orgiasts, and their terrified need *to avoid feelings of tenderness* for their sexual partners, as I have discussed at much further length in

The Fake Revolt (1967), in the closing section, observing that such orgies and trios – the latter being considered the "mildest" type of orgy – "are obvious methods of buffering the sexual act away from any possibility of human meaning, and draining out any meaning it might accidentally develop. Furthermore, the actual 3-in-1 oil orgy, involving kissing-HER-while-screwing-HIM, or screwing several other people (and the dog) simultaneously under the excuse of drugged drunkenness, not only necessarily and permutationally must involve sexual perversion, but is also, in the deepest sense, the setting up of a sexual hall of mirrors, or a thinning-out and cooling-down of the sexual charge and sexual relationship, to the point where there is really nobody present but the drugged orgiast, whose main emotion is an intense and frightened narcissistic concern *to touch no one*, except with the necessary tip of his or her penis or clitoris, and sometimes not even with that. The masturbator's dream."

In normal relationships, the "scissors" position is ideal for coitus out of doors or when dressed, since it can be achieved with ease on any flat surface, such as a bed, sofa, rug, or the ground, and with a minimum of disarrangement of the clothing. The man need merely draw out his penis, and the woman pull up her skirt and push aside the cross-strip of her panties – if she is wearing any, which, after all, she need not. The "scissors" is also ideally suited for love-talk, since the partners' heads are, in fact, fairly close, though not together; and if the woman turns her head downward on its side, to face the man, the couple are gazing directly into each other's eyes. This also makes possible the close observation of the other partner's face at the paroxysm of orgasm, which many lovers are eager to watch; whereas, in face-to-face positions, the heads are often too close for correct focus. The "scissors" posture is likewise suitable for smoking, by either partner or both, during or after coitus. It is particularly so used in the Middle East, where hashish is commonly smoked before or during intercourse, or is placed in powder form on food or desserts eaten beforehand, in the same way that Westerners offer each other alcohol both before and after meals — also during — to diminish their conversational and sexual repressions. "*He that is without sin among you, let him first cast a stone.*" (*John*, 8:7.)

Finally, and perhaps most advantageously of all, "the scissors" is the perfect position for coitus upon waking up in the morning, in the pleasant half-awake, half-asleep, hypnopompic state (or the matching hypnagogic state, just before falling asleep). After coitus in this position, the couple can fall back asleep, which they will probably want to do, without withdrawing the penis and without disturbing themselves by re-arranging their bodies, which might undesirably shake them out of their drowsiness and make them fully awake. In the morning, the disadvantage of "the scissors" in that the partners cannot kiss in it, often becomes a distinct advantage, inasmuch as the unpleasant breath of one partner, which is so common upon waking in the morning — especially among tobacco smokers — cannot irritate the other partner. Since the faces are not too close together, the possible unpleasant breath need not be mentioned at all, nor need any gestures of withdrawal or grimaces of irritation with it occur — much to the embarrassment and hurt of the offending partner — as often may be the case in postures where the partners' faces are close together. The relative impossibility of kissing in this coital posture also makes it ideal for coitus after cunnilinctus with women who object to their own vulvar taste and odor, a subject which will be explored more thoroughly below.

Another position in which the *progression* from cunnilinctus to coitus is simple and peculiarly useful, is that cunnilingual posture in which the man kneels or sits or squats, or kneels on all fours (that is, on his hands – or elbows – and feet or knees) on the floor at the edge of a bed, while the woman lies on the bed or in a large armchair with her legs extended over the edge. The progression from cunnilinctus to coitus is then obviously effected by the man's standing up, or rising to a high kneeling position, depending upon the height of the bed or chair. The ordinary posture for coitus in Western cultures – the man prone upon the supine woman – is not very satisfactory where the woman's legs and feet are unsupported, as in this present posture, for it is difficult for her to make hip movements in coitus when her feet are not solidly planted and cannot be used as anchors or pivots. Therefore, it is not to a prone coital position upon the woman's body that the man rises from kneeling or sitting on the floor before her in cunnilinctus. He rises rather to the position in which he stays kneeling or standing at the edge of the bed, or leaning *up* against the chair, and the woman's legs encircle his waist and are supported by his arms, or else are lifted outward over his arms or upward over his shoulders.

This position, of the man kneeling before the supine woman, is particularly valuable late in pregnancy, as is also the "scissors" position already discussed, since the man's weight does not at all rest upon the woman's belly, and she is in a comfortable supine position. While kissing the belly or mons veneris of the pregnant woman, in loving appreciation of her pregnancy, is very common (it has, for instance, been shown in polite form – through the cloth of the woman's dress! – in the 1960's motion-picture epic, *Spartacus*, and others), some men object to actual cunnilinctus during pregnancy. The reasons for this they find hard to explain, but all seem to involve a definite repugnance for such close association with the unborn child, as though fearing and rejecting the fœtophagic idea that the man might "eat the baby!" In the same way, I have heard a man whose sexual fetich was the sucking out of his own, or some other man's semen from his wife's vagina after intercourse, referred to by his wife as a "baby-eater." This perversion, seminal exsufflation, is more common than is recognized, especially among husbands who are unconscious or non-practicing homosexuals, and keep their wives basically for trading purposes. In any case, during pregnancy the woman is usually passionate enough, and sufficiently unrepressed – since she does not fear becoming pregnant – that cunnilinctus is not really necessary to excite her profoundly, and need only be engaged in if the man desires it too.

IV

THE POSSIBLE connection between coitus and cunnilinctus, and the *progressions* from one to the other, have been treated at length in regard to the preceding postures both because of the particular advantages of these postures for cunnilinctus and coitus and for the combination of both, and because it is important to emphasize the normality and connection of the oral approach to the woman, by the man, to the vaginal intercourse with her to which the oragenital approach normally excites him. Him, even more particularly than her. It is also, of course, desirable to emphasize the use of such combinations – and there are many others – in deriving the greatest possible erotic usefulness from cunnilinctus, since sexual acts are not often engaged in by human beings for the conscious mammalian function of impregnation and reproduction, but rather out of unthinking erotic excitement and desire. Which is as it should be, and as it probably is for the majority of the some *one and a half billion acts of human sexual intercourse which take place on this planet each week.* (Figure it out for yourself: The earth's human population is about three billion, at present, roughly half male and half female, of which each adult couple – representing half of the total – may be assumed to have intercourse twice a week. Those who do not, will balance those who have more.)

The unthinking eroticism of sexual acts is not to be deplored: it is their most vital characteristic. The less consciousness or introspection that is brought to bear on natural activities at the moment of doing them – breathing, eating, sleeping, digestion, and sex in all its spectrum of possibilities – the better these are invariably done. This does not mean one cannot study or experiment as to sexual technique, but that such study must be separated and differentiated from one's intense and immediate *authentic* erotic life. The same is true of all complex physical acts and arts, such as dancing, ice-skating, typewriting, photography, shooting a gun, driving an automobile, or playing any musical instrument; all of which can be done well only when their physical technique has been assimilated beyond the level of consciousness, and is engaged in almost without thought, entrusting the technical part to the reflexes, while the brain and consciousness concern themselves solely with the intellectual and emotional overtones felt or expressed in this physical or artistic act. Unless and until one can engage in sex in the same way, it is seldom done well.

This said and understood, one may continue with the consideration of the actual oral technique of cunnilinctus, a technique involving the interplay of the man's mouth, lips, tongue, head, shoulders, arms and hands, and, in fact, his entire body, by no means omitting his genitals. The woman's part is also not by any means wholly passive, and the woman's own cunnilinctual technique – that is to say, as the recipient of cunnilinctus – will be considered at the end of the present section, particularly covering not only the possible methods of her seconding and making more intense the man's oral excitation of her genitals, but likewise such specifically active motions and techniques (in positions in which her body is kneeling or crouching over the man's head, and her pelvis is therefore free to move violently), as the famous and mysterious "*Diligence de Lyon*" or "Candy Bar."

Of the actions possible to the human mouth, those most important in cunnilinctus, and in all oragenital acts, are: kissing, mouthing, lipping, tonguing (both licking, lapping, flicking, vibrating, and pointing or "stabbing" motions of the tongue), nipping, biting, chewing – with care – oral shaking, blowing, sucking, and swallowing. The simultaneous and subsidiary motions of the man's hands on the woman's external genitals and breasts, particularly at the nipples, mons pubis, labia minora, and clitoris – and aside from actual vaginal or rectal insertion of the fingers or thumbs – are, in relatively ascending order of intensity: touching, holding, palming, squeezing, pressing (*i.e.* exerting downward or sidewise pressure), tapping, tickling, caressing, patting, drumming, stroking, flicking or "finger-skating," pulling, poking, prodding, rubbing, rolling, shaking, pinching, reaming, and actual beating or striking with the fingers or palm. This by no means covers all possibilities and combinations, the mouth – or the fingers or thumbs – moving from side-to-side and in *rotary motions*, with use of other organs also, such as stroking with the cheeks (in the case of the woman, with the breasts and nipples); but this enumeration does include the main and really effective oral and manual manipulations. Scratching, hard enough to leave marks, is raised almost to a science in the *Kama Sutra*, but is too sadistic except at orgasm, when the woman can beat with her fists or dig her nails cruelly into the small of the man's back to trigger his orgasm.

There is also the matter of the speed or rhythm with which each or any caress is done, and *where;* the rapidity or slowness with which they speed up or are toned down, and change or alternate with one another; and the special climactic oral and bodily motions by the man at the moment of the woman's orgasm during cunnilinctus, when the thrashing of her body may require a greater violence in all his maneuvres – both oral and otherwise – in order to stay in operating position, and to force her to allow him to finish. All these can only be considered as they arise in the heat of action, and it is not possible to lay down any hard & fast rules, except perhaps that the order of oral and manual caresses should move from the outer parts or periphery of the woman's sexual anatomy (including her face, breasts, arms and legs, all the way up & down) to the centre of sexual sensation at her clitoris; and that the obvious over-all rhythm must be from slow to fast. The rest must be left to the individual cunnilinguist's personal experience, erotic imagination, and art.

Once in a suitable position for cunnilinctus, in any of the many postures available to choose, the man will find it simple to progress from kissing the mons veneris and vulva, to spreading the pubic hair and the outer and inner vulvar lips, and to pressing his mouth full against the vulva and engaging in various types of mouthing, licking, and sucking of the vulvar groove, the clitoris, and the nymphæ or labia minora. This is the central action of cunnilinctus, and it is assumed that all the preliminaries, both oral and manual, as above, have already been exhausted. One does not *begin* caressing a woman with cunnilinctus. Often one ends there.

The simple motion of the pursed lips from side to side or up-&-down or round-&-round in the well-spread vulvar groove, by means of shaking, nodding, or rotary motions of the head, will usually prove delightful to the woman, and will prepare her for the subsequent application of the tongue to the vulvar groove and the clitoris. The clitoris is the obvious target, of course, but one should not begin there – as stated just above — but should rather make the woman wait, and tantalize her by tonguing her pubic hair and with oral and lingual approaches along the pubic cleft to the clitoris, without actually getting there, except for a few preliminary flicks of the tongue-tip from moment to moment. This will serve to increase greatly her nervous tension and expectation, which are an essential part, perhaps one of the largest, in the sexual pleasure she feels and in her eventually reaching orgasm.

The opening of the vagina itself is one of the most highly sensitive portions of the woman's body, and should not be overlooked at this point. Some men insert the tongue-tip as deeply as they can into the vaginal opening, a penetration sometimes rather superficial owing to the restraining frænum underneath the tongue, similar to that underneath the glans penis. This is really of no importance, as, if the gesture is intended to imitate the motions of coitus itself, it cannot succeed in doing so. It is more valuable to concentrate on the *opening* of the vagina, holding the tongue as deeply as possible in this, while grinding the head circularly, or else licking circularly with the tongue-tip rather stiff, as though reaming or enlarging the vaginal opening. The opening of the urinal passage, about halfway up between the vaginal opening and clitoris, is usually quite small and not very sensitive to pleasure, though easy to irritate. Also, if particular efforts are made to centre the woman's sensations here, this may cause her to urinate involuntarily, which is not desirable except to abnormal and masochistic males.

All the circular motions just described are gratifying to the woman, but especially if they are alternately clockwise and counterclockwise, the man's head — and therefore the position of maximum labial and lingual pressure — rising higher and higher in the woman's vulvar groove at every alternation of stroke, arriving finally at the clitoris. However, neither rotary nor up-&-down motions can be undertaken by the man's head at any great speed, without making him dizzy. But since, in this simple type of pressure-excitation, greater speed of motion will probably produce greater pleasure (after the first few languorous turns), the side-to-side motion of the head is unquestionably the most effective. This can be done with extreme rapidity, more especially when done with a very short side-to-side sweep – the neck being held rigid and only the head moving, almost like quivering – than when done with a longer side-to-side sweep, the neck turning with the head. After a certain amount of experience, the man can do this with great rapidity, and also keep it up a surprisingly long time, as witness the virtuoso execution on the *nai* or pan-pipes, by the Rumanian folk-musicians, this ancient Greek instrument being played with precisely the side-to-side sweeping motions of the head here under discussion.

It is perhaps interesting to note, in passing, that the two principal musical instruments of antiquity (other than the horn and drum), the pan-pipes or flute, and the harp in all its forms – the latter now become the guitar, virginal or spinet, harpsichord, and finally the piano – can thus be considered to imitate, or to allude symbolically to, the two main ways of caressing a woman's body and genitals: the oral and manual. This is almost certainly the secret of the fascination on the part of young people and other sexual beginners, nowadays, with the manual musical dexterity of, for example, Flamenco guitar players, whose quick and supple finger-motions are almost openly identified as a genital strumming or caressing over the sound-hole of the "female" instrument. (See further, on this point, my *Rationale of the Dirty Joke*, 1968, First Series, page 632.) The erotic symbolism of any kind of drum or percussion instrument, as an allusion to violent vaginal coitus, is also perfectly open and ancient; such instruments being thought of, for that reason, particularly in Africa, as possessing powerful "magic." The idolization of Negro jazz, Spanish gypsy Flamenco, Italian rock-&-roll, and similar folk-musics of a heavily rhythmic and openly erotic kind, among modern sub-virile and over-civilized whites, is also a very obvious attempt to approach or imbrue oneself in the sensed sexual magic of such music — and its musicians.

The musical symbol or comparison is of particular value in the matter of speed or stroke in any sexual act, and in the pace and style of the necessary varying, diminishing, and slow increasing of these strokes to the crescendo or climax of orgasm, with a series of lesser and mounting crescendos preceding. The two elements of speed and direction of *motion*, and simultaneous power or relaxation of *pressure*, should be artfully intermingled, comparable to the two matching elements of which music is basically composed: the length and time-intervals of the notes, and their pitch and volume. The different registers and timbres of the musical instruments would thus match, in this parallel, the different characters of the sexual partners, or the key-signatures of the erotic movements: strong, crude, delicate, intense, romantic, *sostenuto*, *andante con moto*, *allegro con brio*, etc.

Actually, it is perhaps best to mingle all of these sexual characters or keys into erotic patterns of one's own choice, precisely as is done in music. The erotic artist ranges from slow to fast, soft to violent, and strong to tender; building up crescendos of emotivity as well as of speed, pressure, and direction of stroke on the organ used, exactly comparable to the "architectural" rising and progression of a Bach organ fugue, or the consecutive overlayering of increasing choirs of instruments, with more and more volume at greater and greater speed, in a continuing and enlarging pattern, as in the symphonic finale of an overture by Beethoven or Rossini. No one but an idiot needs to be told that such finales, and the equally intense rhythmic building-up and whirlingly violent climaxes of such musical works as Ravel's "Bolero" or De Falla's "Ritual Fire Dance" – even the authentic Viennese waltzes! – are intended to represent sexual acts ending paroxysmically in orgasm, under the politely transparent disguise of the dance. It is not an accident that musicians of both sexes have always and everywhere been considered the best lovers, and music – as Shakespeare puts it – the "food of love."

V

ALL THE REMARKS preceding naturally apply as well to cunnilinctus as to vaginal or other intercourse. Of particular value is a special type of mouthing, combined with suction and tonguing, in which a whole mouthful of the vulvar flesh – including, in particular, the upper inner side of the nymphæ or inner lips and the environs of the clitoris – is taken into the mouth, and held there with a strong suction, while the tongue-tip is pressed and prodded meanwhile against the tip or glans of the clitoris, and the cunnilinguist shakes his head from side to side, or nods it rapidly up & down, as described earlier. The prime difference here is that in this type of cunnilinctus *the mouth does not slip or move over the surface of the vulva*, as in the previously described types. Rather is the vulva here seized orally, and shaken against the underlying parts and against the pelvic bones. A very similar manipulation can be used by the hand, pressing against the flatly open vulva, and shaking from side to side or around & around, while simultaneously pressing deep against the underlying flesh, again without any motion over the surface of the vulva. It is probably precisely the transmission of the motions here used – whether orally or manually – to the underlying parts and nerves, that makes this type of excitation one of the most powerful of all, especially of all those in which only the mouth is used. Another exceptionally valuable technique is the "Hummingbird" or "Butterfly": the vulvar skin is pulled open tightly to make the clitoris stand out well, while the tonguetip frisks rapidly from side to side.

An auxiliary pressure of the man's hand, pressing down firmly on the woman's pubis (after the preliminary toying and tracing over her pubic hair), is of enormous value during cunnilinctus, and is obviously extremely simple to do simultaneously. The closer the woman comes to orgasm, the more she usually needs and appreciates such pressure, all through her intercrural groove, from the top of her pubis all the way to her anus and even beyond. It is for this reason that the woman will often lift her hips to force her vulva harder against the man's mouth, as her orgasm approaches, or try to clutch his head closer for the same purpose.

It should be noted, too, that while the man is engaging in cunnilinctus at the clitoris and the top of the vulvar groove generally, his chin can also easily exert a similar pressure against the woman's labia majora and the highly sensitive opening of her vagina, even including powerful motions of waggling the chin and lower jaw-bone from side-to-side, alternately with motions of the tongue higher up at the clitoris. *Caution: To be done with care*, as the jaw can easily be dislocated! The tongue motions and chin-waggling cannot usually be done together, but their up-&-down alternation – in a style similar to "double-tonguing" in playing the transverse flute – gives a powerful and indescribable sensation to the woman, since it comes very close to realizing the wish often expressed (by both sexes) that it were somehow possible for the man to engage in both cunnilinctus and coitus with the woman at the same time.

This point will be returned to again, in connection with

the use of the man's free hand which, in combined manipulations where his other hand is pressing on the woman's pubis during cunnilinctus, should pull and press apart the woman's buttocks and anal area, possibly entering either the vagina or the anus with the thumb or forefinger, or entering both simultaneously (the "Bowling-Hold"). The whole combination of hand-&-mouth manipulations described in this and the two preceding paragraphs is sometimes performed upon a naked woman – traditionally a blonde – stretched out on an altar, as the climax of the so-called "Black Mass." It is also known among occultists as "The Worship of Shiva" (the many-armed god of both reproduction and destruction, in India), and, more irreverently, as "The One-Man Band." The underlying idea, of cunnilinctus as a rite of ultimate evil, is of course not shared by this writer.

As it is obviously impossible to discuss in detail all the various tongue manipulations listed earlier, in their particular use during cunnilinctus, one simple division of all such tongue motions and manipulations should be made. Systematically considered, it is necessary to recognize that all forms of cunnilinctus may be divided basically into two broad types: first, that in which the direction of the man's tongue-stroke, as he licks forward and up, is from the bottom of the vulva to its top – that is, from the fourchette and vaginal introitus upward toward the clitoris; and second, that type of licking in which the man's tongue-stroke as he licks forward and up is from the top of the vulva to its bottom – that is, from the clitoris down toward the fourchette and perinæum.

I believe that the first type, which for convenience will be called *upward cunnilinctus,* is productive of relatively more pleasure to the woman than is the second type: *downward cunnilinctus.* I am of this opinion because it is usually easier orally to approach and titillate the vulva when facing in an upward direction to it, than when facing in a downward direction. This is especially true when the woman is lying on her back, or sitting, or otherwise dorsally supported, particularly in mature women (that is to say, well beyond puberty), in whom the pelvis normally tips somewhat downward, and directs the vulva backward between the thighs, rather than forward and up as in children and immature girls. It is for this reason that, in the previous treatment of common and useful positions for cunnilinctus, no mention was made of the position which is in fact the simplest that can be assumed by the man, in progression from his lying at the woman's side facing and embracing her: namely, that common cunnilinctual position in which the man sits up at the woman's side on a bed or the ground, and then bends forward, curling his legs under him, or passing them beneath his body; then placing his legs almost parallel to the woman as his torso lies prone upon her belly, his face being directed downward between her spread and lifted thighs.

This position is very common, and is convenient to assume. It can be quite pleasurable to the woman, and, being particularly useful for progressions from cunnilinctus to the sixty-nine, it should be considered in connection with the section later devoted to that subject. Even there, however, it must be noted that the sixty-nine is usually not engaged in with the man lying on top of the woman, owing in part precisely to the difficulty of the type of downward cunnilinctus here being discussed (which is that of almost all positions for the sixty-nine except the acrobatic "twisted" form), and owing in even greater part to the woman's feeling choked or impaled by the penis coming down at her orally from above. For cunnilinctus alone, not in the sixty-nine position, the downward form does not seem to be at all as effective or as convenient as upward cunnilinctus. The notes on lingual technique which follow are therefore drafted almost entirely with an eye to upward cunnilinctus, and the cunnilinctor or cunnilinguist who prefers or who must for any reason employ the downward form, can draw from the following notes whatever is useful in, or applicable to, downward cunnilinctus as well.

The reasons for the greater effectiveness of upward positions in cunnilinctus, and for licking motions of the mouth and tongue sweeping upward from the vaginal opening toward the clitoris, rather than the reverse, are the following – quite aside from the down-tilting of the adult female pelvis already mentioned. (In relation to the following, the reader is recommended to examine the splendid drawings of the *true* angle and position of the clitoris – seldom understood and almost never illustrated – in Dr. Gérard Zwang's magistral *Le Sexe de la Femme*, Paris: La Jeune Parque/Pauvert, 1967. This is the only such serious study of the true forms and appearance of the female genitals in existence, and is astonishingly illustrated from the viewpoint of both medical science and erotic art.) The clitoris projects *downward* along the vulva, this being true both of the exposed portion of the glans clitoridis and of the body of the clitoris which is curved backward and down beneath the clitoridal prepuce. Obviously, therefore, the glans clitoridis will receive with greater directness and therefore with greater resistance and therefore with greater force a tongue-stroke directed *upward*, *against it*, than it will receive a stroke travelling *downward*, *over* the clitoris, and striking the upper edge of the glans clitoridis only obliquely and in passing.

Furthermore, situated as the clitoris is, just at the anterior commissure of the labia minora – the point where the smaller or inner vulvar lips join together at the top of the vulva – it is almost certain to be reached and titillated by a tongue-tip stroke running upward between the guiding nymphæ or inner lips (in addition to the excitement to these spread-open lips themselves); whereas a downward stroke of the tongue, having no such guides, is actually likely to miss the clitoris, particularly if it is small or has not yet erected and swelled at its glans, in both of which cases it is especially important that the clitoris should be rapidly found and titillated.

Finally, it is almost impossible for the tongue-tip to be pressed into the vaginal introitus when the man's head faces downward between the woman's thighs, and thus this important subsidiary caress in cunnilinctus is necessarily lost. This is caused in part by the difficulty of getting the head bent far enough forward, down and between the woman's thighs, for the man's mouth to be in accurate apposition to the introitus, and in part because the whole angle of the woman's vaginal axis is upward and back, the floor of the vagina thus rising at a slant and opposing the entry of the man's tongue when he faces downward. Also, and very importantly, this position does not allow the powerful forward and upward thrust of the tongue, in entering the vagina however superficially, but only the comparatively weak downward tongue-thrust. This is a natural quality of the tongue, which is intended to rise upward in the vault of the mouth, and can serve no purpose pressing downward against the lower jaw.

Even if it is possible for the man to press far enough forward and down with his head, entering it well between the woman's thighs, the bony structure of her symphysis pubis is in just such a position – with its lower point closest to the vulva at a spot somewhere between the clitoris and the urinary meatus – as to press against the chin of the downward-facing man, and make a powerful and controlled forward thrust of his tongue in cunnilinctus difficult if not impossible. About the only downward cunnilinctual position in which the tongue-tip can be easily pressed into the vagina is that in which the woman squats or kneels above the supine man, facing his feet — a rather rare posture (except in the sixty-nine), owing to its masochistic tone for the man. The tongue-tip can, however, easily be pressed into the vaginal introitus during upward cunnilinctus, in almost any position, especially if the woman will make the effort to open her vagina to the man's tongue, by straining downward with strong abdominal pressure (Walthard's method in vaginismus), the action being quite similar to straining during defæcation, and employing the same pelvic muscles.

For all these reasons, I consider upward cunnilinctus far & away more important, and the discussion of positions for cunnilinctus at the end of the present essay therefore concerns itself largely with postures in which the woman is supine on various supports, with all the matching positions of the man's body: postures in which it is upward cunnilinctus, and not downward, in which the couple engage. It should be borne in mind, in understanding the concept of upward cunnilinctus, that the tongue is of course able to lick downward with its upper side (by bending the head downward) as well as upward, but not as powerfully. The tongue is also able to lick upward with its underside (by projecting it strongly out of the mouth) as well as downward, but again not so powerfully. Likewise, the alternate stroking and prodding of the clitoris with the upper- and under-sides of the tongue, in a sort of flicking, fencing motion, is most gratifying to the woman, as is also a round-&-round motion of the tongue-tip over the body of the clitoris or just at its glans, a motion which alternately employs the upper- and under-sides of the tongue. The same is true of the up-&-down or side-to-side "double-tonguing," similar to that of flute-playing, already mentioned. "Triple-tonguing," which is sometimes reported, is obviously meaningless or futile, since the tongue has only two sides.

A further property of the tongue and of its motion which should be borne in mind is that there is an appreciable difference between the actions of licking and of lapping. In lapping, the tongue is held out and is kept rather soft, with its tip rounded and with its upper side – or, occasionally, its underside – held flat against the object being lapped. The lapping motion is produced meanwhile in part by an upward turning of the head itself, the tongue usually retreating from the object during the downward stroke of the head, though up-&-down lapping is, in fact, quite simple and feasible, and is very useful in cunnilinctus. Side-to-side and round-&-round lapping should also be mentioned. Licking, on the other hand, is a motion principally of the tongue, which is kept rather tense, with its tip pointed; and the head may or may not assist (with upward and downward motion) as the tongue moves side-to-side, or up-&-down from the lower teeth to the upper, and the reverse, turning its tip sharply upward on the up-stroke, and sharply downward on the down-stroke. Some of the other properties and abilities of the tongue – little known and seldom encountered – especially as regards flicking or fencing motions, will be explored in depth in the later section, under Fellation, entitled "A Practical Treatise." These also have their obvious uses during cunnilinctus. The cunnilinguist's *tongue* should be kept in good condition. Excessively bright red color of the tongue, or heavy grooves or furrows in it, are signs of vitamin B deficiencies, which will also destroy the taste-buds. (Liver, wheat-germ, and brewer's yeast in the diet will remedy this.)

Actually, it would be almost impossible to describe and discuss in detailed fashion all the various oral and lingual caresses possible during cunnilinctus, nor will anyone ever become a master at this art who is not inspired to use his imagination in combining and even inventing new lingual titillations and maneuvres, and long and tantalizing oral itineraries over the woman's whole body before arriving at her genitals, from her mouth, face, ears, shoulders, breasts and nipples, on down; and from her toes, insteps, the hollows under her knees, thighs, and on up. This is known in all cultures among voluptuaries, and is sometimes called the "Tongue-Bath," "Around the World," or "A Trip to the Moon" (alluding to anilinctus during the tour). All such itineraries, and of course most intensely when arriving at the woman's intercrural furrow and her genital organs themselves, must employ all possible actions of the mouth, tongue, and teeth – these with care! – not forgetting the *outside* of the man's cheeks, and even his moustache or beard, and nose. All the actions should be used in any order or combination, and at artistically varying speeds and intensities of pressure. To enumerate again the various oral actions possible in all oragenital acts, these include: kissing, mouthing, lipping, tonguing (both licking, lapping, flicking, vibrating, and pointing or fencing and "stabbing" motions), nipping, biting, chewing – especially of the inner vulvar lips and the area surrounding and including the clitoris, but with great care – oral shaking, blowing, sucking, and swallowing.

When arriving actually at the final phase of lingual excitation of the clitoris and vulva, to bring the woman to (or almost to) orgasm, it should be remembered that the highest excitement to her will be produced only by *continued and concentrated* oral excitation, combined with all possible manual auxiliary assists, and that the man should not stop too frequently. The woman has her own special and increasing internal rhythm as she approaches orgasm, in the mounting crescendo of excitement she feels, and this can easily be lost if the man stops unexpectedly or often. It is then necessary to start all over again in re-creating her rhythmic approach to orgasm, though this will not usually take so long after such an accidental break or pause. To avoid such stopping during cunnilinctus, the man should make sure that his position allows him air to breathe, or else he can come up for air and take a long breath every once in a while, as in swimming. This, however, is likely to have an appearance of gasping that may seem either funny or unpleasant to him or to the woman, or both. It is particularly common during the sixty-nine, when the woman lies on top, often imprisoning the man's face in the grip of her thighs; but in that case the woman's position does not allow her to see his possible grimaces as he comes up — or, rather, pulls back — for air.

The very important problem of avoiding stopping the action while bringing a woman to orgasm is, of course, equally true in vaginal intercourse, but there the man's own matching rhythm of excitement will generally spur him on to stroke without stopping, in fact faster and faster, and sometimes even too fast for the woman to arrive at orgasm with him, with the result that he has to slow down. It is particularly important to avoid stopping in the digital excitation of the woman's clitoris by the man, when her orgasm is close, whether in connection with coitus or cunnilinctus. Very often, and with perfectly normal women, it is necessary to continue such digitation quite a long time without stopping either for rest or lubrication. Meanwhile, a certain amount of lubrication can be brought in without pause by means of the thumb or middle finger of the *other* hand, wetted in the man's own mouth, or he can learn to "change hands without missing a stroke." A difficult point, lubrication! The amount of time involved is sometimes as long as five minutes, at highest speed, not counting any amount of time that has already been spent on protracted foreplay or the caressing of the woman's genitals in a leisurely way. This means bringing her in to a finale while the man counts *slowly* and silently to three hundred (and not by fives!) while the fingers of the hand he is using flick sideways or round-&-round as rapidly as possible, but never losing the grip or placement over the glans clitoris with the middle- or fore-finger, or with the thumb or thumbs. This may involve from a thousand to fifteen hundred wrist strokes, depending on the speed, precisely on the style of piano runs, "shakes," and trills.

Clitoral digitation of this kind requires powerful forearm muscles, and can only come with practice. The best training for the man, other than actual digitation of the woman herself, *bien entendu,* is piano or harp playing, typewriting, or valve-work on wind instruments. The playing of the violin or of the ordinary guitar is perhaps the best training of all, owing to the necessary fingering of the strings at the neck of the instrument, but puts all the needed ability in the left hand instead of the right. This must be borne in mind as to the physical positions assumed by the bodies of the partners, as for instance in the "scissors" position ("*las tijeras*" or "T-upside-down") discussed at length above. People are never so unchanging about their right- or left-handedness as in sexual excitation, whether of themselves or of someone else.

It should be emphasized in this connection that the effective manual or wrist motion of clitoral excitation, for as much as five minutes at a time, does NOT involve either sidewise, circular, or vertical friction of the man's finger against the skin of the woman's vulvar tissues or her clitoris. What actually happens is that the clitoris is gripped or pressed lightly by the tip of the middle finger, or is pinched delicately between the thumb and one finger, while the hand *vibrates* rapidly sideways, circularly, or up-&-down, pressing the clitoris against the underlying vulvar flesh and the pubic bones, *without any friction or slipping* against the vulvar tissues. The motion is almost identical to that of fingering a violin or guitar string, especially in trilling. If actual friction were to be allowed, it would very rapidly dry off the woman's genital sweat or lubricating secretion, and would require endless lubrication with saliva by the man, transferred by his fingers from his mouth. Each such lubricating gesture might involve his stopping – or, if brought in by the other hand, his faltering – in the titillating motion at the clitoris. The probable result would be that either, if he refrained from stopping, the woman's vulva would become very overheated, and her clitoris excruciatingly irritated; or else – if he did continually stop to lick his fingers – the woman would probably never have an orgasm at all. In the lack of the ability on the part of many men to perform this rapid and unremitting wrist motion, or rather in the lack of their learning to do so (it is not really difficult at all), cunnilinctus has the great advantage of carrying all the necessary oral lubrication with it, whether alone or in combination with finger motions. The vibrating massage motor, which will be discussed below, gets most of its real effect from a similar powerful vibrating motion, actual friction against the tissues being unimportant and undesirable at high speeds.

The reference earlier to the counting of time – not strokes! – during sexual activity is worth a brief further note. Such counting is very well known among men, but is usually employed as a way of concentrating the mental attention of the man *away* from the sexual act being performed, and so lengthening his "staying power" in the act, before his own orgasm. Even better than simple counting, which is likely to give the man a feeling of desperation when the numbers get high, or over a thousand, are continuous series of multiplications – two-times-two are four, times four are sixteen, times sixteen are . . . and so forth. One should not use the same series all the time, but change to three-times-three, occasionally, etc., to avoid learning the number-series by heart, which would of course diminish the necessary mental concentration. I have also heard of playing imaginary or blindfold chess in this way, and for the same purpose, and especially attempting the famous and solitary "Knight's Tour" of the chessboard, like checker-jumping. This is more common in the Orient, where certain drugs or ointments are also used for the same purpose, such as rubbing the head of the penis before intercourse with a salve made of macerated garlic in an oil base.

It should be unnecessary to mention that, whatever system is used – even the simple counting of elapsed seconds, as "One hippopotamus, two hippopotamus," etc. – the man must not for an instant relax the physical motions of the sexual act in his original rhythm, even increasing or changing these as necessary. The lips should never be moved, nor any sound be made that could betray the fact of such counting to the woman, as she will unerringly assess this as an insult to her: as though the man were just gritting his teeth and hanging on, to try to satisfy her, which is – alas! – all too often the case. If the woman is so undiplomatic as to *ask*, afterward or during the act itself, whether the man counts or in some other way attempts to distract his attention in order to "stay," he should gallantly deny this. The same is even more true of mental concentration in the opposite sense: where the man or woman attempts to *create* sexual excitement by fantasying that the partner is really someone else, some movie-star, or similar; or by fantasying perverted or orgiastic sexual acts being watched or performed simultaneously. Such fantasies are more common than is realized, and it is both unkind and unwise in many ways to admit to them. Truth is what you feel, not what you do.

VI

ALL GENITAL excitations in which the tongue is used are likely to be more effective if the tongue is moved rapidly and with decided pressure. The tongue tires easily, and cunnilingual movements will usually prove easier and more powerful, as well as more controllable and more effective, if part of the motion is taken by the mouth and lips, and by the head and neck. Again, rapid and forcible motions will produce more excitement in the woman, and this remains true even though the woman's imagination may be more charmed and excited – as the man's is certainly likely to be in cunnilinctus – by a slow, languorous lingual and oral adoration. Some women like, and even beg for, an alternation of fast and slow, in order to rest the irritated clitoris.

Aside from mouthing and lingual motions, the man may nip the woman's nymphæ with his lips, and then suck them, together or separately, or pull them outward lightly – again, separately or together – with his lips or teeth (as, of course, with his finger-tips or thumbs), and worry them playfully; alternating this with licking up between the nymphæ if they have become nipped together like a butterfly's wings. The man can even bite the nymphæ, but this should obviously be done only with great care. The man can also bite the clitoris – lightly! – or scratch it with his teeth, dragging the upper and lower front-teeth against the clitoris alternately, and varying this by biting the woman's pubis and inner thighs. If he has her thighs held well up high, her knees almost folded back on her breast as she lies on her back, her whole intercrural area is open before him and such biting can even include her buttocks and peri-anal area. The clitoris can and should be seized in the lips and, as it were, pumped in-&-out

of the mouth with a strong suction of the lips and cheeks. This is tremendously pleasurable to the woman.

One should remember, however, that the clitoris is a very small organ, for all its remarkable sensitivity. Its exposed portion, the glans clitoris, is seldom more than from an eighth to a quarter of an inch in width, and from a little more than an eighth to three-eighths of an inch longitudinally. That is, somewhere between the size of a very small pea and of a small coffee-bean. These dimensions hold for perhaps three-quarters of all women of the white race, and are not appreciably different in other races, so far as serious measurements are available. The larger clitorides, of the remaining 20-odd per cent of the women, are also not very much larger. *Very* small – rice-size – clitorides are quite rare, as are very small penises: that is, penises of less than five inches (erect length) in the adult; while large penises – seven to nine inches – are rather common, as are the larger than average clitorides.

It must of course be borne in mind that these figures concern only the visible or exposed tip of the clitoris. The curved shaft of the clitoris, which lies hidden under the skin of the upper vulvar groove, where it is supported by the flesh underneath, and eventually by the pubic bone, is naturally a good deal longer; but being far less well innervated than the glans, it is not of equal importance in the excitement of the woman and in bringing her on toward orgasm. Many women, however, feel considerable excitement and pleasure in having the outer part of the shaft of the clitoris – the part just in back of the glans, and hidden under the skin, possibly an inch in length – gripped by the fingers, and its skin pushed & pulled, up-&-down, in a motion similar to the simple masturbation of the penis by moving its skin.

The man can even rub his nose momentarily in the woman's vulva, up-&-down, or round-&-round, or – which can be done more briskly – from side to side. Or he can press the tip of his nose firmly in the vaginal opening or the vulvar groove or at the clitoris, and shake his head from side to side, shaking the vulvar flesh in this way at the same time. He can also rub his chin against the widely-opened vulva, either by shaking or nodding his head, or by moving his jaw up-&-down or from side to side. The latter gesture can be done much more easily, and more quickly and firmly, but, as has already been warned, this should be done with care and without becoming too enthusiastically thoughtless, as the jaw can be dislocated by too great a sidewise effort. Correctly done, however, it can be kept up for a surprising amount of time, similar to the bruxism or "tooth-grinding" during the sleep of anxious individuals, which is similarly done by sliding the back of the jaws sidewise across each other.

Many women do not enjoy cunnilinctus when the man even so much as needs a shave, since the beard-bristles irritate the very sensitive inner thighs. A perfectly smooth, newly-shaven chin is probably best in cunnilinctus, or else a beard long enough not to be stubbly and irritating. Some women, however, specifically enjoy chin caresses of the vulva very much when the man *does* need a shave, and has on his chin a slight stubbly growth of beard, which itches and urticates the vulva and clitoris pleasurably. Other women – surely the majority – find this extremely painful and irritating, although if the man's beard growth is only very slightly prickly, and if the woman will "free herself," in a manner of speaking, to the sensation, she may learn to enjoy it.

Quite a point is made of this matter of the stubbly growth on the unshaven chin, in the absolute pæan to cunnilinctus opening the 17th chapter of *Happiness Bastard* by a hitherto-unknown author signing himself Kirby Doyle (North Hollywood: Essex House, 1968), an extremely powerful, no-punches-pulled novel or personal testimony, in Céline's and Henry Miller's stream-of-consciousness style. Doyle's protagonist or anti-hero, self-mockingly called Tully McSwine, is planning to write a manual of orasexual technique to be called *Oral Dalliance* (another one!), of which the sonorous motto is to be: "The implementation and insurance of a successful performance depend wholly upon . . . Free Improvisation!" Which nobody can deny. He thinks of cunnilinctus plainly as a return to the mother's womb, and fantasies himself as diving into his girl's vagina headfirst, or even stretching it and wearing it over his face, "from eyebrows to chin, like a hot meaty mask." As to his unshaven chin-stubble, when he presses in his lower jaw; "according to her testimony, the blazing sensitivity of the walls of her vagina were heightened to near-insanity if I had a two- or three-day growth of beard on my face, although I would hesitate to make a generalization out of this point, receiving as I have, from females less inclined to this variation, complaints to the effect . . . *take it easy . . . you're scratch'n hell out'a me!*"

The solution to this problem is actually extremely simple. There is no need to leap out of bed to give oneself a quick once-over with a shaving machine, while the woman palpitates impatiently or even contemptuously on the couch. The man in cunnilinctus simply places one of his palms, cupped tightly against his chin, so that only the *back* of his hand touches the woman's vulva, which is completely protected in this way from the touch of his chin-stubble. Meanwhile, he should certainly take the occasion to stretch out the thumb or forefinger of the same hand (the middle finger is curiously immobilized in this position, as in the well-known Violinist's Ring-Finger puzzle), the hand being held so that the thumb does not go up the side of his face, but is jutting directly forward and up from his chin; and drive his digit into the woman's vagina by pressing forward with his hand and chin at every lapping motion of his tongue, simultaneously, at her clitoris or vulvar groove. This is easier to do than it is to describe. Words are lengthy things.

Women and sometimes men often express the wish, quite frankly, that there might be some way to have coitus at the same time as cunnilinctus, but with the same man, and not in a trio orgy with all the emotional confusion – and jealousy – and the homosexual tone inevitable in orgies. The simple thumb-gesture just described is perhaps the closest approximation to simultaneous cunnilinctus and coitus, as felt subjectively by the woman. French voluptuaries of the late eighteenth century refined and formalized this chin-&-finger technique in the chinstrap-dildo. (Actually, a double strap is necessary to prevent it from falling off in the heat of action: one strap behind the neck and another over the top of the head.) But the ordinary thumb or forefinger works just as well, and is *human*. The chinstrap-dildo is, in any case, overartful and something of an absurdity, since it does not do anything that cannot be done – and better – with a simple dildo or phalliform fruit such as a banana held in the hand during cunnilinctus, and pumped simultaneously, or even by one or both thumbs held together in front of the chin. The great advantage of cunnilinctus is that *it requires no mechanical equipment*. Leave it that way! We will return to this point in the matter of vibrating massage-motors used erotically.

A note is relevant at this point concerning moustaches and beards in general, in connection with cunnilinctus. The beard is in a period of eclipse at the present time, being worn mostly by older men as a symbol of their age and dignity, and by young men as a symbol of their Bohemianism and, possibly, virility. Both, in fact, seek in it a virile symbol. Still, there are many fervid cunnilinguists precisely among these two classes: the older men because of advancing genital impotence, which makes cunnilinctus their particular assist, to excite both the woman and themselves; and the arty young men because of an emotional and erotic sensitivity which very often leads to a total pansexuality with women, which must invariably include oragenitalism. There is also – it is useless to deny or overlook it – more than a touch of evident masochism and self-punishment in both young and old men of the types just noted. Masochism in the male is invariably an orally-linked neurosis, of which cunnilinctus is one of the most usual and standard expressions. In fact, it is perhaps the mildest and most normal.

In cunnilinctus, the beard – if soft – is likely to tickle the woman's thighs and vulva in a delicate way which she will probably enjoy. A bristly beard, on the other hand, is likely to irritate her thighs and vulva, and may even become tangled with her vulvar hair – especially if it is curly or long! Just as the woman, during fellation, will often leave one or two of the hairs of her head behind, tangled in the man's pubic thatch, especially if her head-hair is long; just so a man is likely to find one or more of the woman's pubic hairs mixed into his beard or moustache after cunnilinctus. In general, the moustache is not likely to irritate the woman genitally, but will probably tickle her fancy or excite her specially. A silky moustache is more likely to tickle, and a bristly one more likely to excite; though it should be remembered that tickling and titillation are closely related and sometimes interchangeable.

The beard and moustache have in common the tendency to sop up the vaginal secretions, and, if gray or white, to be stained by them. The stain will not show in dark, nor – being amber in color – in blond hair. Of course, during or near menstruation there is more danger of staining, but most men do not cunnilingue the menstruous woman: a point to which we will return. The moustache and beard, even if unstained, are likely to retain the vulvar odor for a few hours, and this may or may not be desirable to the man, depending upon his reaction to this odor. Most men, and especially most men who engage in cunnilinctus, very much like the vulvar odor when it is not too strong or acid, and a trace of it in their moustache may be quite pleasant to carry about with them, or to fall asleep with on the pillow that has been folded or pressed under the woman's thighs during cunnilinctus to raise her pubis to the man's lips.

One last point before leaving beards and moustaches: a man with a waxed and pointed moustache – the so-called British Air Officer or Australian style – should probably refrain from cunnilinctus. If the points are well waxed and withstand cunnilinctus, they may stab and irritate the woman's thighs. If they are not, they will droop and separate, and the sort of fop who would wear a waxed moustache is usually a pretty sorry and romantically uninspiring spectacle with his hirsute glory drooping and bedraggled.

VII

The part the woman plays in cunnilinctus need not be entirely passive, and seldom is. At the very least, the woman must be able to *give herself*, or free herself, to the sensations she feels, and not to fight them. The secret about female impotence or frigidity, is that many women are frightened to "let go," or "jump off the deep end," as they sometimes phrase it, which they conceive of as involving dangers of chaotic loss of personality, or annihilation, as seen in the obvious loss of control over oneself expressed by the man at his own orgasm. There is even often an unexpressed animosity against the man, or all men, involved in the woman's not being able to reach orgasm. This generally stems from leftover fears of parental authority, especially that of the woman's own mother, as though every bit of sexual pleasure achieved were done in despite of the mother – or stolen from her. Orgastic potency is, therefore, a positive sign of emotional maturity, and of freeing oneself from parental lead-strings and trammels, fears, prohibitions, and the like. A man or woman who cannot arrive at orgasm without tremendous emotional effort, or excessively protracted intercourse (half an hour or more), is actually expressing fear and possibly hatred of the opposite sex, and is well on the way to being or becoming homosexual. Psychoanalysis can help.

In all sexual excitation, therefore, and most particularly in cunnilinctus, it is necessary for the woman to achieve this physical and emotional *freeing of herself*, throwing herself fully and willingly into the maelstrom of sensation. A woman who tenses herself desirously to the man's mouth in cunnilinctus, and who lifts and sways her hips to assist him, opening her vulva passionately to him while letting her mind dwell on the pleasure she feels or expects to feel, and on her *love* for the man and how close she is to him, *and especially how much she would like to have his baby and to nurse it at her breast*, as the man may be thought of as "nursing" at her during cunnilinctus . . . such a woman is almost certain to have a complete and satisfactory orgasm – perhaps several. This is seldom the case (and, as to multiple orgasm, never the case) with an angry and unloving woman who lies limp and bored, doing her "marital duty," or holding herself tensely separate, her mind occupied and isolated in narcissistic notions or fears about herself, her body, and her feminist "rights and wrongs," or who may even be letting her mind wander to household worries or some other mundane triviality. Fears about becoming pregnant will also usually prevent the woman from having orgasm. The woman must either feel she is using some birth-control method or pill that protects her from unwanted pregnancy, or she must deeply desire to become pregnant. Without such mental calm and rightness, and *the possibility of erotic concentration*, orgasm is seldom possible. That all this is even more true of vaginal intercourse goes without saying.

The special part the woman plays, by means of her physical motions during cunnilinctus, depends largely on the position taken. In *upward cunnilinctus*, as already discussed and described, which is the usual kind, the woman's physical coöperation is generally limited, by her lying on her back, to lifting and rotating her hips, and opening and thrusting with her pubis and vulva, to meet the man's oral motions. She can also use her hands in many ways, both on her own body (crossed over her breasts and nipples, or opening and pressing closed the lips of her vulva, or pressing on the sides or the glans of her clitoris), and on the man's head and body, including his genitals if his torso is so turned that she can reach them. In *downward cunnilinctus*, and in particular in all positions where the woman is kneeling, lying, or even standing or squatting over the man's face (whether facing in the same or the opposite direction to him), the motions of her body during cunnilinctus are freed of constraint and can become very important and even spectacular.

In these same positions, too, the man's own oral motions are sometimes quite restricted and limited by the woman's body over or upon him, which puts the responsibility for the motion on her. This tends toward a female-dominant and male-masochistic tone, in the action, or rather in the emotions the participants have about it, but it is possible to avoid this. The woman's astraddle motions in this way, over the man's face, are also of extreme importance during the sixty-nine, when – as is usual – she lies on top. This includes the period while she is straddling the man's face, before bending forward to accept his penis orally; and cunnilinctus alone can also be returned to, if he has his orgasm first during the sixty-nine, the woman rising back to a kneeling position astraddle his face, and, as it were, riding out her own pleasure. Kneeling thus over the man, facing his feet, and during the sixty-nine, the woman can sink back and press the man's *nose* into her vagina. He continues cunnilinctus while breathing through his mouth.

All the motions of her hips and torso that the woman can use in coital postures where she lies, kneels, stands, or squats over the man, can also be used when she is in the same positions over the man for cunnilinctus or the sixty-nine. In particular the woman can use – and should make a real effort to try to learn, and learn well – the superb pelvic motion or mysterious gyration first made public in the erotic technique manual, *Les Paradis Charnels* (Paris, 1903, by "Dr. A.-S. Lagail," the poet Alphonse Gallais). This is known in French under the jocular name of "*La Diligence de Lyon*" (The Lyons Stagecoach), about which a famous hoax or shaggy-dog story is told, and in English as "The Candy Bar," from a short erotic film-strip of that title circulated during the 1950's, in which the method of doing this was shown, with extraordinary *maestria* and perfect seat, by a beautiful young American call-girl kneeling astraddle the lucky man.

The *Diligence de Lyon* or "Candy Bar" is a rapid and continuous forward-&-backward rolling motion of the kneeling woman's hips, similar to that known in horseback riding under the name of *posting* or "broncho-busting," where the rider's body sinks and rises rhythmically forward and backward to match the motions of the galloping or bucking horse. In the human version the man may not be making any motions at all, while the woman *posts*. Although her hip motions can also be from side-to-side, in a sort of flat figure-eight (which is also much easier to do), in the true *Diligence de Lyon* or "Candy Bar" the trajectory described by the woman's pelvis, as seen in profile, is that of a figure-eight lying vertically on its edge, the mathematical symbol for infinity: ∞ her whole body riding in this way on the edge of infinity.

At her orgasm during cunnilinctus, if this is taken to the point of affording her an orgasm, the woman is very likely to find the labial and lingual excitation so pleasurable as to be intolerable. In positions where she is lying on her back, or sitting, she will probably try to push the man's head away from her vulva with her hands, or else try to immobilize his head by tightening her thighs around it. Some women, however, want even stronger pressure of the man's mouth at orgasm, and passionately press his head to the vulva with both hands as the orgasm approaches, sometimes clutching his hair and ears painfully, or digging the fingernails cruelly but unconsciously (?) into his face and neck. These are just the hazards of the game, and though they make it difficult for the man to do a good job, they must be accepted with a certain good grace, protecting one's eyes carefully however. The type of woman who tries to push the man's face away from her vulva at her orgasm during cunnilinctus is even more likely to hurt him, in the wild frenzy of her paroxysm, by putting her fingers into his eyes as she pushes his face away, or by scratching his face, or pulling his hair or ears. One man with bushy eyebrows complained to me that the woman grabbed him by these, directing his head as though with handlebars. (I suggested a visor.)

Either type of woman is likely to grip the man's head so tightly with her thighs as to hurt him or make him feel dizzy, not to mention – especially in positions for cunnilinctus in which the woman is over the man – sitting on or clamping his face in such a position that he cannot breathe. In such a case, the man should not panic but should fall back on a sort of mild erotic judo: he must simply arrange to get one hand and forearm wedged up vertically between his mouth and the woman's vulva, and free himself by levering her thighs apart, or simply by throwing her over on her side. With either type of woman, the man should be prepared for her orgasm behavior – especially if he has already experienced it with the same woman before – both in order to prevent her from hurting him accidentally, and to be able to administer those few ultimate strokes to her vulva or clitoris with his tongue, against her will, or to hang on to her vulva and clitoris at the moment of her orgasm by powerful suction or even by careful nipping or biting with the lips.

For it is precisely at, and immediately before and after her orgasm, when the woman feels that she cannot possibly endure the excruciating pleasure of any further excitation, that such excitation will be most poignantly delightful to her. If the woman effectively prevents the man from thus exciting her orally at her orgasm, his fingers can and should be held in readiness for this eventuality, by being near her vulva, or in her vagina and/or anus. He can thus sharpen her orgasm to its finest degree by rubbing or pinching her clitoris, or rolling it between the tips of the thumb and forefinger; or by plunging or twisting motions, if in her vagina or anus, as will be discussed further below, in considering anal digitation or "postillioning."

If the man cannot reach the woman's breasts with his hands during cunnilinctus, either because of his position, or because – she being dressed – he cannot get his hands down under the neckline of her dress, nor through the side-placket, nor up from beneath its skirt; the woman may cross her arms, and fondle her own breasts, either through her clothes or bare, her right hand gripping her left breast, and vice versa. As already noted, she can also reach down to her own genitals to assist the man there with her own hands, opening and pressing closed the lips of her vulva, rubbing these up and down against each other and against the man's tongue and mouth, or pressing on both sides of the glans of her clitoris. This is possible even when she is dressed, her clothes having obviously been pushed up by the man in order to tongue her. (Though it is sometimes practical, if perverse, to cunnilingue the woman *through* her panties, bikini, or nightgown.)

The woman can likewise easily reach down the neck of her dress, when the man is in positions where he cannot, and she will also know better than the man how to pluck and excite her own nipples, either with the fingertips, or between the sides of her forefingers and middle fingers, as women sometimes do with their soapy hands crossed over their breasts in the bathtub. Many women object to engaging in any autoerotic acts of this kind, during sexual activity with the man, but this is usually caused – if not by egoism or excessive romanticism – by false shame: the thought that it is some kind of masturbation. Of course it is, but it would be just as masturbatory if it were the man who were doing it for her. When he is simply not in a position to do so, she should frankly help both of them by doing it herself.

The oral-erotic emotions and sensations experienced by the woman are highly important, though in cunnilinctus one usually thinks only of the man's evident oral desires. The woman, no matter how pudibund she may be as to what she might consider self-masturbation, can at least lick her own lips wetly meanwhile, to reproduce some of the sensation of being kissed, or may suck or bite her own fingers or thumb for the oral-erotic satisfaction she may need. It is thumb-sucking, all right, but then what is cunnilinctus? Love-cries and inarticulate murmurs and avowals by the woman, just before and at the moment of her orgasm, are a very important verbalization or exteriorization of similar oral-erotic needs. It is important that these *should not be repressed*, neither by ideas of dignity or shame, nor by the possible presence of snoopy neighbors behind the wall. If the neighbors do not like it, they can move. The sort of neighbors who count the jouncing of anyone's bedsprings but their own are, in any case, undesirable. Their prudery is really jealousy, of course.

However, children above the age of about six months are likely to be wakened and frightened by the cries of the parents in intercourse or at orgasm, if in the same room, and to come to think of sexual intercourse as a sadistic act. This is very dangerous to the child's own psychosexual development. There are already far too many such identifications in the movies, television, and other irresponsible arts, advertisements, and other propaganda that the child will later be subjected to publicly. Many children similarly misunderstand overseen oragenital acts, which they imagine to involve one parent "eating up the other alive," their crying-out at orgasm being identified as roars or death-groans. This is especially so when these cries involve such verbal ejaculations as "*I'm dying!*" or "*You're killing me!*" and the like, as is quite common since many people unconsciously do identify orgasm and death, as in the polite symbolizations in music of the "Love-Death" in *Tristan & Isolde*.

In all cases, being present at the sexual relations of adults excites the child sexually – it also visibly excites household pets – and often to a degree beyond the child's ability to absorb pleasurably. The excess is therefore necessarily experienced by the child as something frightening and overwhelming. If at all possible, children should sleep in a nursery-room of their own after about the age of six months, where they will not be observing the parents' sex life, and the parents will not be spying on theirs. A screened corner will serve.

The purpose here is as much to protect the parents' own sexual spontaneity, and their right to be as noisy and violent as they wish, both in the sexual act and at orgasm, as to protect the child from unabsorbable excitement and erroneous sadistic identifications. If no separate nursery-room is possible, the parents may have to arrange their sexual lives on the couch in the parlor, after the children have gone to bed, as they doubtless did when they were courting. People who purposely display their sexual intimacy to unprepared children above an age when they can reasonably be expected not to understand it nor to respond to it (six months, at the outside limit), or who actually use or involve children physically in their sexual acts — sometimes in sadistic or other perverted ways — are beneath contempt. The sexual education of prepubescent children by the visible example of the sexual acts of adults or older adolescents, which they are then expected to repeat *among themselves* later, is a different matter, and does not yet exist on any large scale in Western culture. Where it does occur, it is usually thought of as an accidental or deplorable result of the overcrowded living conditions of the poor. Sexual training by live example is essential, but it is still for the future.

Erotic verbalization by men, as part of their customary erotic foreplay and especially at orgasm, is normally quite violent and domineering. This is true of all mammals, many of which also bite and strike the female meanwhile: the unquestionable origin of kissing and caressing, as is often forgotten in attempting to be delicate and refined about one's love-making. The man's verbalization is itself often highly erotic in vocabulary, sometimes threatening and insulting, or merely profane or obscene. Even simply wild animal-like grunts or roars at orgasm. The wife grows to understand this, often to appreciate and expect it. But it is terrifying to very young children, who are certain to misunderstand it as dangerous and cruel. On the other hand, men who talk sweet poetry, or formulate compliments, or who emit charmingly hushed and dove-like sounds of polite passion at such a moment, are faking it.

VIII

After cunnilinctus, and in fact after all oragenital acts, the psychological position of the partners is often delicately uneasy, owing to the unconscious presence of ideas of sexual submission and mastery involved in such acts. Curiously enough this is even true as to the sixty-nine, which is never really the perfect equilibrium one might think, especially not for the person who has taken the bottom position. The oral partner in any oragenital act may feel "used," and the genital partner (especially the man) may feel this even more intensely, or may feel vaguely at a disadvantage, as though having been under uncomfortably close pelvic scrutiny. Women particularly fear such scrutiny by the lover, except during the heat of his passionate approach, in the absurd but very prevalent notion that the female genitals are somehow "naturally ugly" or repulsive. Psychologically this stems from unconscious ideas – shared often by both men and women – that women are "nothing but castrated men," and the revulsion against the female genitals, even by women themselves, is thus based on the lack of the penis, which is conceived of as making the female genitals "inferior." Anyone who has ever held a newborn baby while its navel-cord was being cut is not again ever in any real doubt as to which sex's genital organs really perform the "superior" function! The marvel of phallic erection simply will not compare with the miracle of gestation and birth.

Nevertheless, it is essential, in view of the deeply ingrained ideas of organ-inferiority from which women and many men suffer, to avoid any physical or verbal gestures or expressions of rejection, that might be construed as post-orgasm disgust for any of the bodily liquors of the partner that may have appeared during the act, such as sweat, semen, and the woman's vaginal secretion. Many people do not even like kissing or speaking after orgasm, but wish to rest and regain their forces. This is as true of satisfactory orgasm as of unsatisfactory orgasm, or one that has been missed completely, as often by the woman. If loving conversation is seldom desired, humorous banter is even less welcome. No mocking allusions should be made to the odd positions or appearance into which the other partner may have fallen, limp, at orgasm. It is, for example, rather dubiously humorous for a woman to burst out laughing at the man who has cunnilingued her – on coming to, later, to find his face staring up at her between her thighs – and to ask him why his eyebrows do not match his "beard," and the like.

The man will usually find, after cunnilinctus, that his face is wet from the woman's vaginal liquor, and he will want to wipe it dry. This can be done by turning his face against the woman's thigh – an intimate touch, and one that she can object to only lovingly and amusèdly, it at all – or on the sheets, or on a dry spot on the pillow or a corner of the thrown-back upper sheet or bed-covers, if they are lying on a bed. Note that all the man's motions and positions are generally more free and varied, in cunnilinctus, if he sits on a rug at the side of the bed or sofa on which the woman lies, than if he gets on or into the bed with her.

It is hardly necessary to mention that cunnilinctus cannot easily be performed beneath the bed-covers, as can coitus – if necessary. Most people find even coitus more pleasant and free when uncovered, and like to reserve the covers to warm themselves later if the body feels suddenly chilled in the air after the exertion of coitus. It is not exactly true to say that oragenitalism of any sort is *impossible* under the covers, and there may be people who indulge in it that way. But I am sure they are in the minority, as it would probably result in an overpowering sensation or actuality of suffocation to the partner whose head would be beneath the covers, especially if it were the cunnilinguent man, and to both partners in the sixty-nine. A Vermont farm-girl once told me that both she and her lover had nearly smothered in attempting a sixty-nine while hidden in a haystack. I myself once saw two people on a ski-trip disappear through the snow-crust in the hot frenzy of their lovemaking. Most people do not, of course, make love in the snow, but they are missing something!

Unless the woman objects very much to the odor and taste of her own vulva, which many women do, the man should kiss her *on the mouth* as soon as he conveniently can after her orgasm subsides – especially after the first few times he cunnilingues her – in order to reassure himself, and her too, that she does not hold him in any contempt for having cunnilingued her, and, if anything, only loves him the more for it. This also creates the opposite and matching assurance, for the woman, that the man has not been disgusted by what he has done, to please her, and "still loves her." This nicety is very important – although not so much here as in fellation – because of the prevalent folk-idea of disgust and scorn toward oragenitalism, even on the part of people who imagine themselves to be very sophisticated and to have no such ignorant ideas. In fact, a really intelligent woman will force herself to accept this kiss, in spite of any moderate distaste she may feel for her own odor, or may even pull the man's face up to hers (possibly by the ears, like an amphora

— a playful and affectionate touch), to kiss him in gratitude and in love, or even to wipe his mouth and face with her hair, if it is long. Possibly also she may wish to engage in coitus with him, if she is one of the very many women who can have, and who like to have, several orgasms in quick succession. If the man has not yet had his orgasm, he will certainly want to engage in coitus with her, at that point, or will expect her to reciprocate with fellation. Coitus will probably be easier for her, at that point, as fellation requires quite a good deal of mental and technical concentration, which is not always true of coitus. It is the worst sort of sexual boorishness and bad taste to refuse genital satisfaction of *some* kind to the person who has just satisfied one — especially if orally.

If the woman simply cannot endure her own vulvar odor, or if her æsthetic sensibilities are outraged by the glistening appearance of the man's wetted face and lips — and possibly his moustache or beard — it is better for the man to wash, or at least to wipe his face on the bedsheet, his shirt-tail, or the woman's under-garments lying nearby. (Why not?) There is really no need for him to get up to wash, if there is no water near at hand by the bed, as in a drinking-carafe. Getting up may be quite an effort for him, particularly if the woman has masturbated (or fellated) him to orgasm while he cunnilingued her, as he will then have the usual post-coital pleasant and roseate tired feeling — that is, if he has really had an orgasm, and has not merely ejaculated without feelings of paroxysmic pleasure, as sometimes happens. Women who erroneously believe that a douche after intercourse has contraceptive value, and who leap up after intercourse to rush to the bathroom or bidet, understand very well how unpleasant and undesirable getting up at that languorous moment can be. If adjuncts such as wine, oranges, ice-cream, and so forth have been employed in cunnilinctus, as will be noted later, it will probably be necessary for the man to wash his face, if only for his own comfort, since it will be and will feel drawn and sticky.

When the woman seriously objects to her own vulvar taste and odor, the man should take care – when cunnilinctus is engaged in as a preparatory to coitus, or progresses to coitus after or before the woman's first orgasm – not to kiss her on the mouth, nor to bring his face directly before her own, if coitus is then engaged in, in a position where the mouth-kiss is possible. If he wishes to embrace her closely in such a position, he can still do so by putting his face to the side of hers and pressing his cheek to her, or to her temple; or by burying his mouth against her throat, or under her chin, or against her neck or shoulder, or even, if she openly objects to any contact with her own genital juices, against the bed. However, in the face of actual spoken or grimaced objection by the woman to any approach of his odorous face, the man had best draw up to rest on his hands, or should assume some type of coital position – such as the aforementioned "scissors" posture or "T-upside-down" – where his face is naturally withdrawn from hers.

A completely different approach to this minor problem is also possible, the man simply forcing his kiss upon the woman, after cunnilinctus, whether she objects or not. If this leads to angry words of any kind, he need merely *agree* with her that her vaginal taste and odor are too awful for any sensitive person to bear, and should get her out of his life at once. This is difficult, of course, if the two are married; but few people marry today, at any level of culture, without having very seriously tried out their sexual compatibility beforehand on a very broad spectrum of sexual acts. That is what the engagement period is for. This bold or swash-buckling approach to neurotic sexual difficulties on the part of the woman is the same as that suggested in the later section, on "Irrumation," as to women who purport to be unable or unwilling to swallow the man's semen after fellation. There is a great difference between a man's being gallant erotically, and his being a sexual imbecile. Women appreciate the first very much, but they secretly have the greatest of contempt for the second – sometimes not so secretly. In particular, it is not wise to engage over any long period in oragenital acts with any person who will not reciprocate with the matching oragenital act, whether or not in the sixty-nine form. One-sided oragenital relations are essentially masochistic and sadistic charades, whatever may be the disguise of æsthetic "inability" or whimsical refusal under which they parade.

A final or third solution also exists, in the matter of the woman's objection to her own vaginal fluids and odor. If her objection is only moderate, and she draws the line simply at the mouth-kiss, the man can, with great advantage, put his mouth to her ear during subsequent coitus, blowing or breathing warmly into the ear-hole, and tonguing and circling its ridges and lobe, and the hollow beneath and behind it, during the progress of coitus; ending by inserting his tongue-tip strongly into the ear at the woman's orgasm, possibly with boring or vibrating motions of the tongue-tip at the same time. It is also possible to suck lightly at the ear-hole, which gives one of the most exquisite sensations, but it is important that this be done very lightly, to avoid possible damage to the ear-drum deep inside. The same is true of blowing into the ear, which must be done very lightly. Tonguing of the ear will almost invariably be found to enhance the orgasm considerably – whether of men or of women – and, like anal digitation, when once successfully tried and experienced it will usually become an habitual part of the lovers' ritual.

One last practical point: When a cushion or a pillow has been placed under the woman's hips to facilitate cunnilinctus and possible subsequent coitus, it will almost always be found later to be stained by the woman's vaginal secretions. This stain is not so frequently found on the bed-sheets, when no pillow has been employed, since the woman's hips will usually have been somewhat elevated from the bed by the man's shoulders during cunnilinctus. The rather glairy or mucilaginous female secretion – which is released from the vagina slowly and viscidly – is much more likely to trickle down between the woman's buttocks, when these are elevated by the man's shoulders or fists, than to drip down onto the sheet. Some women have a very profuse secretion, especially immediately before and after menstruation and during pregnancy – but in most women it is not profuse enough to stain any cloth with which the vulva is not in direct contact. At any rate, it is the actually rather slow and viscid flow of the vaginal liquor that makes a pillow more likely than a sheet or cushion to be stained by this secretion, since a pillow is very soft, and will usually press up between the woman's buttocks as she lies on it, and conform to the shape of her perinæal and intergluteal groove, thus, by direct contact, catching the down-flowing vaginal secretion.

The peculiar and unempirical superstition that women ejaculate at their orgasm, as do men, or at least have some appreciable gush of fluid, can most easily be demonstrated to be erroneous during cunnilinctus or in *coitus condomatus*, where there is no backwash of semen to confuse the issue. An exceptionally profuse post-coital flow may exist in some few women, but it never under any circumstances shoots or gushes out like the male semen. The most recent studies of the subject have concluded that the woman's vaginal secretion during sexual excitement is only to a minor degree that of the glands of Bartholin, at the entrance to the vagina, which lubricate the entrance of the penis during intercourse; and that the woman's main secretion is really a sort of vaginal sweat, forming internally. This is similar to the breaking out of sweat across the forehead – as well as in the armpits and the crotch, *n.b.* – during many sorts of emotional excitement, especially fear or anxiety.

Because of the possibility of staining, a pillow is probably more practical than a cushion, for elevating a woman's hips during cunnilinctus – also for coitus – since a pillow is usually cased, and the linen casing can be removed and washed, where a cushion does not usually have this advantage. Also, the surface of cushions is likely to be of some hard or nubbly material not so pleasant to the skin as is linen. Cushions covered with slick plastic dust-covers need not be discussed, since this book is not written for anyone who would make love on a plastic pillow! Finally, a cushion is usually much harder and thicker than a pillow, and therefore more difficult to fold, and altogether less manageable. On the other hand, a cushion may sometimes have a surface more pleasant than the linen or cotton of a pillow, such as silk, satin, or velvet – though these stuffs may cause a rash to some sensitive skins – and the fact that it is harder than a pillow may make it unnecessary to fold it. Practically, however, men who enjoy cunnilinctus usually prefer to use a pillow, precisely because it is likely to sop up a good deal of the woman's vaginal liquor, and they find the vulvo-vaginal odor pleasant and mildly exciting even after intercourse has been completed. They therefore like to fall asleep on a pillow saturated with this odor. I have heard it claimed that sleeping on such a pillow is likely to cause the man to have erotic dreams, which seems both likely and pleasant. Dreams after intercourse or other sexual acts are specially interesting, and have been analyzed by Dr. Angel Garma.

The stain left on white cloth by the vaginal liquor is almost colorless, or of a clear yellowish amber color. Parenthetically, the vaginal secretion is of too clear a yellow, at darkest, to combine with the reddish menstrual blood to produce an orange stain on cloth, first because there is not enough of it, and second because the pigment of the menstrual discharge is much more active than that of the ordinary vaginal secretions. But the stain left after cunnilinctus or coitus immediately before or after menstruation may be somewhat brighter than usual, owing to the presence of a very small amount of blood in the vagina. The stain left by semen is easily distinguishable from the vaginal stain, as the granular lumps in the glutinous semen tend to disappear, and the semen then dries leaving a whitish stain – almost undiscernible on white cloth – and a characteristic crinkled and ridged appearance of the cloth. I have noted, in *Rationale of the Dirty Joke* (1968) First Series, p. 713, under "The Relationship With the Other Man," the concentration in jokes, and in folk-life as well, on seminal stains on towels or handkerchiefs as guilty evidence of adultery by the wife. Absurd as it may seem, this is nothing other than the plot of Shakespeare's *Othello*, reduced to its essentials: the concentration on the 'guilty' handkerchief – though of course Shakespeare makes no mention of semen.

Less hatefully, the stain left by the vaginal liquor upon the bedclothes can be used by the thoughtful amorist to judge the degree of excitement that the woman has experienced. The general rule as to women is the folk-phrase: "*The hotter the wetter*," i.e. "*The more excitement the more juice*," and the greater the area of the stain. The man can conclude from this whether the woman is likely to have really achieved her orgasm or not. Women of sensitivity and breeding will often lie about this — though essentially it is not wise to do so — and will say they have had an orgasm when, actually, they have not, in order not to make the man think that he is ineffectual and a poor lover, which would make him feel frustrated and generally unhappy. And, perhaps just as often, to prevent him from thinking that the woman herself is frigid, or difficult to bring to orgasm, as she may well be.

IX

THE SUBSIDIARY offices of the hands are extremely important and effective in cunnilinctus. This has already been discussed concerning the man's covering his possibly stubbly or unshaven chin with his palm, during cunnilinctus, to avoid irritating the woman's vulva and thighs. In its most primary form, the man's manual activity in cunnilinctus is the holding of the woman's thighs properly apart, and, if necessary, lifted. The woman's legs should not, of course, be lifted vertically from the bed on which she is lying, as this would leave them in the way of the man's oral motions. They should be pressed back upon her chest as far as possible, folding them at the knees, underneath which the man's hands take their grip. This opens the woman's pubic area and her whole vulvar groove most fully to the man's oral caresses. It also somewhat diminishes the part she herself can actively play — in the usual fashion of pressing her feet flat on the bed, and lifting and swaying her hips to the man's mouth. But with a little practice she can learn to do this almost as well by pressing with the hollows of her knees (the so-called popliteals or hocks) against the man's hands for fulcrum. This gives the man the pleasant notion that he is himself shaking the woman's hips masterfully in the air.

More directly, the man's hands can stay close to the vulva to excite the woman by the usual quasi-masturbatory actions at her clitoris and at the opening of the vagina. The very small opening of the bladder, lying vertically about halfway between the clitoris and vaginal opening, is easy to irritate and should not be touched except with the tongue. When the position of the man in cunnilinctus makes it possible for both his hands to be at the vulva at once, he can press his thumbs or fingers against the labia majora and minora, and rub them vertically up and down against each other, especially near the anterior commissure or upper point of joining of the labia, and at the clitoris. The labia minora, or inner lips, can also be plucked or pulled out quite far, since they engorge with blood and enlarge visibly during the woman's sexual excitement. Plucking and pulling at them, whether with the hands or by oral sucking or munching (either or both labia, separately or together), will not hurt the woman, if done without excessive force, but is quite exciting to her. When the labia minora are very long – the so-called "Hottentot Apron" – such plucking or sucking is perhaps best avoided, as women themselves have the notion that long and protrusive labia minora are unæsthetic in appearance (though men find them fascinating), and the woman may assume that such manipulations will make her labia even longer.

Actually, most women's labia minora protrude slightly through the majora, especially during sexual excitement. In women in whom the pubic hair has been shaved, this can be seen happening, and often in others. Most normal men in our culture, however, dislike cunnilinctus or any other sexual relations with women who have shaved off their pubic hair, or removed it in any other way. Shaving in particular will make the woman's pubic mound bristly, between shaves, and it will then be she, and not the man, who must grip her own pubis

— rather than he his chin — to keep from irritating the man's face or chin with her whiskers! In white Western cultures, women who do regularly shave their pubic hair are usually dangerously neurotic and are to be avoided. In certain other cultures, such as that of South America and the Levant, the women are trained either to thin out the pubic hair considerably, or actually to shave or depilate their pubes since the time of puberty. This latter is doubtless to give the men the sensation of having sexual relations with impubescent little girls: again not the cup of tea of the normal adult man. I would repeat that normal men (and women) do *not* like the shaved female pubis, for all the recent cynical advertising lingo about "the bathing-suit shave." No woman will really be driven off a public beach by the police owing to a charming tendril or two of pubic hair curling down her thigh under the crotch of her bathing suit. She might, in fact, have half the men on the beach following her, precisely because of it. The same is true of the natural armpit hair.

Though the physiological purpose of the pubic hair is essentially a mystery, it does serve to concentrate the natural genital odors of the woman, which are her primary attraction to the man, as will be discussed further below. Also, the normal attraction of men to the female pubis necessarily involves its being furnished with the pubic *tressoria* of hair, which — from the psychological point of view — allows it to remain clothed in a certain pleasant mystery. For all the tremendous attraction men have to the woman and to her genital organ, it is still wise for it to remain delicately veiled, if only by its natural hair, even during the closest of sexual approaches. Otherwise, for some men — more than one might think — the female genital risks being thought of as the unconsciously-feared and terrible "face of Medusa," which no man can look upon bare and live to tell the tale. It is this unconscious fear of the naked female genital, visibly and frighteningly "lacking" a penis, which is the true motive of the unappetizing "split-beaver" photo magazines and motion pictures, first publicly arriving from Scandinavia in the 1960's, in which the woman is so posed as to display her genital cleft and vaginal opening – sometimes optically magnified! – instead of hiding them, as in the past. The attraction of men to this type of photo art is by no means as normal as might at first be thought.

Fairness requires that mention should be made here of the one rare cunnilinguistic art or trick for which the shaved female pubis is, in fact, best. In this, the man being in any usual position, the woman lies on her *side*, and draws up her knees and thighs close to her chest, clasping them there with both arms, and thus freeing her vulva to the approach of the man's mouth below her heels, her vulva appearing in the form of a long sidewise slot between her buttocks and thighs. The man now takes hold of her entire vulvar area with his whole mouth, and shakes his head rapidly from one side to the other. He may either allow his lips and mouth to slip sidewise, back-&-forth, along the vulvar slot; or he may hold the woman's vulva somewhat firmly with his mouth, sucking at it strongly, and shaking her whole vulvar area from side to side, without letting go of it or letting his mouth slip on it at any time. This is called "Playing the Harmonica," from the sidewise head-motions of that minor musical art – identical with the motions used in playing its ancestral instrument, the ancient Græco-Rumanian pipes of Pan – and is a cunnilinctual method of choice among men frequenting impubescent (or shaven) young girls in the Levant. The jocular folklore would have it that this is also how cunnilinctus is necessarily performed upon Oriental women, in whom the vulva pretendedly runs from side to side, instead of up-&-down!

During ordinary cunnilinctus, in any of the usual positions, it is fairly simple for the man to lift one arm onto the woman's belly, and to rub her clitoris with the thumb of that hand, introducing into her vagina the thumb or forefinger of the other hand, which lies between her legs, and digitating her vagina with in-&-out strokes, or with a round-&-round stirring or reaming motion – either moving the digit in the circle of the vaginal opening, or else pressing tightly and pulling the vaginal flesh around and around with it in a heavier circular motion. An alternately clockwise and counterclockwise twisting motion can also be used. The forefinger is suggested here, rather than the middle finger, in spite of the fact that in the more ordinary course of events, as for instance when the man is lying by the woman's side and embracing her, the middle finger is perhaps the best finger with which to titillate the vulva and the vagina. The superiority of the middle finger, for ordinary titillation, is due to its being the longest finger, and also – owing to its central position on the hand – to the facility with which the forefinger and ring-finger can then press the whole vulva strongly together simultaneously around the inserted middle finger; the thumb and the smallest finger meanwhile trailing along the woman's lower belly or her inner thighs, depending upon how far down between her thighs the man's hand is thrust, or how far up between them from behind.

During cunnilinctus, however, when the man is in a position to lick the woman's vulva *upward*, it will usually be found that it is rather difficult for him to turn his hand over onto its back, in order to slide the middle finger into the vagina. (In *downward* cunnilinctus, however, the use of the middle finger in this way is both natural and easy.) Thus, with the hand lying vertically between the woman's thighs, the thumb and/or forefinger, which lies vertically the highest, will be found to be the most easily inserted. The great disadvantage of this vaginal excitation with the side-lying thumb or forefinger, as compared to the usual excitation by means of the middle finger, with the palm facing the vulva – either upward or downward – is that, with the side-lying thumb or forefinger, in-&-out motions can be achieved only rather clumsily. Actually, they then require the motion of the whole forearm; whereas the middle finger, when lying as described above, can be moved in-&-out both by its natural crooking motion and by motion merely of the hand and wrist.

This is an important factor when the excitation of the woman goes on for a long while, as the man's hand can tire much more easily when forcing itself, especially for a long while, to motions which are not those natural to the fingers and hand. It is even more important in oragenitalism, since in most upward cunnilinctus the man is supporting himself on just the forearm which must be jockeyed or manipulated to help the thumb's or forefinger's reciprocating motion in the vagina. In such a case, therefore, the other possible finger movements – twisting and stirring or reaming with the finger or thumb, and *shaking of the whole hand while one finger is vaginally inserted and the thumb of the same hand presses on the clitoris* – will probably prove more effective. The man's tongue and lips will limit themselves, during such hand-motion, to flicking and sucking activities inside the circumambient sweep of the fingers and thumb.

The woman's own manual caresses of the man – and of herself – during cunnilinctus, have already been considered, above. It should be added that not only there are women who object to caressing themselves, especially genitally, when in any sexual activity with another person, and who feel that it is strictly for the other person to do this *to them;* but there are also many men who resent and dislike having a woman touch herself in any way genitally (though her breasts are free territory) during intercourse or cunnilinctus, feeling that this is a reproach to the man's own technique. This is a narrow point of view, but it is not possible to make any cut-&-dried rules: often just such little hesitancies and resistances rise from and indicate areas of unconscious conflict between the partners as to their relative positions of dominance and submission, both sexually and otherwise, or are intended – and understood – as unspoken charades of sexual criticism and complaint. Violent and hurting motions at orgasm which can be construed as hateful on the part of the woman should be avoided during cunnilinctus, though, unfair as it may seem, the man is allowed and even expected to show precisely such violence, at least during vaginal intercourse. In particular, if, at her orgasm during cunnilinctus, the woman wishes to make gripping, pulling motions with her hands, or to strike out with her fingernails, she should carefully try to restrict this to her own breasts or mouth, or to the bedclothes, and not to the man's hair and face, ears, neck, or shoulders.

It is, as has already been observed, not necessary to limit the man's manual caresses of the woman during cunnilinctus to her genitals. One of the man's hands, meanwhile, the one not occupied at her genitals, may reach up under one of her thighs – which is perhaps being supported by the shoulder on the side nearest that hand – to stroke, rub, handle, press, grip, squeeze, knead, shake, jounce, pat, tap, pinch, nip, tickle and scratch (even poke and prod!) and generally fondle and caress both the sensitive flesh at the side of her waist and her buttocks and thighs, or her breast itself, rubbing and rolling the nipple *deeply* between his wetted thumb and forefinger. Obviously, caresses of the breast should not be as violent, nor involve as much pressure, as those on the simple body-flesh, as for instance at the waist or buttocks. Caresses of the fleshy globe of the breast are also not as exciting to the woman as those concentrating specifically on the base of the nipple where it enters the breast. If the man grips *both* the woman's breasts during cunnilinctus (or coitus), this is more likely for his own psychological needs than to excite the woman.

It is important to understand that, despite what most men believe, it is not the tip of the woman's nipple nor even the nipple itself that is the most sensitive part of the woman's breast, but rather the milk-head, a thickened spot or centre well below the level of the areola where the nipple joins the breast. As the name implies, the milk-head is the centre where all the woman's lacteal ducts come together, like the bay at the mouth of a complex river-delta. It is this centre, below and beyond the nipple, against which the nursing infant's mouth presses violently when sucking, in order to pump out the milk; and it is this which must be pressed and pinched when it is necessary to draw out the woman's milk by hand, as for a premature baby.

It is therefore precisely here and nowhere else that the pressure of the man's thumb and fingertip will create the greatest excitement to the woman, in a sexual situation, especially if the fingertips have been wetted beforehand in the man's mouth or in the moisture of the woman's own vagina. The man's mouth can, naturally, be applied directly to the nipple – precisely as is that of the nursing child – with even more exciting results. When the woman is actually in milk, and nursing her child, it is a charming romantic touch for the man to taste her milk during the love-play (the woman may herself offer this to him), but he should certainly not drink up any appreciable amount of her milk in this way: that is stealing from the child. The pressing out of a small amount of the woman's breast-milk, to lace a shared glass of brandy or a midnight cup of cocoa, is also well known among men and women still in love with each other, though married.

X

A VERY valuable but seldom mentioned technique possible during oragenital acts is the titillation of the perinæum — the space between the vulva and the anus in women, and the scrotum and anus in men — and the introduction of a finger into the anus. While to many people anal digitation seems and is unpleasant, there can be no doubt whatsoever that *the quality of orgasm* produced by genital and anal excitation combined is immensely more piercing, high-pitched, and pleasant than orgasm produced by genital excitation alone. This is partly psychological, to be sure, representing an admission of feminine urges to be penetrated bodily — as much in the case of men as of women — but it is more largely physical, since it carries the motions and excitations of the sexual act deep into the pelvic musculature where men, at least, seldom otherwise experience it. When even once properly experienced — that is, properly executed *and properly submitted to*, without panicky emotional resistance — it will usually be returned to again and again, and is very likely to become an integral part of the erotic technique and ritual of the pair. However, clumsily done, or without proper lubrication, and without the proper relaxation of the sphincter by the submitting partner, it can be most unpleasant. A few unfortunate experiences of this kind with it, combined with outraged moral and æsthetic sentiments, can so affect some women or men as to inhibit orgasm in them, and even voluptuous pleasure of any degree, when anal digitation is even so much as attempted.

The best lubrication for use in digitating the anus is probably oil or cold-cream or vegetable or petroleum jelly. However, in connection with oragenitalism it is obviously not desirable to lard up the sexual parts or their environs unpleasantly, both for olfactory and gustatory reasons, and for the further reason that the grease may soil the bedclothes just at the point where the man's (or, in fellation, the woman's) face or chin must rest. Saliva, therefore, or the vaginal secretion transferred externally by means of the finger, will usually best serve, and most practically, to lubricate the digitating finger. So lubricated, anal digitation will be insured against being accompanied by any real pain, if the finger is introduced slowly and carefully, even if the subject does not understand how to relax the sphincter, or is antagonistic to digitation, and must be convinced by demonstration that it can be made enjoyable. When the subject has already had some experience with anal digitation, the relaxation of the *sphincter ani* is easy to perform, as is also a further motion or slight downward and outward pressure of the muscle in such a way as to extrude the anal border, like the corolla of a flower. The digitating finger is then, as it were, drawn or aspired into the anus when the muscle relaxes and draws upward. These images may seem absurdly poetic, but will be found to be exact.

One particular advantage of using the vaginal secretion as a lubricant for anal digitation is that this secretion will not appear unless and until the woman is aroused, and it is only when she is aroused that she will be likely to be insensitive to, or willing to endure, the occasional slight preliminary pain of anal dilation and digitation. It hardly needs to be mentioned that "postillioning," as anal digitation is colloquially called, is not practical when the subject suffers from hæmorrhoids, as it is likely to prove painful and to cause bleeding. The finger should not be dipped several times into the vagina for the lubricating secretion. The amount that can be taken up at one time must be made to serve. Women object strongly to the idea – more than to the sensation – of any cross-motion between their vagina and anus, in the direction of the former, and there are evident sanitary reasons, not necessary to insist upon here, for this objection.

The anus should not be groped for — and possibly missed — but should be found by slowly running and pressing the fingertip along the perinæal and intergluteal groove. Once the finger is inside the anus, it can be moved back-&-forth, care being taken always to keep the tip past the sphincter, or the finger is likely to pop out and will have to be re-inserted, again with the possibility of pain. Or the finger can be held still, within the grasp of the sphincter (sometimes surprisingly strong), and the whole hand shaken vigorously, agitating the whole anal, lower rectal, and perinæal region. At the point of orgasm, frankly in-&-out coital movements of the finger, or even two fingers together, will usually be found most gratifying to the subject. Postillioning can best be done by the middle finger, as explained previously concerning vaginal titillation; but in cunnilinctual positions it is usually necessary to use the forefinger, or — after the woman has become accustomed to anal digitation, or to anal coitus — the thumb, with the same disadvantages.

Anal digitation can be very painful if the fingernails are too long on either the fingers used or those adjacent, which grip hard at the perinæum meanwhile or "spider-claw" the subject's genital area. The fingernails should therefore be clipped. Women who wish to postillion the man during fellation or coitus, but who do not care to clip their fashionably long nails, may gouge up soap from a hard soap-cake under the nails of the thumbs and fore- and middle fingers, and this will usually smoothe out the nail by filling the space between it and the fingertip. The soap can easily be removed or washed away afterwards, which also assists in perfectly cleaning the finger used.

If soap irritates the mucous surfaces of the anus (or vagina), wax may be used similarly, although wax is probably less commonly available nowadays than soap, nor can it be put under the fingernails as discreetly. Soap can be scraped up quickly and unostentatiously while washing the hands. It is perhaps relevant that women have been known to wear kid gloves while masturbating men (which would solve the difficulty under consideration), a special type of prostitute being said to exist — called a "flipper" in America — whose specialty is such manustupration, and who wears soft thin gloves during the act, the outside of the gloves being oiled. In a well-known American novel, *Of Mice and Men* (1937) by the late John Steinbeck, there is mention of a manual laborer who wears a glove lined with vaseline on his left hand: he is "keepin' that hand soft for his wife."

The finger should be removed carefully after anal digitation. It cannot usually be pulled directly out of the anus — especially when only a non-oleaginous lubricant such as saliva has been used — without both pain to the subject, and a disagreeable noise, like the *pop* of a champagne cork. This is the so-called "American Corkscrew" of French prostitutes of the nineteenth century and early twentieth, who would purposely do this to themselves while standing with their knees spread, as an erotic joke or scatologic clownery. Actually, it is very gross, and of the style and level of humor of people who make the same "popping" noise — sometimes rhythmically and repetitively — by pulling one finger or the thumb rapidly out of the mouth along the inner surface of one cheek. Anyone who finds this funny would doubtless find the same manipulation, done rectally, absolutely hilarious. It is a matter of record that the most hysterical and long continued laughter ever created on the stage, and among endless mixed audiences, was that greeting the trained crepitational specialty (actually a Yoga trick of anal aspiration of air) of the "*Pétomane*" in the French music-halls of the turn of the present century.

At orgasm—when this is profound—powerful and rhythmic contractions of the sphincter occur in both sexes, and are felt by the intruded finger in postillioning, usually at intervals of about one second, slowing and disappearing after orgasm. (When experienced vaginally, this is the so-called "vaginal orgasm," which is, however, in no essential way different from a clitoral orgasm. The vaginal contractions or spasms can be created just as well by bringing the woman to orgasm strictly by clitoral titillation, without in any way entering or touching her vagina. The specifically "vaginal" orgasm is a myth.) To avoid any pain to the subject, or undesired noises, it is best to remove the postillioning finger in the pause between contractions of the sphincter. To withdraw the finger, even when lubricated with oil or jelly, it should be bent downward toward the rectal floor, while the hand itself is turned upward and is drawn away simultaneously, thus levering the finger out, as one might say, on the fulcrum of the anal orifice's anterior edge. If, meanwhile, the subject will press down slightly with the sphincter, in exactly the way such pressure is exerted during defæcation, the finger will be forced as well as pulled out, and there will be no pain whatsoever. The relaxation or pressing down with the sphincter to allow entry of the finger (or of the penis, in anal coitus) is also very similar to the defæcatory exertion used in extruding the finger, but is more diffused and not so powerful.

After anal digitation it will usually be necessary to wash—or at least wipe—the finger used, as it may have an unpleasant odor, and, if lubrication has been used, it will be greasy. Also, there may be tiny brown fæcal particles around or under the fingernail. This is only to be expected. As is not very well known, the rectum is quite empty of fæcal matter except immediately before the sensation of requiring to defæcate is felt, this sensation being itself caused by the action on the rectal nerves of the down-moving fæcal column. It commonly occurs, therefore, that the subject to anal digitation – postillioning – is likely to feel the desire to defæcate immediately after being postillioned, or to imagine that this desire is present. This is usually due to the sympathetic excitation of the nerve centers controlling defæcation when the *sphincter ani* is titillated, and the person may find, upon going to stool, that there is really no necessity at all. However, in some people, anal digitation or anal coitus causes an acute looseness of the bowels. Both of these sympathetic nervous manifestations will probably disappear upon continued acquaintance with such excitation, but when the couple are out of doors it may be useful to have some soft paper or a handful of dry leaves near at hand, just in case . . .

It is possible that occasionally a tip of fæcal matter may be felt by the finger in the rectum, but this, while not particularly æsthetic or pleasant, is a matter of very little real importance. It should certainly not be mentioned – or displayed! – at the time, as the subject is probably just as aware of it as the person who is postillioning, and is also probably twice as horrified and embarrassed. Though this is doubtless perfectly natural – "a place for everything, and everything in its place" – there is also such a thing as the right or wrong moment. The soiling of the partner's finger or penis occurs almost invariably when actual anal coitus or pedication is commonly used, which is why most men of any real cultivation dislike and avoid anal intercourse with a belovèd woman. Boys and "dirty girls," or even lower animals, especially in situations of sexual starvation such as distant army outposts and jails, are doubtless something else again, if one's catholicity of choice extends that far — or far back.

When anal digitation accompanies cunnilinctus and not coitus, it may take the place of vaginal digitation concomitant with cunnilinctus, or it may accompany it, the thumb being introduced into the vagina, and the forefinger or middle finger into the anus. The whole hand is then shaken or turned backward-&-forward rapidly, a quarter-circle, without moving or slipping the fingers within the tissues, thus shaking the whole vaginal, anal, and perinæal area strongly. Or, of course, the thumb and finger (or fingers) can be driven rapidly in-&-out in simili-coital motions: this is, however, best only when the subject's orgasm is close. The combined digitation of the vagina and anus in this way, whether or not accompanying cunnilinctus, is graphically termed "the Bowling-Hold" in American slang, from the similar position of the thumb and middle finger in holding a common bowling-ball. This type of excitation combined with cunnilinctus is productive of so tense and high-pitched an emotional state, and such excruciatingly enjoyable sensations at orgasm, as to cause women to thresh about wildly, and scream (into a pillow or against the palm of the hand, if one is forced to live too close to one's neighbors), or even to faint, especially the first time it is experienced.

A type of excitation which is associated to both cunnilinctus and anal digitation, and which cannot be omitted from any exhaustive survey of oragenitalism, is anilinctus: the licking, tonguing, and sucking of the anus. If the woman's body is clean — really clean — no tenable hygienic or olfactory objections to anilinctus can be advanced, and those that are made can stem only from psychological considerations, or prejudice and training. It is therefore a matter of personal choice, and I will enter into no æsthetico-psychological theorizing about it. Obviously there has been some contamination of its use as an oral caress by the well-known folk phrase or insult in many languages, in which ultimate contempt is expressed by inviting another person to kiss one's arse. When intended seriously, as an erotic invitation, this is quite another matter, and even more so when one makes the offer – preferably by simply doing it, and without words – rather than makes the demand.

Anilinctus is usually extremely pleasurable to the subject, once the feeling of shock is discarded, and it is therefore going to be practiced by people, by sensitive and loving people who wish to give each other the utmost possible pleasure, and to express their affectionate subservience to that pleasure. It is also going to be practiced by vicious and unpleasant people who wish to wallow in whatever eroticism seems to them to be nasty and lubricous, and profoundly sado-masochistic, and therefore expressive of and satisfactory to their peculiarly ambivalent love and hatred of sex. At any rate, the genitals are excretory organs too, of a sort, but the erotic application of the mouth to them is quite coolly undertaken and enjoyed by many millions of the world's approximately three thousand million people. It should be recollected that none of the world's great religions makes any dogmatic objection to any oragenital act when practiced as an excitant to eventual vaginal intercourse.

Anilinctus can be just as sanely considered and employed. Meticulous cleanliness is, of course, a prime consideration; and it hardly needs to be mentioned that the breaking of wind during either oragenitalism or anilinctus is at all costs to be avoided. A good deal further as to the actual oral techniques of anilinctus will be given below, in the final section of the present monograph, following the treatment of the Sixty-Nine, to which the interested reader is referred. One possibility not mentioned by the author there cited is that of cunnilinctus and anilinctus combined, which is most easily performed in the position already described above, as "Playing the Harmonica," the man's mouth sweeping rapidly back-&-forth along the pudendal and perinæal groove of the woman lying on her side with her knees pulled up tight to her chest.

XI

But to get out of the rectum and back to our tour through the vaginal canal with gun and camera, I might mention a rather extreme method of heightening the woman's erotic sensations during cunnilinctus – or, for that matter, during any sort of sex-play, or during coitus. Namely, the use of an electrical vibrating device at her clitoris. These appliances are of two types: one in which the motor is held by means of a handle, while a vibrating shaft extends from the axis of the motor and terminates in a rubber or ivory tip which touches the flesh and transmits the vibration. (I have seen another erotic use of this type of motor, in which an artificial penis was attached to the end of the vibrating shaft so that vibration could be added to the in-&-out and stirring about motions of the artificial penis within the vagina.)

In the second – and, to my mind, better and more *human* – type of electrical vibrating device, the vibrating mechanism straps over the back of the hand, and the fingers themselves are made to vibrate, and can transmit this vibration to the partner's flesh by touching it. Although this use of vibrating mechanisms as an adjunct to the sexual excitation of the woman and to cunnilinctus – as well as to fellation and masturbation of the man – is extremely valuable, one writer claiming that the woman is likely to faint during her first orgasm brought about by coitus combined with the vibrating mechanism applied to her clitoris (it has not been my experience that anyone really faints), most average people will probably consider an electrical appliance and its wires extremely out of place in the lovers' bed, and even, indeed, a damnable encroachment of science on private life. They will probably never employ this technique; or will do so, if at all, only exceptionally and occasionally, and rather more in a spirit of fun than of harried and scientific lechery.

The above two paragraphs, which are printed here almost exactly as they appeared in the original edition of this monograph in 1940, have been more prophetic than I could have imagined. Every suggestion in them has been turned assiduously into fact since that time, in particular the opening allusion to a camera tour through the human vagina, in the Drs. Masters & Johnson's *Human Sexual Response* (Boston, 1966), based in part on photo-studies of the inside of the vagina during orgasm. The erotic use of the vibrator has become not only something of a fad, but even quite an industry in the intervening three decades, and particularly over the last ten years. When I first wrote, few people had ever heard of such a thing, though the use of vibrators by masseuses-prostitutes, for masturbatory purposes on their clients, had of course immediately come about on the invention of these vibrators and their public availability for scalp-massage by barbers. Now, the vibrator as an erotic adjunct is so widely known that a large part of the interesting illustrated pocket-volume, *Sex Gadgets* (cover-title: *The Stimulators;* Cleveland: Century Books, 1968), by Roger Blake, Ph.D., apparently in collaboration with John Trimble, Ph.D., is devoted to various vibrating mechanisms, dildoes in particular.

Dildoes, or artificial penises for use in female masturbation (and rectally by the male) have been known since antiquity, and machine-operated dildoes delivering the obvious simili-coital reciprocating motion have at least been fantasied since the middle-nineteenth century. This was an inevitable sexual adaptation of the then-popular science fiction fantasy of the human automaton or Machine Man, which can play chess, dance, whistle – and make love, never stopping until its motor is turned off, of course, as with the earlier occult versions in folktales, where the Sorcerer's Apprentice or Magic Penis (in expurgated forms, the Magic Cudgel) cannot be stopped without the magic word. The original vibrating dildo, mentioned above, was constructed at my suggestion in 1937/8 by the late Dr. Vladimir Fortunato, the greatest anatomical model-maker of this century, who also built the Transparent Woman that created a sensation at the 1930's World's Fair, and has since been endlessly imitated as an educational doll.

Both the transparent models – including another showing the genitals in intercourse, on the inspiration of Leonardo da Vinci's famous "Venus Obversa" drawing – and the vibrating dildo were intended for use in connection with the early private marriage-counselling clinic of Dr. Robert Latou Dickinson, dean of American gynecologists, whose amanuensis I was. Further materials prepared for marriage-counselling, but then considered premature in America and not used, included a beautifully posed series of coital posture photographs, and an erotic training film. Western society is now ready for this, and such photographs and drawings (and, in Scandinavia, films), of conscious didactic purpose, are now appearing in all countries, as once, immemorially, only in the Japanese "pillow-books" or engraved posture-book calendars, given to every young bride, and on the walls of the Hindu love-temples from which the pillow-books were probably derived. The beautiful and sincere tone and purpose of these have now been crudely parodied – with an unacknowledged bow to the famous eighteenth-century "Petits-Pieds" engraving – in a mock Japanese pillow-book, showing, by way of expurgation of course, only the partners' *feet*, as the centre-spread of the men's magazine, *Playboy* (15th anniversary issue, January 1969), usually devoted to expurgated color photographs of pubic-hairless nudes.

Dr. Fortunato's vibrating dildo was made of milk rubber, and in three sizes, with a stiff undulating wire fixed into the rubber inside; the external end of the wire, at the base, being threaded to attach to a hand-held massage motor. It was attempted in this way to reproduce the sensation of sexual intercourse, or the use of an ordinary dildo, with the simultaneous application of vibrating sensations to the woman's pelvic region, though obviously not to her clitoris, where, in fact, these are much more effective. It will be understood of course that the reciprocating motions of ordinary intercourse or masturbation can be achieved in many ways, both natural and mechanical; but *human beings cannot vibrate*. That is both the exceptional value, and the real but hidden human danger, in the erotic use of massage vibrators. A fluted dildo with a rotating motor was also tried out, with sensational – but, again, oddly inhuman – results. Extreme lubrication was needed with this, to avoid vaginal pain when rotating at high speeds, or actual brush-burns. More recent versions of the vibrating dildo take advantage of its phallic shape, and use self-contained flashlight batteries to power the mechanism, thus getting rid of the intrusive wall-socket power wire. However, battery-powered vibrators and dildoes are seldom sufficiently powerful, for all their advertising claims, and sometimes run down just at the wrong moment, as in the prophetic – if politely modified! – scene of "The Singing Doll," in Offenbach's opera *The Tales of Hoffmann*, based on the story "Undine" (1816) by E. T. A. Hoffmann.

Also, and much more importantly, the real area of the body where the specifically vibrating sensation is of greatest value is not inside either the vagina or rectum, but externally, at the clitoris in women and deep over the perinæum in men (prostatic massage). The vibrating dildo, in any form, is really therefore only an erotic gadget or toy, and is self-evidently intended to *replace* the man in sexual intercourse, and not to act as an assist or adjunct to help him excite or satisfy the woman. My own studied conclusion is that the real but unstated purpose of dildoes, whether vibrating or not, among modern "swinging" groups, is to excite the sub-virile or perverted men – not the women – by watching the women use these on themselves. That is certainly the implication of the fact that men are known to pay prostitutes to observe them using dildoes, and to pay extra if the woman will suck the dildo after her (purported) orgasm. This is all obviously an erotic charade or play-acting, for the benefit of the psychologically crippled or impotent male.

The apparatus of real value remains the simple and original hand-strapped massage vibrator, and it may be observed that only the best and most professional models give satisfactory results, or can stay the course. The cheap drugstore items and battery-operated forms are worthless rattles, intended for the sucker market of immature and neurotic "swingers." Two final warnings, both very serious: First, *vibrators must be kept away from water*. If used in the bathtub or shower, on either 110- or 220-volt curent, they can electrocute the user, who may be rigid with shock and unable to turn the apparatus off. This is a gruesome way to die. Vibrators should also therefore not be used on women who have an uncontrollable tendency to urinate at orgasm, which may cause at least a highly unpleasant shock. Any woman who knows this to be her case should refuse, with thanks, the offer to use a vibrator on her genitals.

Second, *the erotic use of the vibrator is habit-forming!* Women who learn to depend on its supplementary use at their clitoris, to bring them to orgasm during intercourse or cunnilinctus, eventually find that they cannot have an orgasm any other way. As an occasional erotic delight, or as shock-treatment for psychological frigidity — to prove to the woman *that she is not frigid* — the use of the vibrator is a remarkable and unforgettable adjunct, especially when used in intercourse in the "scissors" or "T-upside-down" position. It also has great value in the exciting of the older man to erection, especially for the wife who may have lost some of her exciting freshness for him, after many years of marriage. But it should be obvious that an entire adult erotic life cannot be based on orgasm or erection achieved with a massage vibrator.

The concept of playfulness, mentioned earlier in connection with the erotic use of such mechanical toys, is very important in oragenitalism, in which the necessary position of the bodies inevitably draws the partners' heads apart. Oragenitalism therefore requires some other — some less intense — form of emotional communication between them than that possible in deep vaginal intercourse, with the lovers plastered together belly-to-belly by their sweat, kissing each other with probing tongues, and aching to be even deeper in each others' bodies & souls. (Some people are never satisfied.) Most people, either from sexual shame or nervousness or training or romanticism, are likely to be just a shade too serious in bed; often very much too serious. Many writers on sex technique "in marriage" — always in marriage, to evade the admission that unmarried people have sexual needs and lives too — have furthered this attitude by writing about sexual relationships and sexual acts under an offensively mock-pious façade, and in an adviseering tone and heavy-handed manner better suited to the exposition of Swedish setting-up exercises or the workings of an internal-combustion gasoline engine. (The coldest work in tone, though most detailed as to technique, is probably Dr. John Eichenlaub's *The Marriage Art*, New York, 1961.) Or else they affect an unctuous and hallowed ministerial tone, more to be expected over a death-bed than over a bed devoted to sexual love.

By thus treating the fascinating subject of erotic technique – which is one of the most ancient and honorable of literary forms, and need apologize to no one for anything, in a culture where murder-mysteries are the most popular and best-selling of books – with far too much distant, and presumably scientific, cold and antiseptic timidity, which is really only intended to sneak it past the censorship of sex (there is no censorship of murder-books); or else by garnishing it with a wealth of bogus overtones and undertones of sacred, scared, and sanctified romanticism; these writers have managed now, for a century or more, after hastily dishing up the most barbarous rudiments of eroticism, to leave the reader more or less apprised of the fact, if not really of the technique, of sexual connection, but entirely in the dark as to why in the world anybody would want to try it.

Any person who wishes to arrive at the fullest development of his or her sexual life and capacities should remember that sex is only in part the oft-observed ultimate gesture of amity and tenderness toward another person. There is also a wild and savagely egoistic undercurrent, which is the real biological substructure of all sexual acts: shifting, moving, and always somehow unpredictable – especially in its choice of partners and of acts – except that what it is *really* after is, for the man, sexual gratification; and, for the woman, a similar gratification but one leading to impregnation and the birth of the child, at least in possibility. Romantic overtones aside, the proper purpose of sexual experience is *one's own* as well as the other person's sexual gratification and orgasm. This requires and involves erotic pleasure and enjoyment for both, even a certain amount of violence, and certainly the approach to sex as playfulness and joy and fun.

It is quite unnecessary for the man to lie, during cunnilinctus, burrowing his face assiduously into the woman's pubis. A man engaged in cunnilinctus is likely to look ridiculous, if not actually ugly, and the only way to make a ridiculous-seeming operation appear less clumsy and ridiculous is to undertake it and engage in it with at least an overtone of playfulness and banter. Such banter is almost always out of place and ill-received after orgasm, when the partners are resting and – one or both – floating up out of their orgastic trance. But it is precisely the tone which is most pleasant when beginning cunnilinctus, especially, where the man must sometimes crawl about the woman, leaving his knees at the side of her face while his shoulders and head disappear toward lower pastures. A charming word of farewell, or laughing admonition to hold the fort, for the moment till he gets into place, is sometimes very welcome to the woman at this point.

In cunnilinctus the man can throw his head back occasionally and toss his hair out of his eyes. If his hair is cropped short in the bristly crew-style haircut, he can, instead, rub and tickle the woman's vulva and thighs and lower belly by turning his bristly head from side to side. He can nip the woman's nymphæ in his lips and mouth and munch them, even worry them lightly with his teeth, tugging them from side to side, between licks at her clitoris. He can rub his mouth in her pubic hair, or bite her thighs, or scratch them lightly by rubbing his unshaven chin over their inner surface; or he can even rub the tip of his nose in the woman's vulva or vagina briskly though momentarily.

He can vary his perfervid tonguing with breathing spells, remembering that only the "dream lover" – who does not exist – has, in the laughing folk-phrase, "a nine-inch tongue and can breathe through his ears." It is not difficult to breathe shallowly at all times during cunnilinctus, unless the woman crosses her legs passionately behind the man's neck, or tightens them too much at the sides; but it helps to vary this shallow breathing with coming up for deeper breaths occasionally; avoiding, of course, gasping and snorting like a sperm-whale in rut. The man can also speak to the woman during his breathing spells, asking her if she likes what he is doing. Many men, however, and quite a few women, dislike having the mood broken by conversation during sexual intimacy of any kind, particularly those who make love with their eyes closed in narcissistic fashion, who may even be fantasying someone else! All normal men object – and especially during cunnilinctus – to having the woman advise or tell them what to do, especially if repetitively; but then, she really knows best what pleases her most, and what she would like, and how and where. It is often wise to arrange verbally beforehand just what each partner is to do, and not to do, if such arrangement can be made without breaking the mood of foreplay, or sounding like a partnership agreement on how to paint a barn. Even so, this is better than recriminatory post-mortems afterward, like those after card-games or the visits of in-laws.

It has been observed earlier that the woman should not tell the man on her coming to after orgasm in cunnilinctus, that he looks as though her pubic hair is his beard. However, if the man himself finds it amusing to pretend this, or even, for that matter, to put eyeglasses over his penis and a peacock feather up his rectum, that is his joke on himself, not hers, and there can be no serious complaint. More to the point, he can also pretend to stop cunnilinguing the woman, just as she is about to have her orgasm, and thus torment her deliciously, though this often results in her tangling her fingers violently in his hair and dragging his face back down to her vulva again. He can do anything jolly and tender and exciting that comes into his mind, and that means things that are exciting to himself as well as to her, except that he should not harm or frighten her. In a word, he should remember that he is *making love* to the woman, and not performing a surgical operation upon her. And always, he should bear in mind that art consists — among other things — in the concealment of art, and therefore to pretend that everything he does has just come to his mind spontaneously that very instant, and for that special woman's especial benefit. It may even be true.

He should remember, above all, that a manual such as this is not intended to be hung over the bed on a string, to be referred to ever & anon. Even its shadow should not fall on the bed, to be cited as an authority on positions or technique in the heat of action, nor (Aphrodite forbid!) during arguments afterward! I will not sleep easy in my grave if I must lie there thinking that lovers in future decades are using the pages I have written, in laughter and in love, as though they were torn out of Hoyle on Whist, or Culbertson on Contract Bridge. Surely the most biting reproach that can be made to a lover is that made by Juliet to that hopeless duffer, Romeo, toward the end of the first act of Shakespeare's play: "You kiss by th' book."

XII

A VERY effective preliminary to cunnilinctus, and one which is delightful and gratifying, in its possessive playfulness, to the cunnilinguist as well as to the woman, is the act of licking and mouthing the woman all over her body as a tantalizing preparation to cunnilinctus, usually beginning with kissing her mouth, and ending at her vulva after having covered any one of a variety of possible itineraries. This is even more common as a preliminary to fellation, and is much used by prostitutes under the names, in America, of a "Trip Around the World" or a "Tongue-Bath," for clients who are desirous of something special. It will be discussed again, in this connection, in the later sections of the present monograph, on Fellation, Irrumation, and the Sixty-Nine.

The most elaborate progression over the body probably consists of kissing the mouth (kissing with the tongue as well as the lips), then licking up over the cheek, over the closed eyes (kissing, licking, and very, very soft suction), back to one ear (tonguing the ear-hole and breathing warmly into it: this will even quiet crying babies!), then behind and under the ear, and down past the ear, and under the side of the chin (strong licking and prodding or "fencing" with the tongue-tip); then over the throat, chest, and the midriff (very sensitive), spending a little time licking, sucking and lightly biting the nipples (even on a man); then under the armpit (licking, and biting of the hair with the teeth), turning the subject over onto her belly at this point; then licking over the shoulders and down the spine, with side-forays in along the sides at the waist, and particular concentration at the small of the back (licking); then over and between the buttocks, possibly with a flick of anilinctus at this point; then over the backs of the thighs (licking and biting), the hollows or hocks behind the knees (licking and suction), the smooth insides of the calves, over the ankles, the heels, the soles of the feet (licking and tickling by touching with the fluttering eyelashes, which is exquisitely unendurable to ticklish people, especially when done to the soles, the insides of the elbows, the midriff, or the lips); the subject being turned over onto her back again at this point as the man continues by licking and sucking her toes (possibly in the game of "This Little Pig Went to Market"), then over the insteps (very sensitive just at the flat plain where the toes join), at the inner calves again, continuing up the inside of the thighs, and then, just as cunnilinctus seems finally attained, a momentary and tantalizing delay by skipping the genitalia and tonguing the navel will usually add just the proper fillip of piquancy; and then . . . dragging the mouth around the edges of the pubic hair to come in upon the vulva from the sides of the crotch, ending with cunnilinctus, which should be especially vigorous, frenzied, and protracted.

Other itineraries are common, some much shorter and omitting the legs, or progressing down the front of the body and up the back, ending with anilinctus and *cunnilinctus from behind*. Or the tongue-bath may be engaged in after cunnilinctus has begun, leaving the vulva and travelling the mouth all over the body, to return to the vulva again as though the honeycomb centre of an enormous figure-eight. It is sometimes asked how long a bodily itinerary like this "should" last, and the same question is also often asked about cunnilinctus. Obviously, no exact answer is possible, as different people are more excitable than others — and more patient. But the full itinerary described in the preceding paragraph can hardly take less than twenty minutes; the half-itinerary, ending at the vulva and omitting the legs, from ten down to as little as five minutes, though this is hardly worth the trouble. The real rule is: if you're counting minutes in love-making, don't bother with human beings at all — stick to rabbits.

The amount of time to be spent on cunnilinctus itself naturally varies with the time it takes the woman to come to orgasm: from ten to twenty minutes, or half an hour, is usually long enough. If the woman has not had her orgasm by then, the man should simply proceed with vaginal intercourse — *to avoid tiring or wearing out both her and himself* — on the assumption that she has been sufficiently excited lingually, but will probably not come to orgasm in that way. Many men find that they take less and less time about cunnilinctus as they grow from adolescence to middle age, their desire for vaginal penetration becoming more intense at maturity, and the emotional primacy of coitus itself becoming too powerful to spend as much time as before on the oragenital preliminaries. It should be mentioned, finally, concerning oral itineraries over the body, that it will usually be found that the wet progress of the tongue leaves the skin somewhat cold and nervously creeping, owing to the evaporation of the saliva. It is this, as much as the actual caress of the tongue, that makes the tongue-bath so very enjoyable.

Probably the most playful practice in connection with cunnilinctus is the application of liquids such as wine, champagne (or bubbling soda-pop for the poor!), orange juice, honey, melted ice-cream, whipped cream, etc. ad lib., to the vulva, either to camouflage or to enhance its characteristic taste and odor, and to amuse both the woman and the man. It should be realized that such applications will leave the woman's crotch and pubic hair quite messy unless the cunnilinctus engaged in afterward carefully involves licking, or drinking, or even eating away the totality of the ice-cream, honey, or similar. These in particular should not be daubed on the woman's vulva or into her pubic hair, followed by a few brief licks, leaving her badly in need of a bath or bidet. Every drop should be licked lovingly out of every hair — that is the whole point. Where the material is solid or semi-liquid enough actually to be pressed part way up into the vagina, this should be done, even in the case of ice-cream which will, of course, give something of a shock owing to its coldness, of which the woman should be warned. Whipped-cream is best, and the vagina can be quite filled with it by means of air-pressure cream-dispensers for kitchen use, but great care should be taken not to inject compressed air into the woman's body. This is *very dangerous*, as will be discussed below.

Orange juice in particular is mentioned surprisingly often in common speech and jest, in connection with cunnilinctus, and, indeed, orange juice squeezed over a woman's pubis or on her vulva does have the quality of neutralizing any unpleasantly hircine or piscine odor of it, and giving it a rather warm and heady taste and odor, when licked up with the vaginal liquor or sucked out of the pubic hair. Lemons or limes should not be used, as their acid quality will cause an unpleasant burning sensation to the woman's sensitive vulvar tissues. They are also harder to squeeze. Obviously no one but an imbecile would attempt to squeeze fruit juice on a woman's vulva with a lime-squeezer in hand. It is also not very romantic to pour canned grapefruit or pineapple juice into a girl out of two holes punched in a metallic can. If you can't use a blue-glass carafe, this book is not for you.

In using oranges in cunnilinctus, the pre-frozen reconstituted juice should of course be avoided: like making love with a condom. Blood-oranges (and tomato juice) are also undesirable, owing to their color. The seedless type of orange is by far the best to use, and any orange used should be cut in half against the grain of the sections, as the juice can be more easily and cleanly squeezed from it when it is cut in that way. The juice should be *dripped* onto the vulva — not poured! — at the lower point of the pubic triangle at the top of the vulva, or through the pubic hair mat. It will flow downward into the vulva by itself if the woman is lying on her back.

After or during cunnilinctus in this way, or with any other fruit or cream added, the liquor can be shared with the woman, mouth-to-mouth, especially ice-cream. The woman can also endear herself to the man by licking his face clean with her tongue, making it unnecesary for him to stir himself and get up to wash his face. Or, equally endearingly, she can wipe the man's face with her hair if it is long, but this is just a tender gesture, and will not really clean his face very effectively, and it may start them kissing and eroticking all over again, which is nice.

A similar and very heady flavor is given to the vulva, though its odor is not neutralized, by the application of sweet still wines, such as a good Port, Muscatel, or Malaga. The wine can be poured over the woman's mouth and chin abundantly, or between her breasts, to run down her body – unless she is very fat and convex – over her belly and navel and through her pubic hair to her vulva, where it can be drunk and licked up by the man. The whole winey trail can later be licked clean by him. The use of wine in this way is a very ancient erotic gesture. It is implied in the ever-present jugs of wine at the orgies depicted on the ancient Greek figured vases, and is rather specifically described in the orgiastic banquet-scene of the *Satyricon* of Petronius Arbiter, about 65 A.D. Champagne is nowadays sometimes used in this way – being classically caught in the woman's slipper and drunk as a toast to her – and while its bubbly effervescence will cool and tickle the woman's skin pleasantly, its rather vinegary flavor does not really combine well or flatteringly with the vulvar taste. This is true of all dry wines.

Sweet still wines usually contain about one-fifth alcohol, or twice as much as dry wines, and this will often occasion a rather exciting tingling, and a warming sensation to the woman's vulva – and to the vagina if rubbed inward by subsequent coitus. An anonymous work, *L'Amour Saphique à travers les âges et les êtres*, published in Paris in 1902 and actually the work of Dr. Paul Garnier, mentions that a mouthful of brandy blown into the vagina during cunnilinctus causes "a burning sensation on the mucous surfaces which doubles the pleasure." Great care should also be taken to avoid blowing air simultaneously into the vagina, as it will probably escape with a flatulent and embarrassing sound. There is also a much greater danger involved. Just to begin with, there is the "burning sensation on the mucous surfaces," as mentioned. Before exposing a woman to this, on the theory that it will please or excite her, any man might do well to dip his erect penis, with the foreskin retracted, into a large glassful of whiskey, and see if this really "doubles the pleasure." Most men who have tried this do not think so. The "*Suçage à la Menthe*," noted under Fellation later, in which the fellatrice sucks a mint-candy before beginning on the man, is about as far as most men care to go.

Oil of wintergreen (methyl salicylate), aside from its well-known use in procuring strong erection of the penis – mostly in the form of the rubefacient salve, Baume Bengué, can also be used to cause burning and excitement of the vulva. But it should be used only externally, and great caution must be exercised to employ only the most minute amount of this substance, as more than a very few drops will cause the most agonizing pain, far in excess of such pain as can be considered tingling, or moderately maddening and exciting. Such excessive pain is very likely if any of the oil runs down over the anus, or the scrotum if it is applied to the man's penis, or rubs off onto him during subsequent coitus. If any is gotten into the cunnilinctor's eyes, it can do appreciable damage to the mucous conjunctiva of the eye. A drop or two – at most – applied to the clitoris will usually be more than sufficient, and a very small quantity can be rubbed on a finger and inserted into the vagina. Oil of cinnamon (or cassia) combines more felicitously and warmly than does oil of wintergreen with the intrinsic vulvar taste and odor, and has about the same effect. Cinnamon or cassia oil can also be mixed, in small amounts, in the wine used in cunnilinctus as described above, and also gives the wine a delicious flavor, rather like certain Greek wines.

The use of such oils, or brandy, as mentioned earlier, is immensely pleasurable to some women, but many – perhaps most – find it intolerable and extremely painful, although when the pain subsides a feeling of restless and squirming eroticism is usually felt. This is not some last, frantic resort of desperate voluptuaries – or perhaps it is – as the application of stinging nettles to the vulva to produce sexual excitement and swelling is quite common among certain primitive tribes of Africa and Oceania. Actually, the use of such nettles, or of brandy vaginally, is likely to be only an obvious sadistic trick disguised as a promised erotic delight, on a par with the East Indian "aphrodisiacal" rubbing of hot chili peppers on the fingers before handling the genitals of the opposite sex. This is simply a form of torture, as is any use (internally or otherwise) of the vesicating green blister-beetle, "Spanish Fly" or cantharides, once considered an aphrodisiac among the ignorant, the only persons, still, who believe in aphrodisiacs.

One is coming close here, perhaps even flirting dangerously with the sado-masochistic entertainments of a sub-flagellational type, like that never-to-be-forgotten "Ice-Spurred Special" in Dr. Eichenlaub's *The Marriage Art*, in which wives are seriously recommended to prepare a bowl of ice-cubes by the marriage bed, and to jam a handful of these into their husband's crotch or the small of his back at the climax of their marital intercourse, presumably in order to increase the intensity of his orgasm! The husband of any such wife is probably lucky she does not use *real* spurs. I am not suggesting for a moment that Dr. Eichenlaub's "Ice-Spurred Special" does not work, as I have not tried it and do not intend to. But I would recommend that any husband whose wife has picked this up as part of her regular sexual repertoire should also try it out on her, unexpectedly, once in a while, to make sure that she finds the temperature of the ice-cubes just dandy. As with the vaginal use of brandy, hot chili peppers, and the like, these activities are nothing but sado-masochistic tortures directly attacking the genitals, when used on people who do not like, do not expect, and cannot stand them. It is always wise – not to mention more honorable – to try them out on oneself first, full-strength.

Certain recent popular works concentrating on oragenitalism have made the extremely dangerous suggestion – promulgated as the *ne plus ultra* of erotic delight – that air should be blown into the vagina during cunnilinctus, so that the woman may enjoy the "swelling of her passages" or the rippling sensation as the air bubbles out again. This is specifically described and tacitly proposed in Dr. David O. Cauldwell's *Oral Genital Contacts* (Monogram Books, 1967), middle of supplementary note 3, as part of the case-history of a boy of fifteen having sexual relations with two goofy twin-sisters, named Merry and Sherry, *eleven years old:* "We did everything we could think of in about two hours time . . . They had me do something I had never done before; they had me stick one of those tubes that go on [clothes] hangers into their vaginas, and slide it back and forth, and had me blow air into their vaginas through the tube. It would swell up their passages and seemed to provide keen feeling." Talking about the blind leading the blind: Merry and Sherry, eleven years old, offering the reader their latest discovery!

The same dangerous idea is taken even farther in a curious and very neurotic work, entitled *Sex Rebel: Black*, signed "Bob Greene" (Greenleaf Classics, 1968), which purports to be, both from its statements and style, the sexual autobiography of a well-known Negro psychiatrist, largely concentrating on cunnilinctus, urine-drinking, and wife-trading, for unavowed homosexual purposes of seminal exsufflation. I have not been able to determine whether this work is an authentic Negro autobiography, though it does appear to be. It is subtitled – which should give some idea of the *tone* of the whole thing – "Memoirs of a Gash Gourmet." Giving of his best as to cunnilinguistic technique, page 321, the author observes: "It's an art learned by practice. There's no textbook called, 'Frenching Made Easy'," which is peculiar, considering that on page after page he appears to be popularizing, in autobiographical form, the original edition of the present monograph; for example (his page 102) as to the use of wine. As his final recorded experience, or bit of ultimate propaganda, concerning his own unspeakable racial self-humiliation in acting the part of the "Negro rapist" for an orgy-gang of sadistic swingers in an expensive Los Angeles suburb (page 358), he makes the following almost direct recommendation:

> I could have nibbled on Flame the rest of my life. Isolating the long lip, I sucked, bit, chewed. Then placing my mouth between them and over the hole itself, I took a deep breath and blew into her vagina. Flame jumped slightly in surprise, and the air rushed back out noisily like small firecrackers. "*Do that again*," she asked immediately afterward, and I complied. (Later she told me it felt as if all her internal organs were trying to escape through her pussy, producing an exotic and erotic thrill she had never previously experienced.)

With the above recommendations of Drs. Cauldwell and "Greene" should be compared the following somewhat less dithyrambic passage from Dr. Eugene Schoenfeld's no-nonsense medical advice column for hippies and swingers, in the *Los Angeles Free Press* (November 15th, 1968), not reprinted in his *Dear Dr. Hip-pocrates*:

> A few years ago, one of the psychiatric journals carried a paper on an unusual accidental death of a woman during coital foreplay.
>
> Her lover had an impulse to blow air into her vagina, which he proceeded to do vigorously. She had just stopped menstruating and her vascular system was therefore directly vulnerable. She complained of pain immdiately, and died within a few minutes – a rather gruesome outcome to what began as an erotic whim.

Not all women, of course, who allow their lovers to try this – with or without the wooden tubes taken from clothes-hangers – will die within a few minutes of an air-embolus in their blood-vessels, as did the woman reported above, who "had just stopped menstruating and her vascular system was therefore directly vulnerable." The powerful and repeated vaginal insufflation suggested in *Sex Rebel: Black*, however, could easily spell sudden death for any woman, whether or not recently menstruating, and especially when pregnant. A few further kooky California items, of equally unconscious danger or irresponsible sadism, connected with oragenitalism, will be warned against in the later section of this monograph on Irrumation.

In connection with the use of wines and other liquids inserted into the vagina as erotic "clownery," it should be mentioned that the presence of a bottle on the scene may suggest to the man that it might be playful to pour the wine directly into the woman's vagina, and to masturbate her with the neck of the bottle, pressing this into her vagina. It might indeed; but care must be taken not to press the bottle in too deeply, as women have died as a result of vulvo-vaginal lacerations and peritoneal puncture from a bottle pushed in too far, as can easily happen owing to the funnel-shaped shoulder of most bottles. I am also given to understand that a suction may be created, especially when the bottle-neck is inserted into the vagina and the bottle's contents then poured in, or when the bottle is inserted empty and warm, which will make it very difficult or even, it is said, practically impossible to withdraw the bottle. This may be simply folklore, stemming from the gruesome Fatty Arbuckle and Bix Beiderbecke tragedies in the 1920's and '30's. It is not folklore, however, that American highschool girls, unable to get the contraceptive Pill, are known to shake up a warm bottle of soda-pop with their thumb held over the mouth of the bottle, which is then thrust into the vagina as a foaming douche after intercourse. This has absolutely *no* birth-control value, and may, in fact, drive the boy's semen even further into the uterus than it might otherwise have arrived, with the serious additional dangers as to air-embolism already noted.

Sophisticates often insert into the vagina fruits such as strawberries or cherries (sweet, pitted cherries), or sections of an orange (a seedless orange), or slices of apple deliciously dipped in honey; thereupon sucking or drawing them out of the vagina again, and eating them with relish. The classical fruit used in this way is the banana, which is (with the serpent) the oldest and most famous of all phallic symbols, and one of the commonest objects used by women as a natural dildo, as are cucumbers and carrots. According to Mohammedan legend, the fruit of Eden with which Eve sinned was a banana — the large red banana of the tropics, is meant —

since the Bible does not specify anywhere that Eve used an apple: "the fruit of the tree" says *Genesis*, 3:1–7, without details. I have been told that it is possible for a woman with good muscle-tone in her vagina to peel back a ripe banana a short distance, to insert the peeled tip into her vagina, and then to peel and draw in all the rest of the banana simply by exerting the vaginal muscles. I have never seen this done, but am assured that it is a common trick among Levantine belly-dancers, who certainly are able to, and do pick up folded currency with their vaginas from the edge of the spectators' tables.

I have also heard very often of using oysters and mussels in cunnilinctus, inserting these into the vagina and then sucking and eating them out again, and I believe these reports to be entirely authentic. Karsch-Haack has reported of certain primitive peoples of the South Pacific that they insert small fish into the vagina and eat them out again — he does not say whether the fish are raw or cooked or even scaled! — and, after that, *any*thing seems likely. Oysters and mussels are apparently used in this way, in Western cultures, in preference to clams, since the taste of clams is very salty and fishy, and as such is thought too similar to the taste of the vulva to be added to it . . . too much of a good thing, as it were. There is also an evident ritual or religious idea hidden or unconscious in such practices, since fish and the ocean are everywhere connected with the cult of Aphrodite-Venus, the goddess of love. The obviously vulviform external shape of certain shellfish of the cowrie type (*Cypræa*) has caused these to be used as sacred amulets or money in many cultures. It cannot be overlooked, too, that the inner lips of the human vulva, when closed, are extremely similar in appearance to the soft inner parts of any bivalve of the oyster type, sometimes even including the pigmented edge.

In any case, the practice of inserting any solids into the vagina and sucking them out again should probably not be attempted by persons with false teeth or a dental plate, as such persons usually cannot produce any strong oral suction without displacing their dentures. As a matter of fact, this practice is not easy even for the most enthusiastic amorist, as the fruit or oyster or what-not can prove quite difficult to suck out – particularly if the woman's vagina is quite deep – but that is, of course, all part of the fun. If the object actually cannot be retrieved by sucking it may have to be fished out with the fingers. This is easier if two fingers can be inserted vaginally to grasp the object with their sides, tweezer-fashion, than if only one finger is inserted and must be hooked into or around the slippery object, or must press it against the upper vaginal wall and so draw it out.

Another objection to this practice is that while inserting the object, if the insertion is done with the lips and teeth, as is often the case, one is quite likely to blow a certain amount of air into the vagina, and this air will then escape with an unpleasant and suggestive vibrating or "raspberry" sound, which is rather embarrassing to the woman and unappealing to the man. This is the same sound, and caused by the same unintentional intrusion of air into the vagina, that is often encountered in coitus from behind when the woman is kneeling on all fours or in the knee-chest position, with her buttocks up and her breast and face down.

XIII

WITH THIS we arrive at the whole subject of the vulvar taste and odor, and the psychology of the cunnilinguist. There is a minor literature on sexual perfumery and osphresiology, remarking upon the sexually exciting quality of certain odors, and mentioning among these, in the case of very many people, the genital odors of the opposite sex. This is as true of women as it is of men. The most important work on the subject is that of the great sexologist Iwan Bloch (published under the pseudonym of "Albert Hagen"), who unfortunately has this to say about the genital odor and oragenitalism. After remarking that he has "emphasized the point that no sense impression calls forth so strong and prompt emotional reactions as olfactory sensations do," he goes on to state that "the normal man is, at the most, attracted by a generalized body scent [in the woman] when it is not out-and-out disagreeable, but is altogether repelled by genital odors. Such an inverted condition as is manifested in *cunnilingi* is an atavism to manipulations of a sort frequently observed among animals. Healthy and normal people experience the strongest repugnance to all odors localized in the genital areas." This is both true and untrue, and in any case highly misleading, since it exactly reverses who the normal and abnormal individuals really are!

To begin with, the human being is not really so very different from the less loquacious animals, such as dogs, in whom the rôle of smell in sexual selection is well known, as is the prevalence of oragenitalism, specifically cunnilinctus, as a coital preliminary. Nor is the repugnance that men feel toward the vulvo-vaginal odor very deep, being more of a jocular and affectionate distaste, as an examination of the multitude of jokes and the mass of disparaging slang terminology relating to the femino-genital odor will amply demonstrate. The contention that healthy and normal people experience "the strongest repugnance" to the vulvar odor is, in the case of men, absolutely and demonstrably untrue. Normal men, and in fact all adult males of the mammalian order, are very much attracted to the ordinary genital odor of the female, and are sexually excited by it. Other genital odors, such as that of menstruation, also excite non-human males, though human beings generally express a pronounced dislike or revulsion for it, but only after the blood of menstruation has been exposed for some time to the air. Otherwise, they are incapable of distinguishing it from the blood of a rare beefsteak that they may very much relish.

As Bloch himself says, the olfactory sense is capable of powerful emotional evocation — of both distant memories and immediate excitement — to a greater degree than any other sense. Surely the sexual impulse is as easily stirred by odors as any "emotional reaction" that Bloch may have had in mind. To contend that the well-known *odor di femina* is merely "a generalized body scent which is not out-and-out disagreeable," and to aver or imply that this much-prized odor is simply perspirational and not at all genital, is in direct contravention of the most obvious empiric facts. The Drs. Kronhausen, in *The Sexually Responsive Woman* (Grove Press, 1964), ending their chapter on "Women and Oral Sex," neatly express the circular logic and essential mental confusion of persons wishing to argue, like Bloch, against the naturalness and the natural attractiveness of the human genital odors and of oragenitalism: "As to the . . . contention that mouth-genital contacts are 'unnatural,' one can only gain one's point by losing it: if one states the fact that mouth-genital behavior is very common in all mammalian species and can therefore hardly be considered 'unnatural,' one is told that this just proves it to be 'animalistic'."

While the olfactory is not the strongest factor in making a man desire, or derive pleasure from, cunnilinctus, it is surely present in most men who so desire and who derive such pleasure. Aside from the normal component in the average sexual impulse of fetichism directed toward the genitalia and their appertinent sensible qualities – sight, touch, taste, and smell – there are, for the man, indirect psychological motivations and satisfactions in cunnilinctus which the vulvar odor could hardly suppress and is much more likely to enhance. Such motivations and satisfactions are the desire to arouse sensual passion in the woman, and to satisfy that passion – particularly when ordinary coitus does not usually suffice to bring her to the point of orgasm, or when she cannot otherwise be sufficiently excited preliminarily to assure her orgasm in subsequent coitus – cunnilinctus being here almost the ideal solution of the difficulties of the man with a frigid wife, or the impotent man, or the man afflicted with premature ejaculation. Or other, deeper motivations and satisfactions – the desire for the closest possible intimacy with a belovèd partner; or sexual excitement and urgency of such intensity as to move the man to loll and revel in the vulva, which is, after all, the ultimate object of his passion. In the face of desires and uses such as these, it seems incredible that merely a pungent odor could deter human beings from cunnilinctus, when the same human beings can eat with the utmost relish such substances as Gorgonzola and Limburger cheese, preserved herring, and rotted meat – under the designations of "high" and "gamy." And if the exceptional vulva should really smell so unattractive and downright repulsive as all that, well, it can always be washed.

This washing need not seem a reproach to the woman, and an insulting necessity; but can be made into a charming erotic game by having the man wash the woman with his own hands in a perfumed bath (bath salts), concentrating playfully on her vulva – making a rich lather in her pubic hair; trying to put the soap into her vagina, et cætera – with a wealth of bubbles and suds, and much splashing and laughing. This is even more pleasant as a preliminary to fellation, the woman washing the man's penis, and masturbating it with the soap-lather for lubrication when the man erects, as he probably will, as a result of her handling. However, the man may find that after such masturbation with soap, the touch of the bath-water causes a burning sensation to his penis.

The soap may be washed off the woman's vulva by having her lie flat in the tub, with the under-sides of her thighs up along the foot of the tub – and her legs over the edge at the knees, unless the foot of the tub is against the wall – and with her vulva directly under the faucet or tap, from which the warm water splashes down on the vulva to wash it clean. This is distinctly masturbatory, and occurs to many women spontaneously as a very effectual form of auto-excitation. With her hands crossed over her lathered breasts, exciting their nipples while the warm water pours over her vulva and clitoris, a woman can make of the washing of her genitalia preliminary to cunnilinctus a ritual of preparatory excitation that will put her in just the mood for cunnilinctus or eroticism of any sort. (Compare the notes on the shower bath, in the second paragraph following.)

At any rate, if a woman's genitals are reasonably clean, and the woman herself is neither disliked, too old, menstruous, or diseased, the odor and taste of her vulva and of her genital secretions should not be unpleasant to the average *and uninhibited* man, and should, in fact, be darkly pleasant, attractive, and definitely sexually exciting to him. But few people are truly uninhibited, or can even distinguish between what they really feel and what they believe they ought to feel. "Togetherness" cannot replace sexual authenticity.

To the reminder that the genitalia are excretory organs, it may be countered that there is seldom if ever any appreciable odor of urine about the genitalia of either sex, and that persons of any sort of taste and intelligence are not likely to prepare for oragenitalism or for any type of sexual contact by urinating – particularly in view of the fact that sexual pleasure is usually more acute in the presence of moderate tension caused by a somewhat distended bladder. There is even, furthermore, a component of mild urolagnia – attraction of urine – in the normal sexual impulse, as witness the fairly common practice of a man and a woman taking a shower together and urinating over each other's belly and legs. Or this may be done while swimming, or in a bath-tub, before engaging in the very jolly – and very slippery – coitus in a soapy bath-tub. The interest of men and women in watching the urination and even defæcation of the opposite sex is well known, and has even been briefly mentioned by Goethe in *Wilhelm Meister*, and in the autobiography of Havelock Ellis, *My Confessional* (1934).

In any case, if there is an unpleasant odor or taste of urine on the genitalia, they can always be washed and even perfumed. Plain water only and no soap should be used in brief ablutions, as soap is likely to be more noticeable and more unpleasant to the taste than a trace of urine could possibly have been. If the genitalia are perfumed it should be remembered that most perfumes are largely alcohol, and that alcohol may sting and burn the genitalia – although this may be pleasant – and, further, that most perfumes are manufactured with a base of either musk, ambergris, civet, or castor (which, ironically enough, are all derived more or less from the sexual or defæcatory organs of the musk deer, the whale, the civet cat, and the beaver respectively), and that these substances tend to fix and combine with the genital odor, and not to conceal it.

Many men do not even object to cunnilinguing the menstruous woman, immediately before and after, and also while the menstrual flow is actually in progress. This penchant was recognized even in antiquity, the Greek language having terms to distinguish ordinary cunnilinctus from cunnilinctus during the menstrual period; and if there was a word for it, it seems quite likely that the practice was by no means unknown, or even rare. I have brought together, for the first time I believe, a large amount of material on the subject of cunnilinctus during menstruation, but from the psychological and historical, rather than practical point of view, in *Rationale of the Dirty Joke* (1968) First Series, pages 567–84, under the heading "Cunnilinctus and Masochism," to which the reader is referred. What is emphasized there, on the basis of folk materials from many cultures, is the unspoken attraction that many men must feel for cunnilinctus upon the menstruating woman, an attraction which cannot really be based on any special attractiveness of the menstrual odor, but must be of far deeper emotional roots. What is perhaps involved, at the deepest level, is not the man's attraction to the vagina but his *fear* of the vagina, of its strange "penisless" conformation, suggesting to him unconsciously a castrated being, with all the anxiety this creates in him; and especially of its ability to bleed for days at a time without its possessor dying – an ability he knows he does not share.

If, however, the man does find the vulvar odor and taste a shade or two too pungent, or even definitely unpleasant during or around the period of menstruation, or at any special time of the woman's month, he had best refrain from cunnilinctus then unless she especially desires it or requires it to assure or procure her orgasm, and unless he feels affectionate enough to endure the odor for her sake, or has a cold in his head, and can't smell anything anyhow. The factor of taste is almost negligible then, since what is called taste is largely really odor, as can easily be demonstrated by the simplest sort of experiment. When the man just cannot bring himself to the point of engaging in cunnilinctus upon the menstruous woman, in spite of her desires; other types of stimulation than oral can usually be made to suffice, particularly since the menstruous woman is often, if not almost invariably, more passionate than usual, and her vulva softer, more turgid, and swollen, and sometimes rather open.

Some women have an unpleasantly sharp, acid and acrid vulvar taste between their menstrual periods, but whether or not this is a chronic condition in the specific woman, and exists in her at all times in her month and throughout her life, it is difficult to say. There is a common belief, however, that young girls — between nubility and their early twenties — have in general a sweeter and more pleasant taste than older women. Their labia minora are also said to be of a softer and more velvety texture; the nymphæ of older women being said to have a rather rubbery or leathery feel. Also, and relevantly, many men prefer the pinkish color of the vulva and nymphæ of younger girls — especially when these parts must be approached as closely as is necessary during cunnilinctus — in preference to the successively darker pink, red, brown, purplish, and even inky black coloring of the vulva of progressively older women. The vulvar coloring is not, however, exclusively related to age, and considerations of general coloring — blonde, brunette, et cætera — and racial pigmentation are very significant; but little systematic and scientific information seems available concerning such relationships.

An interesting amateur statement on this subject is made by an American aviator in World War II, quoted in Cauldwell's *Oral Genital Contacts*, supplementary note 2, concerning a young girl of Spanish and Indian descent with whom he had sexual relations in the Dominican Republic: "She was 18 and very pretty. Her pubic hair had been thinned out somewhat, and was not as coarse as most Latin pubic hair . . .

Her labial area was neat, nice to look at, not ugly or irregular in shape. She had a feature that I have seen only in Latins, that is, a mottled pattern of dark gray just inside the inner labia. This I took to be some disease when I first saw it. It isn't. These people have a darker than average pink color in both the inner and outer labia. The gray pattern does not follow any set lines, such as blood vessels. It is not unattractive, when you know it is normal." It should also be added that, in all races, the inner and outer lips of the vulva become redder or darker as they become congested with blood during sexual excitement: a sort of "dusky flush." (This is true even in infants.) Many men also prefer small nymphæ to large ones, not to mention the practically universal preference among men for a small vulva and vagina generally. In Lesbians this is often reversed, the large vulva being preferred.

If cunnilinctus is considered indispensable even in the presence of a definitely unpleasant vulvar taste and odor, the man – unless he is conveniently afflicted with a head cold, in which case it is very difficult to breathe during cunnilinctus – can momentarily but effectively dull his sense of taste, though not of smell, by holding a piece of ice on his tongue for half a minute or so. This can be done with the least obvious "business" and open affront to the woman's feelings if liquor, in the form of iced cocktails, is present at the sexual séance, but it should be remembered that while eroticism and intoxication go quite well together, an even partly intoxicated man may find ejaculation very difficult to achieve, which can be most distressing especially if fellation is attempted, and, lesserly, in the case of coitus. This use of ice will probably diminish the man's sensitivity to taste long enough for him to begin cunnilinctus and to continue it to such a point where he is himself so much excited by it – or by the gratifying spectacle of the woman's excitement, or by her concomitant caressing of him – that the well-known diminution during erotic excitement of the acuteness of the sensory perceptions (hearing, feeling, sight, taste, and smell; diminished in about that order) sets in, and the man becomes more or less unaware of any unpleasant odor or flavor.

I wish at this point to re-emphasize my contention that the ordinary vulvar odor will usually be pleasant and exciting to the man. During cunnilinctus the man must, in the very nature of things, practically *live* in this natural odor and taste and in the somewhat viscid vaginal liquor, and far from dissuading men from cunnilinctus – although, of course, it does dissuade many – this combined olfactory and gustatory experience may be a large or even the largest part of the man's desire to engage in cunnilinctus.

For, ideally, cunnilinctus is *psychologically* as pleasurable and as exciting to the man as it is, *physically*, to the woman. The same holds true even more definitely of the psychological pleasure that many women take in fellation, and this aspect of the subject will be discussed at greater length further on. That cunnilinctus and fellation are – or, at least, can be – delightful and satisfying (even to the point of orgasm) to the active party – the cunnilinctor or fellatrice – as well as to the passive party, is the most important single point that can be made. The fact that the pleasure experienced by the cunnilinctor or, more often, the fellatrice can even reach the point of spontaneous orgasm is probably the reason for the usual psychiatric categorization of fellatorism and cunnilinguism as "perversions" (as "variants" or "deviants" by those of greater skepticism as to the demonstrable existence of a rigid norm). And, in fact, if oragenitalism habitually takes the place of coitus for the cunnilinctor or the fellatrice, it may indeed be considered a deviant from whatever rather fluid and flexible norm there may actually be in sexual activity. One thing is obvious: such exclusively oral acts do not directly serve the natural impulse toward the coital acts that are our biological purpose.

Before leaving the subject of normalcy and oragenitalism, mention might be made of the oragenital employment of animals. We are, of course, animals ourselves, but one of our most serious miscegenational taboos is that against intercourse with animals even so closely related to us as chimpanzees or baboons – assuming that anyone other than another chimpanzee or baboon is seriously interested in them. The xenophobic taboos against intercourse with persons of other races, places of origin, skin-color, etc., obviously are connected, nor is this the place to discuss the subject, which is largely psychologically determined. Oragenital relations with animals are very common, and do not seem so much a matter of abnormal sexuality, as one of ingenious or ingenuous pansexuality. It is observable that the human individual almost always takes the genital part in such relations, and seldom or never the oral part, clearly implying that the animal is simply *faute de mieux*, in the lack of a human companion.

Many young girls and boys attempt to induce a dog or cat to lick the vulva or penis, the organ sometimes being rubbed with cream or honey to attract the animal: a childish or anthropomorphic error, since these animals do not like honey. Cats and kittens are less frequently used than small dogs, since all cats are likely to scratch, and their tongue is also unbearably rough. Similar use of calves, lambs, and other farm animals is often reported. Actually this is quite dangerous, as such larger animals often are overpoweringly strong in their sucking reflexes and are likely to bite disastrously if disturbed when sucking. I myself know of a girl, for that matter, who put sugar on her vulva, and let flies walk on it because she enjoyed the tickling sensation; and I have heard of a boy who put his penis into a can of wriggling worms. But this latter is apocryphal, and neither is really oragenitalism.

Psychoanalysis, with its remarkable ability at getting people to reveal their deepest secrets, has again and again recorded the pleasure of the active party in oragenitalism. The consensus of opinion among those who have considered the subject at any great length or depth is that oragenitalism satisfies in the active party not only very deep reminiscences of sucking experiences at the breast — or deprivations of these — but also the desire for the most intimate, and at once the *most submissive and most possessive* sexual contact possible with the later sexual partner. Oragenitalism is therefore a practice to be expected among the more emotional and intelligent, in whom derived and complex psychological urgencies and gratifications are likely, as well as among persons of powerful erotic propensities. When an individual is both highly sensitive and erotic, he or she is extremely likely, faced with any sort of opportunity, and relative freedom from inhibitory influences, to attempt, to enjoy, and finally to be habitually given to oragenitalism, at least as coital foreplay. But this is conjectural territory, and I wish to confine myself to facts.

XIV

THE ATMOSPHERE for sex-play of any sort is a very important coefficient of the amount of pleasure and gratification to be derived from it. The imagination is powerfully heated and excited by certain surroundings, and depressed and diminished by others. Obviously there are also individuals to whom we are attracted, and others to whom we are not, but it is surprising how large a part imagination plays even in such sexual choices. As Dr. Johnson is supposed to have said to

Boswell: "Sir, were it not for Imagination, a man would be as happy in the arms of a chambermaid as of a duchess." (Maybe happier.) All this is even more true of oragenitalism than of coitus, especially in what regards the surroundings, since in coitus both partners are usually physically close all along their bodies and much occupied with each other, and are also probably kissing with their eyes shut; while in oragenitalism one partner is very likely to be lying supine, fully conscious of the surroundings.

Ideally, all these surroundings should be comfortable whether indoors or out of doors – a bed, a sofa, a couch, a rug before a hearth, a garden, under a tree, a forest clearing, a haymow, a wheat-field, a mountain top, a lakeside, a river's edge. It is sometimes unavoidable that sexual intimacy be engaged in in an automobile or behind bushes, but neither of these is recommended, being both cramped and unæsthetic. If indoors, a private bathroom and toilet are almost essential, or, at the very least, water and towels and a basin.

There should be no fear of interruption or discovery, especially if the woman has any vague – or decided – feelings of wrongdoing. If indoors, the man should lock the doors, and should make a definite mental note that he has done so, or he may worry about it, repeatedly getting up to make sure (mild *folie du doute*), and even proving temporarily impotent because of nervousness on this score. Freedom from possible interruption can be further secured by taking the telephone receiver off the hook, but this should not be done in a hotel or small town where the operator is likely to listen-in to the partners' love conversation, which may prove very inflammatory to her. The doorbell can be blocked or disconnected too, or a "Do Not Disturb" sign hung on the door, if in a hotel. The doorbell can be blocked most easily and without breaking it by putting a heavy rubber band around the periphery of the bell, thus reducing any possible ring to a quiet buzz which can conveniently be disregarded.

There should be no necessity for hurry or for remaining dressed or for being quiet. This latter is very important, since many people have an uncontrollable desire to moan or sing or shout or scream at orgasm, and it has a definite inhibitory effect on the degree of pleasure of the orgasm, or even on any orgasm at all, to be required to bear in mind that the neighbors will hear it if one screams, or may already be listening snickeringly to the jingling music of the bed-springs.

At the beginning of the pair's intimacy light can be entirely absent, or dim-colored (blue or red), moonlight, or a shaded bed-lamp or table-lamp. As their intimacy progresses, and they become used to one another, more in love, and, possibly, more unabashed and unashamed, they may go on to intimacy at dawn, in the morning, or in the full sunlight, although this unfortunately cannot be recommended to people who are ugly or fat or very thin or crippled.

Love-making easily follows such preambles as walking in the woods or meadows, feasting, drinking, dancing, bathing, swimming, reading poetry, driving very fast in an open automobile, taking drugs, reading erotic books and looking at erotic pictures, listening to music, or any of a hundred other exhilarating experiences. Many of these preamble experiences can be had in bed or on a hearth-rug with the partners lying side by side, or even lying on their sides, in a sort of sixty-nine, with their heads resting on each other's curled underthigh, and their faces near each other's genitalia. Very often the man can lie between the woman's legs with his cheek on her pubis, to revel in the feel of her pubic hair and the heady odor of her vulva while he eats or drinks (possibly dipping the leg of a squab into her vagina for sauce, or pouring his wine over her vulva and drinking it up from there), or sings

— possibly accompanying himself on the guitar — or talks, or listens to concert music, or even reads or smokes. A modified hookah (or even a real narghile, water-bottle and all) will keep the ashes out of bed.

In oragenitalism the partners need not undress, but they should be able to do so if they wish to, and the man should always undress if he can before being fellated, as his trousers will get in the way if only opened and pushed down, and their cloth may irritate the woman's face, not to mention that they will certainly look a little ridiculous, and that his underwear is sure to bind and annoy and get in the way. A woman, on the other hand, has only to pull up her skirt and lift her hips while the man pushes or pulls down her drawers — if she wears any, which she can easily remember not to do if she intends to enjoy sexual intimacy with the man if the occasion arises — and takes them off (or leaves them hanging on one foot, if she thinks she might lose or forget them); and her belly and vulva and crotch are then entirely open to the man's caresses.

If the pair are in bed, the room should be warm enough for them to throw the covers back during oragenitalism, and also for them to move to the floor or an armchair without having to put on dressing gowns or robes for warmth. While most lovers wish to sleep entwined with each other after their passions are spent, fore-thinking voluptuaries are likely to prefer twin beds — one to pummel and disarray and wet with sweat during sex-play, and the other to remain cool and fresh for them to sleep in afterwards. The use of twin beds otherwise is, of course, intolerable, as depriving the partners of precisely the closeness in sleeping that normal people — in fact most mammals — naturally seek.

The room, or the lovers themselves, particularly the woman, may or even should be perfumed. The woman may apply the perfume to the lobes of her ears, to her lips, to the tip of her tongue, to the nape of her neck, behind her ear-lobes, in her armpits, between her breasts, to each nipple, and to her pubis. Only a touch is needed at each of these, particularly if a touch is given to all of them. The woman may also touch up her nipples with lip rouge, if she is to be naked – otherwise it will stain her underwear – and such high coloring of the nipples will seem jolly, and will probably taste good, to the man.

The choice of a perfume is, of course, a personal matter, but as an adjunct to sexual intimacy, heavy, provocative, languorous, and even Oriental-seeming perfumes are perhaps best. I am not well enough acquainted with the composition of perfumes to explain the fabrication of the heavy, sultry, "sexy" perfumes, but these qualities will usually be found in perfumes largely containing musk, civet, ambergris, or castor, as well as frangipanni, ylang-ylang, patchouly, benzoin, sandalwood, verbena, or jasmin. It is difficult to describe perfumes, and it is dangerous to name trade products since they disappear from the market sooner or later, but of perfumes available at present, those best suited for sexual enhancement of a person or bed or room are perhaps Ciro's "Danger," Lanvin's "My Sin," Fabergé's "Aphrodisia," Schiaparelli's "Sleeping" and "Shocking," Caron's "Can Can," Leigh's "Risqué,' Corday's "Toujours Moi," Patou's "Moment Suprême," and the heady "Drumbeat" of Charbert. The generally sexual tone of these trade-names is significant, the manufacturers recognizing, and capitalizing on the sexual use and erotic tonality of all perfumes. One "forbidden" perfume should perhaps be avoided, despite its provocative name, since most men find that it smells like unadulterated skunk. Note, incidentally, that any perfume can be experienced even in silence and in the dark.

Incense can also be used to perfume the room, and the incense-burner, with the smoke curling slowly up before a candle which may be the room's only illumination, creates a rather seductive and dreamy atmosphere for many people. Care should be taken to avoid oriental incenses of too heavy an odor, which make many Westerners sick or groggy. Despite their advertising, incenses – and even shaving-lotions – with a smell like pine trees are nowadays to be avoided, since they are less likely to make city-bred people think of virgin forests, etc., than of the so-called "chlorophyll" destinking agents used in toilets. I am reminded at this point of the subsidiary use of drugs in heightening sexual sensations, aside from the drinking of the obvious wines, whiskeys, liquors, and liqueurs which are legally acceptable in the West. Though one certainly does not wish to recommend their use in countries in which they are illegal, certain other drugs are also used in similar social and sexual situations in both East and West. In particular, the dried flowers and leaves of the hemp plant (hashish, technically *cannabis*, in America called marihuana and many euphemistic terms) are nowadays often smoked by both partners before or even during sexual intercourse, in certain convenient postures such as the "scissors" position earlier described, and by the subject during oragenitalism.

A paragraph appearing here in the original edition of this monograph, discussing the sexual use and presumed sexual effects of a number of narcotic and euphoric drugs has here been omitted as being now more dangerously likely to create converts than it was when originally written. No person not living in a cave needs to be told of the tremendous, media-sponsored vogue of LSD, peyote, and other hallucinatory drugs during the 1960's in America, particularly among adolescents easy to influence by irresponsible propagandists and cynical peddlers. I have written bitter pages on this scourge, which I have seen from close, in my pamphlets *The Fake Revolt* (1967) and *Models of Madness*, particularly emphasizing in the latter the seldom-told truth that the use of these drugs leads a large percentage of their habitual users to schizophrenia, that is to say insanity. Some of the most dangerous drugs known, of vegetable origin, such as henbane, snakeroot, and Jimson weed (which even the American Indians treat with caution), have been blithely taken by young people looking for "kicks," and finding only sudden death – if they are lucky – sometimes prolonged agony and convulsions. Poisonous hallucinants of this kind, particularly those of mushroom and cactus origin, have in any case almost nothing to do with sexuality, and are not sexual excitants. If they were, it might be another story, nor would they stay illegal long.

I have been censured for mentioning narcotics here at all, or for saying anything further about them than that most narcotics usually make the person who takes them feel bored with sexuality and beyond it. Few drug-addicts are sex-addicts too. It would be insincere, however, to deny that certain euphoric drugs (not the hallucinants) can be, and often are, quite pleasant adjuncts to sexuality. The hysterical and ridiculous disapprobation evinced by Occidental society toward all drugs but alcohol – when not *forcing* these on "lesser breeds," as in the Opium War of the 1830's, in which England forced opium on the Chinese – seems to me excessive and hypocritical. In India, today, persons of excellent family will sprinkle powdered hashish on cakes being served to visitors (who seldom react in Peter Sellers style), with the same benevolent attention as a European or American host pouring an after-dinner glass of cognac – with coffee and cigars: two further drugs – for honored guests. Taken in moderation, neither culture has found that its favorite drugs are anything but pleasant enhancements of civilized life. Of course, moderation is the privilege of only a very few. The rest swill like pigs, in all countries. There are also sex-pigs. We all know several.

Drug addiction is a terrible and shattering affliction, and is likely to make the individual socially useless and even dangerous. Drugs, however, have a definite value in the sexual sphere, and are used for that reason and with satisfactory effects by many people, of whom only the weak and maladjusted become drug-addicts. I have therefore mentioned drugs in relation to sexuality, and maintain that they can there be quite useful, although I hardly wish to recommend their use. It all depends on which drug you use, and how you use it. The deadliest habit-forming drug widely used is tobacco.

A rather mild and fairly harmless way of accentuating sexual pleasure, or any other pleasure (such as listening to music) is hyperventilation: the practice of inhaling as deeply as possible during sexual intimacy, or whatever the pleasure may be. But *really* as deeply as possible, dragging in great lungfuls of air. This is possible only to the subject in oragenitalism, of course, and can very easily be done by her or by him. The breaths should be taken one after another in quick succession, and held only very briefly. If oragenitalism is being experienced at the same time (and also if violin music or other music of high-frequency vibration, or of pronounced and protracted rhythm – such as Ravel's "Bolero" – is being listened to at the same time), the unusual amount of oxygen inhaled will usually, in combination with the other excitations, make the subject mildly light-headed, and will create a feeling of exhilaration and a desire to laugh and shout. The effort itself also creates a certain auto-intoxication or hypnosis, as can easily be observed nowadays among crowds of young people listening to rock-&-roll and other heavily rhythmic music.

The use of music to heighten sexual pleasure is very ancient, and very well known. Shakespeare begins his comedy, *Twelfth Night*, with the lover's plea: "If music be the food of love, play on!" Religious attempts were once even made to ban certain kinds of music as "wanton," in particular the so-called *modus lascivus*, which is, alas, nothing but the Ionian mode or key of C, to which every piano is tuned! Nowadays, the phonograph and the radio make music easily available at any hour of the day or night, once the prerogative only of the richest voluptuaries. The music is of course played not only beforehand, to help create the erotic mood, but also during the erotic act itself, sometimes matching the action to the rhythm of the music.

The radio, however, has the enormous disadvantage (television is even worse) that after the music – be it a peaceful or fiery sonata, a majestic organ selection, a sweeping and surging symphony or symphonic tone-poem, or even headily rhythmic and drum-beating jazz – after the music has produced the desired state of languor or excitement in the lovers, an announcer's sleek and insinuating, or brassily nasal and foppishly smug voice is sure to disrupt the atmosphere completely by suggesting, nay practically demanding, that a million listeners drop whatever they're doing and rush out at once into the street to buy-*buy*-BUY! Mexican Mentholated Toilet Tissue – the Perfect Paper for People with Piles! This is the reason, of course, for the continuing popularity of the phonograph among people who love music, of whatever kind, and who wish to use it as background for their sexual lives. The phonograph is particularly welcome now that disc-recordings and tapes have an extended period of play, and no longer require changing the records every few minutes (except for the worst kinds of musical *kitsch*) in hearing an extended composition through to the end.

Violin music, particularly if it is very fast, high-pitched, and brilliant, reacts well and enhancingly on many people in connection with sexual excitement, exciting them the more. This is very well understood in the formal alternation in Hungarian Gypsy folk-music and dances, of the sensuous *ritardando* followed by a break-neck climax of speed (the *lassu* and *friska*). It is unnecessary to underline the symbolic sexual miming here. For people who respond to this type of music there might be recommended especially the violin concerti of Bach, Beethoven, Brahms, Bruch, Chausson's "*Poème*," Dvořák, Haydn, Lalo, Mozart (also his superb *Sinfonia Concertante* for violin and viola, K.364), Mendelssohn, Paganini, Sibelius, Tchaikovsky, and Vieuxtemps (No. 4, one of the most sexual), and in particular the tremendous outpouring of baroque concerti by Vivaldi and Locatelli (*L'Arte del Violino*), which explored and almost exhausted all the possibilities of the genre at its very beginning. Special mention should also be made of the Violoncello concerto in B-minor of Dvořák, in which the low and throaty tones of the 'cello react as excitingly as the higher and more vibrant tones of the violin. Piano and organ concerti can be most effective, too, with different types of people, as well as symphonies, sonatas, symphonic tone-poems, fantasias, overtures (such as those of Mozart and Rossini), and even string quartets, in most of which, however, many people – myself included, incidentally – are able to discern only that the tail of a horse is being dragged over the entrails of a sheep, excepting always the quartets of Schubert.

Music in which rhythm and the drumbeat are very pronounced – such as jazz, rock-&-roll, recordings of primitive drum-music, or violent orchestral exercises like the well-known "Bolero" of Ravel (who called it a "*danse lascive*") – have a profoundly sexual reaction upon many people, as well as one of general excitement and tenseness; but it is also a fact that these are much more likely to leave them emotionally limp than sexually ready. In general, slow dreamy music of a delicacy hiding great depths, such as the music of the Spanish guitar (for which the three quintets by Boccherini are masterpieces of unassuming simplicity and emotion) and Debussy's famous "*L' Après-midi d'un Faune*," will be found to be more pleasant, as erotic accompaniment, than many violent musical orgies of overwhelming volume and beat, which are really replacements of, rather than excitants to sexuality. Massive-volume "rock" music of distorted tone and overwhelming beat is absolutely not an aphrodisiac, except perhaps in the sense that dying on the gallows is said to give the victim an erection. No future in that!

Except for very simple souls, the proper mood and rhythm of love-making is more closely that created by Chopin's nocturnes or his "Raindrop" prélude, or Beethoven's "Moonlight" sonata, or even his "Sonata Appassionata," than that of the finale to Rossini's "William Tell" overture – I mean the part with the horses: *Rump-titty, rump-titty, rump, rump, rump!!* – or Schubert's "Marche Militaire." Which is not to say that there are not moments when the last two are perfectly right! It should be remembered, finally, that the nostalgic music of a hurdy-gurdy down the street, or of wheat soughing in the wind, or rain on the roof at night, or branches tapping on a window-pane, or even the unearthly rustling of curtains blowing in the inquisitive moonlight, can make any two lovers, who have not forgotten what love is really all about, feel just as erotic or just as peaceful afterward as any more elaborate music ever can.

XV

THERE REMAINS now only the consideration of postures to conclude this analysis of the technique of cunnilinctus. To avoid fatiguing the reader with the formal analysis of possibilities, only the most common posture used – that in which the woman lies supine on her back – will be analyzed at length. Other postures will be noted briefly, with the thought that anyone who wishes to do so can easily dress the table of possible variants in all of these, on the style of the variants shown for the first.

To begin with, let us consider the theory of human posture. Just as faces are distinguishable through the divergent combination, and the moderate variation, of features which are in general quite similar in all persons; just so postures differ in the divergent combination of the parts of the body. These parts are the torso, the legs, and the arms; each of which may be divided into two movable parts: the torso into the hips and shoulders, the leg into the thigh and lower leg (that is, the part of the limb below the knee), and the arm into the upper arm and forearm.

There are eight primary positions of the torso; the hips and shoulders being in a line with one another and untwisted: *1.* supine – lying on the back; *2.* leaning – the hips on the supporting surface, and the shoulders and head lifted, the torso making a quarter-angle (about forty-five degrees) with the supporting surface; *3.* vertical upright – the torso resting on the hips, and at right angles to the support; *4.* bending – the torso bent forward at a quarter-angle declination from the upright; *5.* prone – lying flat on the face; *6.* stooping – the torso bent far forward and downward at a quarter-angle from a horizontal position; *7.* downward vertical – the hips held straight above the shoulders and head; *8*. hanging supine — the torso bent far backward at a three-quarter-angle from the upright (or may be considered upward at a quarter-angle from the downward vertical position).

It will be seen that in moving forward or backward through these postures consecutively, the torso will have described a complete circle, itself as the radius, the hips as the more or less unmoving center, and the head describing the imaginary circumference, of the circle.

There are five distinct leg positions: *1*. full lifted — the entire leg (thigh and lower leg) at an acute angle to the torso; *2*. half lifted — the entire leg at right angles to the torso; *3*. quarter lifted — the entire leg at an obtuse angle to the torso; *4*. straight — the leg at no angle to the torso, and a straight continuation of it; *5*. backwards — the entire leg at an obtuse angle to the back of the torso. In each of these leg positions the entire leg is straight, the thigh and lower leg in a straight line. There are three possible variant positions of the lower leg: *1*. quarter bent — the calf at an obtuse angle to the underthigh; *2*. half bent — the calf at right angles to the underthigh; *3*. full bent — the calf at an acute angle to, or touching, the underthigh.

At any time, both legs can be held in the same position and state of straightness or bending, or the other leg may assume any of the twenty other possible leg positions (5 primary leg positions × 4 positions of the lower leg). The legs can also be held together at their inner sides, or can be held open in three variant positions of spread: *1*. spread — both the thighs and lower legs separated; *2*. dropped open — the feet close together, at either ankles or soles, while the knees drop completely outward and away from each other; *3*. splayed — the thighs together, and the lower legs spread from the knees downward.

There are also two twisting motions of the torso: the *twist*, in which the hips are held relatively still while the torso twists half or full to either side, in the full twist the side of the torso being in the direction in which the feet face; and the *side-bend*, in which the hips are held relatively still while the shoulders dip half or full to either side, in the half-dip one arm, if it is extended, being at an acute angle to the legs, the other extended arm being at an obtuse angle to the legs.

The positions of the arms are not considered, being more or less irrelevant in a discussion of cunnilinctual postures, and too complex to be treated understandably or completely in the space here available.

A little multiplication at this point will give a slight idea of the myriad postures possible to the human body. 8 torso postures × 5 thigh positions × 4 lower leg positions = 160 × 20 possible positions of the other leg = 3200 + 160 original leg and torso positions = 3360. Furthermore, 5 thigh positions × 4 lower leg positions = 20 side-lying positions × 20 possibilities of the other leg = 400 + 20 original positions = 420 side-lying possibilities + 3360 "straight" positions = 3780 possible positions.

If every combination were possible, 3780 positions of the woman × 3780 positions of the man would give the alarming sum of 14,288,400 possible combination-postures for one man and one woman in coitus, cunnilinctus or fellation, not counting the twisting and side-bending of the torso and the positions of the arms. Luckily, this is only theoretical, and I leave it to the very ambitious to conceive and test all the actually possible combinations and permutations of postures for the different types of sexual intercourse, genital, oral, and otherwise.

Now that all of two pages has been spent on theoretical body postures and combinations, let us forget all about it, and consider the matter briefly and practically. For all practical purposes, the fullest range of body postures can be found by *following the body during a forward progression*, from lying on the back, through standing, to lying forward on the belly. (Or a backward progression, from prone to supine.) 1: *Supine* – the body lying flat on its back, forming a straight line from head to foot. Two sub-postures should be mentioned; *A*: Hanging – in which only the lower torso, hips, and legs lie flat, and the upper torso, shoulders, and head hang down backwards from the horizontal plane; and *B*: Leaning – in which the hips and legs are still supine, but the upper torso is lifted to a quarter angle from the bed, supported either by the bent and backward extended elbows or by the backward extended, or forward extended and gripping hands.

2. *Sitting* – *A*: the legs still supine, but the torso lifted vertically; or *B*: the legs being curled to one side; or *C*: the thighs still resting on the supporting surface, and the lower legs dropped more or less vertically as when sitting in a chair. 3: *Squatting* – roughly the same sitting position as 2C, only without any supporting surface under the thighs, the body being supported upon the feet or toes. 4: *Standing* – the body is extended upward from the squatting position. 5: *Bending* – continuing its forward progression, the body bends in the middle, the legs remaining vertical while the torso bends forward toward or beyond the horizontal. 6: *Huntsman Position* (one leg kneeling, one leg squatting) – the body drops to kneel on one knee, while the other leg squats, its thigh horizontal and its lower leg vertically downward. The upper torso may return to vertical, or may remain bent forward or even downward. This position is called the huntsman position because it is used by archers and riflemen. 7: *Kneeling* – the squatting leg of the huntsman position joins its mate and kneels too. The upper torso may be vertical

or may bend forward to the horizontal. 8: *All Fours* – the upper torso in the kneeling position bends forward and is supported by the hands or elbows, which hang downward to the supporting surface. The legs may remain in a kneeling position, or the knees may be lifted while the legs are supported on the feet. 9: *Prone* – the legs are extended completely backwards and the support of the arms is withdrawn, the body falling forward to lie flat on its breast, belly and legs. Two sub-postures should be mentioned; *A*: Leaning up – the head and shoulders and upper torso lifted and supported on the elbows; and *B*: Hanging – in which only the lower torso and the hips and legs lie flat, and the upper torso and shoulders and head hang down forward from the horizontal plane, as over the edge of a bed.

This itinerary is probably not quite the one that would be followed by a person really intent upon progressing from supine to prone as quickly, and through as few intermediate positions as possible (such a person would hardly bother to rise to a standing position in the process); but the nine positions given represent the full practical range of body posture, leg positions not being considered, nor twists and side-bends. The body may also lie on its side, with twenty possible positions of each leg (420 combinations), and with twisting and side-bending (upward) variations of the torso – here very important.

The reader may think that an undue amount of space has been spent on this consideration of general body positions and combinations preliminary to a consideration of cunnilinctual body positions and combinations. But this space has by no means been wasted. Without the analysis of posture given above, no systematic treatment of cunnilinctual postures could be made, nor could it be readily understood by the reader. It would be necessary to welter in a miscellany of postures, known and imaginary, and probably derived from erotic art (which is anatomically almost worthless, since the artist can and does distort anatomy to suit the needs of design), and from erotic photographs – which are likewise almost worthless because they depict possible but impractical postures which have been chosen not for their erotic effectiveness but for the voyeuristic displaying of the genitalia to the camera. Art and photography, however, are useful, and have been useful to me, in synthesizing a system of postures, in verifying the actual possibility of specific postures, and in clarifying methods of support and other details.

In the outline of postures which follows, the woman's position is to be given through the practical progression of nine possibilities described above; progressing from supine, forward to prone. Under each position of the woman are to be given the possible positions of the man, first those in which he can lick the vulva upward; second those in which he must lick the vulva downward – the man's positions progressing from prone, backwards to supine; side-lying variants being given last when any exist.

I. *The Woman Supine:* A. – *Upward.* 1. *The Man Prone* – He lies on his belly between her spread legs, his legs extended behind him or curled at his side. It will probably be necessary to place a pillow under her hips to raise her vulva fully to his mouth, as described and commented upon at length earlier in this monograph. The higher her thighs are lifted toward her torso – until finally her knees are at her breasts – the easier it is for the man to cunnilingue her, he rising onto his elbows if necessary, and supporting her legs on his shouders. Or she can lift her knees directly upward, bringing her heels back toward her buttocks, under which a pillow may or may not be placed. In this way, resting her weight on her shoulders and feet, she can lift her hips and move them up and down and around to assist the man and to add to her own tension and pleasure; meanwhile relieving the man's shoulders of the weight of her legs.

2. *The Man on All Fours* – (a) As the woman's hips are raised higher, till her torso itself is lifted on the pivot of her shoulders, the man rises to all fours, on his knees and hands, his hands resting in the hollow under the woman's knees which he presses apart, and down along her body to her breasts. This may be done on a sofa or at the edge of the bed, and his outer leg may be extended down along the edge to rest on the floor, and give him greater support and equilibrium, so that he need rest none of his weight on her through his hands. She may support her hips on her elbows, her hands under the small of her back and her forearms more or less vertical. (b) The man may also be on all fours on the floor facing the bed, while the woman lies supine with her hips at the edge of the bed and her thighs apart and resting on the man's shoulders, or together bent back toward her breast, one or both of her forearms clasped under her knees to support them. If only one, the other hand may play with her clitoris.

3. *The Man Kneeling* – As in 2.a, 2.b, and 5.c.

4. *The Man in the Huntsman Position* – As in 2.a, 2.b, and 5.c.

5. *The Man Bending* – (a) Except by tipping his head uncomfortably, the man cannot cunnilinque the supine woman while he bends forward from a standing position, unless her hips and vulva are raised very high. This can be done by means of several high cushions on a rather high bed, but cushions may slide and slip, and he must support the weight of his forward-bent upper torso on her hips or buttocks or on the cushions, which are thus even more likely to slip. (b) A better place for this position than in a bed is therefore in an upholstered armchair, or it can be done in an automobile, the

woman in the front seat, the man in the back, the woman lying with her shoulders on the seat and her hips and legs up along and over the sloping back of the seat, with her spread knees at the tip of the back, over which they hang, and on which the man's belly is resting between her knees, as he leans far forward to cunnilingue her. (c) Or she can lie sideways in the chair, with her hips resting on one arm of the chair, over which a pillow or cushion has been bent to make it less sharp and to lift her hips and vulva a little higher. The man can rest his weight on his elbows on the arm of the chair at both sides of the woman's hips, or may hold her legs under the knees, and rest there.

6. *The Man Standing* — As in 5.b, the woman's hips at the top of the chair's back, and her legs out over the man's shoulders. This may drive her chin unpleasantly into her chest, so this combination is probably better with the woman as in 1. or 2. on a high table or other support, such as may be found elsewhere than in the bedroom — the crotch of a tree, a packing case, or the first landing of a staircase, with the man standing in the well of the staircase, if there is no balustrade.

7. *The Man Squatting* — As in 2.a, 2.b, and 5.c.

8. *The Man Sitting* — (a) He may sit on the same surface as that upon which the woman is supine, his legs encircling the ottoman or stack of cushions which raise her hips to the height of his shoulders. (b) Or she may be supported without cushions, by her thighs on his shoulders, and her own shoulders on the bed or ground, between his spread legs. He may lift his knees, his lower legs sliding back and upward under her armpits, and can rest his legs firmly on his feet, so that she can wind her arms around his lower legs between the calf and the knee, and hold herself in position. A little woman with a short torso will find this difficult with a tall man with long thighs, as his knees will lie under or past her shoulders,

and she must lift her arms to allow him to raise his knees properly. (c) He may sit on the floor before her, as in 2.a, 2.b, and 5.c. (d) He may sit above the surface upon which she is supine, as on a sofa or armchair while she lies on her shoulders on the floor on a few pillows before him, and lifts her hips onto his knees, he bending his upper torso and head forward, and drawing her upward and to him with his arms wrapped around her thighs from underneath. Or he may sit in a deck- or beach-chair, while she lies back on the foot-rest, and lifts her thighs over his shoulders to entwine her lower legs behind his head, giving herself extra support, while his elbows are on the arms of the beach-chair, preventing her entwined legs from dragging his upper torso too far down. The deck-chair has the advantage of supporting the woman on her back instead of on her shoulders as she is when on the floor before the man.

9. *The Man Supine* – In this position of the man, and in its variants in which the man leans slightly up toward a sitting position, supporting himself on pillows or on his elbows, and in which the man's upper torso is hanging back downward, the cunnilinctual postures mentioned in 8. are possible, with this difference that the man's body is straighter now than when he was sitting up, and the distance between his shoulders and knees is much increased. Since the woman's thighs must remain at his shoulders, her head will move forward along his body, to about his hips. She may lie there, supine on his thighs, her head on them or between them; or she may twist her upper torso to one side and down to fellate the man simultaneously – which is most easily possible with a tall woman and not too tall a man – thus achieving the "cross-back" or twisted sixty-nine, later to be mentioned. Or she can slide her upper torso off his thighs onto the bed, while he twists more or less onto his side to keep his mouth at her

vulva. This position of the woman supine and the man on his side, with his legs toward her head, and his head under her near thigh, which rests on his shoulder, has been mentioned earlier in this monograph with mention of how it may be reached from a position where the man is lying at the woman's side, facing, embracing, and kissing her.

I. *The Woman Supine:* B. – *Downward.* 1. *The Man Prone* – The man lies on his belly, facing the woman's feet, with (a) his knees resting on the bed at either side of the woman's waist, or (b) with his legs straddling her, her legs spread, her knees and hips up. In *b.* he can press his penis to the woman's mouth, for a sixty-nine – see later – or he can let it lie pointing downward between her breasts which she squeezes together to form a groove (if her breasts are ample) in which he can rub his penis, while she kneads and "bag-pipes" her breasts together with her hands, until he too has an orgasm. If her breasts are sufficiently large for him to press them together with his thighs while he goes through coital movements between them, the woman can use her hands to caress his penis at its root, or his testicles, or to digitate his anus. If his precoital distillation does not suffice to lubricate her intermammary groove, she can wet the inner curve of each breast with her wetted palm or palms – using saliva – before he straddles over her.

If he reaches an orgasm in this way, care should be taken, contraceptively, that his semen, which will spurt down along her belly, does not get on her vulva, either by spurting that far, or by trickling down. A very satisfactory termination to a bout of this sort is for the man to draw his penis back when he feels his orgasm is approaching, and ejaculate into the woman's mouth, if she enjoys that. Intermammary coitus is more exciting to many men than is fellation, so if he engages in the above finish, he should be sure that his orgasm is actually upon him before he shifts, or fellatory movements may be necessary to bring him to orgasm, or he may even have to return temporarily to intermammary rubbing, which may make either him or the woman feel ineffectual and inexpert.

2. *The Man on All Fours* – As 1.

3. *The Man Kneeling* – (a) As 1.a, the woman's hips being lifted very high on pillows; the man kneeling high or sitting back on or toward his heels. Or (b), if the man straddles her, he may hold up her hips with his hands down around her waist, but pillows will help. With him kneeling astraddle her supine body she will be almost forced to anilingue him, so this position should best be avoided with women who are much opposed to anilinctus. However, in the presence of great excitement and the proffered possibility of anilinctus as in this position, many more women are likely suddenly and spontaneously to do it than would if coolly asked beforehand, when they would almost certainly refuse. It is always best *never* to ask a woman for any sexual intimacy, but to suggest it to her by actions. If she is sufficiently excited, as by cunnilinctus, there are usually few things she will refuse. (c) With the woman's hips elevated very high and her thighs drawn back on her breast, the man can very easily sink back, while astraddle her, to irrumate her – that is, to press his penis to and into her mouth for her to fellate. Or he can press forward, rising to a high kneeling position, for intermammary coitus.

4. *The Man in Huntsman Position* – (a) As in 3.a, in which case the kneeling leg should be closer to the woman, and the squatting leg farther, for the man to rest his elbow on, as he passes his arm around the woman's hips to support her. (b) As 3.b, on which it is a great improvement, as the woman's head is free on the side of the man's squatting leg, and she can both breathe and turn her head away from the possibility of anilinctus, if it does not appeal to her.

5. *The Man Bending.* As 3, the man dropping to an all-fours or kneeling posture to ejaculate in the woman's mouth, if she has been titillating his penis and anus with uplifted arms. However, she may have to support her hips with her arms, resting on the bed or floor on her elbows, with her hands under her hips. But if this position is assumed at the side of the bed or before a chair, so that the woman's hips can be lifted to rest on the edge of the bed or edge of the chair-seat, her arms need not support her, and will be free. However, it is very painful to keep the arms lifted very long, and this may prevent the woman from bringing the man to orgasm by manipulation; and when her arms become tired he may sink to a sixty-nine.

6. *The Man Standing* – As 3, and with progression to the sixty-nine as in 5. Conveniently done at the end of sofa, with the man standing with one foot on the ground and the other kneeling at the woman's side on the sofa, or astraddle her, and the woman's hips raised on pillows, or without their aid, to the arm of the sofa. The sofa here spoken of is considered to be of the type with shoulder-high arms, and not with elbow-high arms, in which latter case the man would be bending, and this would be a type of 5.

7. *The Man Squatting* – As 3, it being possible for the man to extend one of his squatting legs sideways to give the woman air and freedom of movement for her head. Better than sitting, inasmuch as the man can rise easily on his legs whenever the woman wants him to, without the scrambling clumsiness of rising from a sitting position.

8. *The Man Sitting* – (a) As 3, and compare 7. (b) The woman lying with her hips over the edge of a bed, the man sits near the edge of the bed on the floor, facing away from the bed, and tips his head all the way backwards to cunnilingue the woman. However, he would probably twist his upper torso and head sideways and backwards in preference

to this extreme, uncomfortable, and almost impracticable back-bend, making of this position a form of upward rather than downward cunnilinctus.

9. *The Man Supine* – As 8.

I. *The Woman Supine:* C. – *Sideways.* 1. With the man lying on his side under the woman's raised legs, cunnilinctus of a sidewise and upward type is easily possible. 2. With the woman's thighs drawn up quite high, and her hips supported appreciably above her head either on her elbows or on pillows, the man can lean over her exposed vulva and cunnilingue her from either side in almost every position possible to him but the supine. He may also progress from upward to sidewise to downward cunnilinctus, in most positions.

XVI

This analysis of cunnilinctual postures – the woman being more or less supine irrespective of the man's position or the upward, downward, or sidewise direction of his licking – will serve as a model for the analysis of cunnilinctual postures with the woman sitting, squatting, standing, bending, in the huntsman position, kneeling, on all fours, and prone. This method of outlining postures by considering the one partner to remain in a single position while the other partner progresses through all nine postures in upward, downward, and sidewise oral or genital sex has the advantage of fitting the facts, which is more than I honestly thought it would do when I undertook to develop it. All the variants for other basic postures of cunnilinctus than that in which the woman lies supine on her back, can be worked out on the preceding model by any interested reader who will take the trouble. The warning should be expressed that this should be done in bed, not on paper; otherwise a good many physical impossibilities will creep in, if done theoretically only. Erotic photographs are useful for such systematization, but a great deal more can be learned from erotic moving-pictures, when such are available and artistically done (which is not often!) as to motions used, and *progressions* of the bodies from one posture to another.

A few notes on special postures of cunnilinctus, other than those with the woman supine in the usual fashion, may be useful: In upward cunnilinctus by the man, who is lying on his back, the woman also on her back but lying along his torso (I.A.9), it is immediately observable that this is similar to the disposition and relation of the two bodies in the classic sixty-nine, except that the woman and man are both facing upward, and the woman is therefore not fellating the man. However, if her torso is long, she can twist her upper body sideways to fellate the man without inconvenience. This is the "crossback" or twisted sixty-nine, to be discussed again at the end of the present monograph. Even if she cannot do this, any woman can throw her upper body somewhat to one side and off the central line of the man's torso, so that instead of her head being between his legs, or supported on both his thighs, it is now supported on or beyond one of his thighs. In this position his erect penis will fall precisely in her armpit, and she can also crook her elbow to hold it there with her hand, or to touch the tip of his penis to her breast. Axillary masturbation or armpit-coitus easily follows.

Another possibility in the same original position, this time leading into an interesting progression: The woman can bring her legs back slowly, one at a time (while turning her body briefly outward in the opposite direction to each leg), until each leg is finally bent or folded, her heels now touching the man's shoulders instead of lying straight out beyond his face. Aided by her hand, she can now progress easily to a kneeling position over his face, thus changing their relative positions completely. He is now still lying on his back, but she is entirely up off his torso and is kneeling over his face and head, his arms still clutching her thighs from back-to-front as before. She can now bend even farther forward until she is on all fours, resting on her hands or elbows and her knees. The relationship of the partners' bodies is now that of any two-person "link" or set, in the human *spintry* or "daisy-chain" commonly in use at orgies of three or more persons erotically entwined, since the mouth of any one partner in each link or set, and the genitals of the other, are now as far apart as possible.

The twisted sixty-nine, abovementioned, or something quite close to it, can also be developed by an entirely different progression, again from the same original cunnilinctual position in which the man lies on his back and the woman lies on her back along his torso. In the first step or phase, the man simply sits up, thus drawing the woman's knees up onto his shoulders, her legs hanging down behind, while continuing cunnilinctus upon her. The woman's own shoulders have slid back simultaneously from between the man's thighs or knees to between his ankles, her hands now falling at about the level of his knees. (I.A.8.*b*.) The man now continues to rise, by the same turning out and back of his knees described in the paragraph here-preceding, until he is in a kneeling position, with the woman hanging from him. The woman's hips will now have slid partly forward off his shoulders, and he should be supporting the weight of her pelvis on his two hands, his elbows bent and jammed back against his own midriff for solidity. The woman's upper torso is now supported on her own shoulders and upper arms, which now touch the ground.

The man now rises, first to a huntsman position, on one kneeling leg and one foot planted on the bed or ground; then

– possibly with the woman helping him by doing a "Wrestler's Bridge" or back-pushup with her arms and hands – to a standing position. The woman will now be hanging from his shoulders by her crook'd knees, some part of her weight also being taken by the man's hands strongly holding her wrists. If her torso is long enough, she can now half-turn her upper body (which is now the lowest part of her, in fact), to fellate the man simultaneously in the twisted sixty-nine. The man should never have stopped the action of cunnilinctus during the entire progression, from lying on his back with the woman lying on top of him, to standing vertical with her hanging from his shoulders. This is an elegant and quite difficult progression, at which not everyone will succeed the first time it is attempted. Even without the final twisted sixty-nine, it demands a woman who is moderately light in weight and very supple, as well as strength – and single-mindedness! – in the man. It is most effective if the woman does not know beforehand that it is going to happen, and slowly finds herself being lifted completely into the air. Another finish is for the woman to sit up, at the end, with the man pulling on her wrists to help her, until she is sitting high up on his shoulders facing him. The two then collapse gracefully backwards, the man beneath, ending in the same "link" position as that ending the progression described just before.

All erotic progressions should be performed slowly and smoothly, like the motions of a dance, those involving oragenitalism even more so than those of coitus, to avoid any sudden jolts or falls and the resultant danger of biting the partner's genitals. There should be no floundering or scrabbling about. The next phase or position should be clearly visualized *mentally* before it is attempted, until enough experience has been had with such progressions that one can trust one's body-motions and reflexes to do the right thing by themselves. Above all, there should be no nursery-playpen ordering about of the partner: "Now you must put one foot on this roller-skate, and the other over the chandelier, etc." Even signals and taps with the hand on the back or buttocks, in wrestler fashion, to indicate that the next step is to be taken, should be as unobtrusive as possible, with no tossing back & forth of any imaginary gymnasts' handkerchief nor shouting of the acrobatic "*Allaaaay*-OOP!!" Even when being done before live audiences, over the educational television chain of the year 2069: "Oragenital Progressions – Advanced" (we will see then whether I am joking now), a quiet and underplayed style will best set off the beautiful and flowing eroticism that the lovers are attempting to achieve.

One is conscious of the absurdity of any numbered analysis of oragenital or coital positions, such as that preceding, almost as though preparing the act of love for computerized programming. There is little danger of this. As the observation of any ten erotic acts or photographed erotic scenes in motion-picture form will show, the invariables of sexual posture – those parts that can be analyzed and scheduled – are only the framework for almost an infinity of touches resulting from the partners' personal *styles* of both acting and responding. For example, the motions of the hands and arms, touching and encouraging the partner's head or body during the act, which are sometimes as complex or frozen at unexpected angles as those of Balinese temple dancers, derived from the *mudrás* or ritual hand-poses of the Buddhist priests. The combination of postures also makes almost impossible any too precise codification. The woman may, for example, lie in cunnilinctus half on and half off the edge of a bed or couch, her body almost precisely in the huntsman position (half-kneeling), though she is actually lying on her back. When standing on one's head, in the modified form known as

"The Bicycle," where the shoulders touch the ground and the hips are supported on the hands and elbows, the posture is quite similar to that of sitting in a chair; yet a woman with whom one engages in cunnilinctus in this posture can hardly respond as though she were really sitting down – though she can pedal with her legs! – nor is cunnilinctus performed upon a woman standing on her head as it would be if she were actually sitting, where the chair would be in the way of her vulva unless she slid well forward to the edge.

Some postures are, by their nature, impractical in the erotic sense, as either or both partners cannot remain supported in the strained positions involved long enough to arrive at orgasm. These are intended simply as "clowneries," erotic games to amuse the other partner, both partners falling or modulating into more practical positions soon. For example, cunnilinctus with a woman whose body is arched up from the floor – facing upward – in an extreme "Wrestler's Bridge" or "Rainbow," her weight supported on her feet and on her hands cast back beyond her head, while the man stands at her side, or kneels between her legs, supporting her hips while he cunnilingues her. Or the posture reminiscent of a vertical sixty-nine: the woman standing on her hands with her open thighs on the shoulders of the man sitting on a chair facing her breast – or else she facing upward and away – he helping to support her hips with his hands at her waist. This is similar to the famous coital posture called "The Wheel-Barrow."

Certain positions, especially those involving twisting of the head, or side-approaches, do not permit the man's mouth to approach the woman's vulva in such a way as to allow his head freedom of movement: for example, when he comes in from the side under one of the supine woman's uplifted legs. Good thigh opening (abduction) is possible for the woman in upward cunnilinctus, when she sits on a chair with one foot lifted up onto the seat of the chair with her, and the other on the floor beside the man. He sits – legs forward under the chair, or crossed tailor-fashion, or curled at his side – or else kneels (sitting back on his heels, kneeling high, or on all fours), or squats before the woman.

A modern French manual of erotic technique, *Les 32 Positions* ("Mexico: Editions F.O.B.," really issued in Paris about 1958), signed "Dr. Pieli," who is presumed to be the French free-verse poet, Isidore Isou, is the only printed work other than the present monograph that gives any serious group of postures or advanced techniques for cunnilinctus, or in fact for any oragenital act. Under the over-lapping headings of "*La Féllation clitoridienne*" and "*La Féllation vaginale*" – certainly a peculiar use of the term *fellation* – Pieli/Isou makes the following recommendations:

"*Clitoridal Fellation.* This is done with the tip of the tongue, in a 'titillating' way. The tongue should move rapidly from right to left, or up and down, with the agility and rapidity of the finger. Women are very sensitive to this type of caress. It is to the man's interest to engage in this practice, as certain women are quite long in coming to orgasm. As soon as the woman has come, it is wise to stop this maneuvre, for – except in rare cases – the clitoris then becomes as irritable as the man's penis does after his testicles have been emptied. [*Translator's Note:* The male ejaculate does not actually come from the testicles, but from the seminal vesicle deep inside the body, behind the bladder.]

Tonguing. The woman should be lying on her back, with her thighs spread. The man places his mouth on the genitals of his partner and licks her clitoris, while increasing his rhythm. The movements of his tongue finally assume the speed of the tick-tock of a clock.

The Ice-Cream Cone. With the thumbs and forefingers spread, place both hands at the sides of the vulva, and pinch the flesh together vertically. Then press the hands together sidewise, so that the vulva becomes a sort of mound in which the clitoris is almost buried. Pass the tongue over the vulvar groove. The sensation that the clitoris feels is diminished by its wrapping of flesh, and the woman's orgasm will arrive almost imperceptibly at first but irresistibly.

The Peter-Puller. The woman is stretched out on her back. The man straddles her at about the level of her breasts, and bends forward to reach her genitals and to suck and titillate her clitoris. This position is reminiscent of the sixty-nine, but does not engage both partners. (The title, however, suggests the woman's probable response.)

The Squatter. The man lies on the ground and the woman squats over his head, lifting her skirts as though she were going to piss. She presses her genitals down to the man's mouth, and allows him to suck her.

Dog-Style. The woman is on all fours, her hips thrust up backward, her thighs and buttocks well spread. The man approaches her from behind, and, taking the same position as his partner, he lowers his head deeply to suck her clitoris.

The Hoop-Snake. The woman lies on her belly, and the man straddles the back of her neck, gripping it with his thighs as he kneels. He places his hands under the woman's groin and lifts her hips into the air, his elbows serving to support their weight. The woman's body now forms an arc, her head lifted between the man's legs, and her buttocks and hips being lifted by his hands. He then places his chin in the woman's vaginal opening, and licks her clitoris with powerful strokes of the tongue. When he feels that she is close to her orgasm, he speeds up the motions of his tongue, and, pressing down with his feet, lifts her head off the bed and into the air in the grip of his thighs. At the same time he presses upward with his elbows to curve the woman's body backward even more. A remarkable position, best seen in profile.

The Lollipop. The mouth is placed at the vaginal opening, and rubs hard against it with the flat of the tongue.

Bird-Pecking. The mouth is at the vulva, and the tongue travels over the inner and outer lips, which are wet with the woman's vaginal moisture. The teeth nibble at her vulva very lightly, and the tongue enters into the vagina, but the man does not attempt to suck out the moisture.

The Glutton. The man's mouth is pressed avidly to the woman's vulva, glistening with her vaginal moisture. He laps up and then swallows with relish this delicately bitter liquor, which represents her ultimate femininity and the sum of all pleasures. His tongue penetrates into the vagina, his lips kissing the woman's inner lips. (Also called *The Suction-Pump* or *Vacuum-Cleaner.*)

Dog-Style Backwards. The woman is on all fours, as in Dog-Style. The man straddles her waist, his head facing her rump, and he bends all the way forward to reach her vulva, which he can either lick or suck as in the two preceding forms.

The She-Wolf. The woman is still on all fours. The man lies down on the ground, his head facing the same way as his partner's but just underneath her hips. He lifts his head and nurses at her genitals like Romulus and Remus being nursed by the Roman she-wolf. (*Note:* To observe that this is not the sixty-nine, but a spintrian 'link' position, as described earlier.)

Upside-Down. The woman lies on her belly, her hips thrust up backward to open her crotch to the man. He lies face down on top of her, but in the opposite direction, his head at the level of her rump. He places his chin against the woman's anus, and 'cleans up her kitchen' with powerful strokes of his tongue at her humid vagina, also licking occasionally at her anus. When the woman feels her orgasm coming inside her womb [!] she lifts her rump and spreads her legs as wide as she can."

Not a posture, nor yet precisely an erotic clownery, since it works very well, is the French "Escarpolette" or Swing, never before published, except in pictorial form in the *Diableries* of Le Poitevin. When the woman is supine on her back before the man, he prone or on all fours, she can catch up her thighs – her hands hooking under her knees, which are brought up high – and rock her body forward and back, to and away from the man's mouth. The same motion is possible, though in a more mechanical way, in an actual swing, or, better, in a double-seat garden frame-swing, the woman sitting well forward on her seat and jutting her vulva forward over its edge, while the man kneels before her on the floor of the moving swing for cunnilinctus. The alternately acute and obtuse angle made by the upright of the seat with the floor, as the swing moves back & forth, produces cunnilinctual movements more or less automatically, the partners remaining still, except that they must exert their weight rhythmically – the man at least – to keep the swing going.

The frame-swing can also be used for coitus, the man remaining standing on the floor of the swing (unless the seats are very low, in which case he can kneel, as for instance on a children's frame-swing), and pillows are built up under the woman's buttocks on the seat until her vulva is at a height to meet the man's penis, while her arms are held up and out over his elbows. A swing-posture for fellation, probably intended as a clownery, is described in the following section, "A Practical Treatise on Fellation," under the names of "Hammocking" or "Coconut Roulette." More or less automatic fellation is also easily possible in a frame-swing, by the same method just discussed for cunnilinctus, the woman kneeling on the floor of the swing.

XVII

Positions in which the woman is above the man for cunnilinctus are not popular with normal men, except during the sixty-nine, involving as they do an extreme implication of the man's being forced into, or accepting, a completely submissive rôle. The implication that the woman is urinating on the man in such postures, or could do so – note Pieli/Isou's "The Squatter," just above – is also unacceptable to most normal men. It is typical of the irresponsible use made of case-history material in current popular sex manuals, without questioning whether the ideas being suggested to the readers do not stem from perverted or otherwise mentally sick individuals, that Dr. D. O. Cauldwell's *Oral Genital Contacts* (1967) end of supplementary note 3, gives the following brief run-down of cunnilinctual postures as supplied by a 27-year-old Englishwoman with a long experience of Lesbian group-cunnilinctus in a private girls' school, and a subsequent sexual career with men largely consisting of refusing intercourse. She would, however, allow cunnilinctus during petting sessions, sometimes in automobiles, she *sitting* on the steering-wheel, or lying across the hood of the parked car with the man standing before her. Later she and her husband became habitual "swingers," reporting having had oragenital relations with twenty-four other couples in twenty-seven months. She writes: "Four basic positions have been utilized for cunnilingus:

1. Woman on hands and knees above prone [*supine*] male.

2. Woman sitting on upper chest of male.

3. Woman on edge of high table, with man kneeling or sitting in chair drawn with [in] proximity.

4. Woman prone [*supine*], with knees raised and calves dropped over male's shoulders."

This is very much like the classic joke about the man collecting all possible postures for sexual intercourse, but forgetting the so-called normal one. The "swinger"-instructress here puts the most usual posture for cunnilinctus last, her three first choices concentrating on obviously dominant positions for the woman and submissive for the man. Positions of this kind are, of course, those preferred by male masochists, almost all of whom are compulsive cunnilinguists, advertising for partners in classified ads in the far-out press in California and New York and in special magazines, in absurdly obvious coded phrases such as: "*Willing but inexperienced young man searching for French culture with fat girl who will teach him how.*" When women partners are found, however – fat and dominant, or not – they are often disgusted and driven away by the frequently expressed desire of such male masochists to combine cunnilinctus with either the fact or fantasy of urine-drinking or other urolagnic defilements ("The Golden Shower," in the tub or shower-bath). A particularly common fetich among such men, not very well hiding its hidden homosexual desires, is for seminal exsufflation, the man sucking or attempting to suck out after intercourse his own semen, or, preferably, that of some other man to whom the woman has been offered or "traded" with that intention. But enough of these pitiful shifts!

The most important cunnilinctual positions where the woman is above the man are those in which she sits, kneels, or squats over the face of the supine man. She can face his head – upward cunnilinctus resulting; or his feet – downward cunnilinctus; or either side – sidewise cunnilinctus, in which last a rapid combination of cunnilinctus with anilinctus ("Playing the Harmonica," earlier described) is possible. When she faces his feet, sometimes beginning from standing, and sinking to her knees over his face, the posture of her upper body may fan or progress in a whole half-circle, all the way from leaning far back on her own hands, to bending forward to titillate the man's penis with her hands or breasts; finally falling completely forward to end in a sixty-nine.

Sitting is not good, as when the woman sits over the man's face – whether facing his head or feet – her whole weight is on him and she cannot control it, nor can he move his mouth well. All that he can actually do is to attempt to thrust his tongue up as deeply as possible into her vagina (or anus), pushing his tongue up-&-down in imitation of coitus. The frænum under the front of the tongue, similar to that under the glans penis, is likely to be sore after prolonged effort of this kind. Squatting – perhaps on the low arms of an armchair in which the man is sitting – gives the woman the best control of her pelvic movements, with the possibility of forward-&-backward, side-to-side, and round-&-round motions; but the crouching position soon tires her, and she also looks least æsthetic in it, with more than a suggestion of squatting to urinate, etc. The huntsman position combines the advantages of both kneeling and squatting, the woman resting and levering her upper body on one forearm placed on her uplifted knee. Probably best of all is kneeling, facing the supine man's head for upward cunnilinctus, while he grips her breasts, though only back-&-forth motions are possible to the woman, and a sort of shimmying side and rotary movements. The back-&-forth motions, however, can be quite sensational, as earlier described under the names of "*La Diligence de Lyon*" or the "Candy Bar," well worth any woman's learning.

Where the woman stands over the man for cunnilinctus – he sitting, kneeling, lying with his back on a stool or hassock, etc. – she will, if she is facing him, have to bend backward and rest both her elbows on a chair or table (or low branch of a tree) in order to jut her hips sufficiently forward for upward cunnilinctus. If she is facing away from him – that is to say, facing in the same direction as his head, for downward cunnilinctus – she may bend forward, or rest her whole torso on a small table under which he is sitting and clinging, while she spreads her buttocks with her own hands reaching back; or she must "sit down on the air," or in some other way should arrange to tip her pelvis backward and to present her vulva to the man's upturned mouth. She may also stand with one foot lifted, to rest it on his shoulder. Or, facing him, she can stand with her legs *behind* his shoulders, on which she rather sits, as she leans forward to support herself with her arms or hands on the wall or some piece of furniture, as she is not in equilibrium. Or, either facing him or facing away as she stands over him, she may spread her legs, forward and back, as though running, and put one leg before him and one behind him, while he turns his head upward to cunnilingue her. Here, as always, he can tip his head further back, and is in better equilibrium when he sits, or when, while kneeling, he sits back on his heels, than when he either squats or kneels high.

Downward cunnilinctus really comes into its own when the woman is on all fours or prone (lying facedown), and the man is behind her, he being in almost any position. This is probably the original form of approach of the male to the female during that presumed historical or pre-historical period when the proto-human beings were quadrupeds, or had just risen partly to the palmipede stance of bears and most of the apes. Almost all other mammals still approach the female sexually by beginning with cunnilinctus from behind in this way. Many humans never try this posture at all, thinking of it as humiliating for the male, on the style of the folk-phrase or invitation concerning kissing the buttocks as an expression of contempt. The actual position the man chooses, in this approach to cunnilinctus, depends on the height of the woman's hips above the bed or support she is lying on, facedown. If she is kneeling, he kneels behind her "dog-fashion," or stands beside the bed on which she is kneeling. Or he lies prone with his head and shoulders lifted, if the woman is lying prone before him with her belly and pubis on a pillow and her legs spread. If there is no pillow under her, the man will have to pull open her buttocks and thighs strongly with his hands to get at her genitals, and will in any case not be able to approach with his mouth toward her vulva very deep.

Three progressive variants of the woman lying prone over the supine man for cunnilinctus: *First*, he leans back in an armchair, and she straddles his face, facing his feet. Only one of her legs is on the floor; the other will probably not reach, and must curl behind her along the back of the chair. *Second*, the man sits in an armchair and the woman lies down on his body facing his chest and legs, her head toward his feet, her thighs over his shoulders, while he cunnilingues her "downward" (that is, in this position, *up* from her belly to her buttocks). Her shoulders are on his thighs and her head is turned, resting on his knees, or is hanging down between them. Her breasts will usually be just right in this position for intermammary coitus with the man simultaneously, his penis lying "up" between her breasts. In describing the man's penis here as lying "up" between the woman's breasts, gravitationally "up" is meant. Actually it is directed "downward" through her intermammary groove, toward her hips. The woman kneads her breasts together over the man's penis, to form a groove for his coital motions, using her hands or her shoulders turned or splayed inward. She can also telescope her breasts softly back-&-forth against his body in time with his penis motions, by turning her shoulders alternately forward and back, as is often done by women in dancing close, or when kissing mouth-to-mouth.

Third, the woman slides still further forward till she is standing on her hands on the floor, while the man bends forward to hold her at the waist and support the weight of her hips with his arms while cunnilinguing her. This is rather more playful than practical, as has already been noted in discussing this same final posture as reminiscent of a vertical sixty-nine. It is also very similar to the famous coital posture known as "The Wheel-Barrow" – appearing in engraved sets of the pseudo-Aretino posture drawings, since about 1700, along with other baroque postures such as the "Whirling Basket" – the woman sometimes being outfitted with a wheel-&-axle to hold between her hands (nowadays a skate-board), or even with two cakes of wetted soap in her hands to use as casters, while the man slides her along a tile floor in this position. Whether practical for cunnilinctus or not, the posture described above can easily progress, if the man is strong and the woman not too heavy, to his standing up with the woman hanging down along his body in a sixty-nine, and ultimately to his tumbling her forward on the pivot of her hands so that she lies on her back, while he kneels and falls forward prone over her for a sixty-nine. A very neat progression.

II

FELLATION

ORAGENITALISM

II. FELLATION

As WITH cunnilinctus, so with fellation, there is no serious literature of its technique. A few passages mentioning it appear in books on advanced sex technique, especially in French, and one brief manuscript has recently been discovered, describing some of its more exotic forms from the purely passive position of the man being fellated. This will be translated completely, below. A pathetic note is struck, in the first published work actually entitled *Fellatio,* by Donald H. Gilmore, Ph.D. (Torrance, California, 1968), where, halfway through the book – which is largely composed of case-histories and irrelevant illustrations – at the opening of a chapter hopefully entitled "Fellatio Techniques," the author confesses: "Technique, that individual variable, comes into play in any sex act, and especially fellatio . . . Censorship, combined with the fact that sex is a very personal subject, has prohibited any instruction manuals on sex technique. I, for one, think it's high time we had one, and I'd very much like to see a serious study on this subject published." Meaning, only too evidently, that his book is not it.

Even less will be learned, as to oragenital technique, in the sudden group of similar Hollywood publications, all issued in this and the preceding year: *Cunnilingus and Fellatio*, by John F. Trimble, Ph.D., author also of *5000 Adult Sex Words and Phrases* – one wonders what the *childish* words may be – and several volumes imitating, sight-unseen, the title and presumed contents of the present work: *Oral Geni-*

tal Contacts, *Oral Love*, *Oral Lovemaking*, *Oral Techniques* (straight fiction), *Oralism*, *Oralism the Forbidden Fruit*, *The Love Kiss* (actually by Dale Koby and Dr. Leonard Lowag, and the best of this group), *The Lips of Eros*, *Anatomy of Oral Love*, and *Techniques of Oral Love*, this last particularly inept; ascribed on their respective title-pages to Drs. David O. Cauldwell, Hagerman, Fenmore, C. C. King, John Raymond, Robert Edwin, David Davidson, Jory Sherman, Kantor, and Jerome Williams, some or all of which are apparently pseudonyms. This must be the world's record for an impossible and largely incompetent sub-literature, flung together in a very great hurry to catch the "New Freedom" audience. More recent entries include – again all from Hollywood – *Oral Love Illustrated*, by E. V. Douglas; *Cunnilingus*, by Douglas H. Gamlin, Ph.D., with a companion volume, *Soixante Neuf* (69), by Donald H. Gilmore, Ph.D.; *Oral Orgies*, by H. Courtney, and a purported case-history collection, *A Woman's Look at Oral Love*, of which the absurd title is probably intended less as neo-feminist *kitsch*, than as an invitation to reader-voyeurism on female sexual acts. Seventeen volumes, not one actually on oragenital technique.

Other works of the kind also exist (and are planned!) at the chapbook level, generally with marvellously promising titles if not contents, all attempting to make good the former general publishing rule of silence as to oragenital acts, a silence forcing even so detailed a sex technique manual as Dr. John Eichenlaub's *The Marriage Art* (New York, 1961), with its sub-flagellational "Ice-Spurred Special" in chapter 6, to omit all but the most superficial treatment of oral sex. These new catchpenny paperbacks are pitifully inept and unilluminating concoctions, products of the West Coast "Grease-Ball" school of sex-exploitation and psychofakeology, mushrooming into existence in America since the

New Freedom. They are largely composed of bogus case-histories and an occasional faked illustration, driven out to book length with long quotations from standard pornographica and sexological drivel of equal stature, ventilated here and there with some perfunctory psychological drool. It has been seriously suggested that the authors of all or most of them are really one and the same person, or — more likely — that these items are being produced automatically by a sex-crazed computing machine with an erection, programmed by a eunuch.

Their single most striking contribution to human knowledge is their frightening demonstration that cynical and incompetent "psychological consultants" all over the United States today not only can make an excellent living destroying the lives of desperate neurotic patients with cretinously permissive advice — coming on strong with recommending homosexuality, orgies, and the most dangerous sadistic perversions, often with children, or whatever else the "psychologist's" own private perversion may be — but that the tape-recorded case-histories thus swept together, and doctored up for publication with page upon page of fictitious erotic dialogue, can then be turned profitably, and with very little effort, into paperbound gunk for selling in midnight bookstores at inflated prices to a very special clientèle. Whatever else need be done or said about this sub-literature, it is painfully unedifying to read, and the technique of oragenital acts will not, unless accidentally (in the case-histories), be discovered in it.

At an even lower level, if such a thing is possible, there is also *Sexual Techniques during Prescribed Continence* (New York: J. R. Brussel, Medical Press, 1968), signed "Dr. Betty J. Cox." This is largely composed of long, unacknowledged quotations from the Masters & Johnson *Human Sexual Re-*

sponse (1966) and from the first edition of the present work – solely on cunnilinctus – gruellingly hacked together and *improved* with eccentric verbiage and sentimental gush. It alternates curiously between the magniloquent and pious goober-talk of retitling the simple sixty-nine "duorallation" (credited to Dr. J. E. Schmidt, President of the American Society of Grammatolators [!] who is also believed to be the book's author), and retitling itself, for advertising purposes, "Brave New World of Sex" – long after Aldous Huxley – "The New Sexuality," and "*Femina Libido Maxsisimus Sexifaction*," which should make whoever invented the Ph.D. degree go whirling in his grave. The illustrations of coital postures supplied – the male and female figures being pudibundly separated on superimposable sheets! – have nothing whatever to do with the text, being taken from drawings (by Mahlon Blaine) for a German work of the 1900's by a gymnasium-professor, Dr. Josef Weckerle, and from a Japanese acrobatic series. All in all, a museum piece, and a masterpiece of ignorance, pretention, and bad taste.

Actually, the main question in all oragenital acts is not physical but psychological, and the same is also true of the problem of orgasm in women – when this is a problem. The primary question in fellation is: *active or passive?* The vocabulary of the art mirrors this choice. Latin erotic terminology actually distinguishes two acts in fellation, or rather two approaches to the same act. First, *fellation*, in which the man's penis is sucked or otherwise orally excited by another person (the fellator or fellatrix). Second, *irrumation* – from the Latin *irrumare*, to give suck, as a mother gives the nipple to her nursing child – in which the man (the irrumator) presses his penis actively into the fellator's mouth, and engages in coital motions by moving his hips and body in a rhythm of his own choice. In both cases the oral friction is usually continued until the man's orgasm, the semen being swallowed then by the fellator.

The bodily positions taken will also generally signify whether the act is to be considered fellation or irrumation. In *fellation, the man is passive and the fellator is active.* The man is usually sitting, leaning, or lying on his back, while the fellator or fellatrix lies or crouches over him, or kneels before him, holding and directing the man's genitals with her hands at first, or seizing him by the buttocks to force him deeper into her mouth. *In irrumation, the man (the irrumator) is active, and the fellator is passive.* The man almost always stands, half-kneels, or lies face down over the supine or kneeling fellator, whose face and body he purposely dominates in a virile and sometimes cruel way, often seizing and immobilizing the fellator's hair, ears, and head with his two hands. In the standing position the man sometimes even pulls the woman's head to his groin by her hair, especially if this is long or in braids, as though directing her with reins. Obviously, both fellation and irrumation involve the same action of oral friction, in the sense that the mouth and penis are in both cases joined in a quasi-coital fashion. But the emotional effect on each of the participants is extremely different.

It should be observed specially that no reference is made here to homosexual fellation or irrumation, the word *fellator* being used interchangeably with *fellatrix* or *fellatress.* The oragenital act is considered here as deriving from the normal erotic foreplay between a man and a woman, as it does throughout the mammalian order. The technique is not, of course, in any way changed by the sex of the participants. But it is worth noting that the distinction of the act, according to the active and passive rôles taken, is particularly evident in homosexual relations, where the presumably very feminine and submissive type of homosexual will usually prefer to engage in fellation or in passive anal intercourse, while the violently masculine and aggressive "wolf" or "hero" type of homosexual will insist on irrumating or pedicating his submissive partner. Actually, the relationship is more subtle than this suggests, since the fellator may often be (among homosexuals, almost always is) the dominant partner, no matter what the other person may think. This demonstrates again the essentially active quality of fellation.

The accepting of the penis into the mouth is not, for a woman, so very different from accepting it into the vagina. From the unromantic biological position, *the goal or purpose of all human and higher animal life is the insertion of the penis into the vagina,* so that the life of the species may continue. The female of the species is therefore normally willing, and – in periods of heat or rut – violently anxious for this vaginal insertion. Human females who are not willing, under reasonable circumstances and with a male who attracts them, are not normal, or are being skewed and abnormalized by social influences or unwisely prudish training which damage the normality of their sexual impulses. However, the human female will also accept as an erotic preliminary the similar insertion of the penis into her mouth, though this has no direct biological purpose, in the same way that she will generally welcome the erotic preliminary of the male's tonguing or orally caressing her vulva, as a prelude to intercourse and sometimes even as a substitute for it.

Here the similarity to the other animals ceases. Though most mammals regularly engage in the licking of the female's genitals before intercourse – basically *to excite the male* by means of the female genital odor, and not to excite the female – few males of other species than the human will venture to entrust their penises between the teeth of the female, though licking of the penis by the female before and also after intercourse is commonly observed. Without meaning, therefore, to suggest in any way that fellation is a "higher" activity than that of other animals, it is ultimately a different type of sexual activity than any known to them, and its purposes and motives will not be found in the broader area of biology, but must be sought in the deeper reaches of human psychology.

The motives of the man who wishes to be fellated are presumably very simple: he wants the sexual excitement and satisfaction involved. Yet why does he prefer this type of excitement to that of sexual intercourse itself? Originally, in the child, there is no special type of sexual activity, aperture, or partner that is more attractive than any other; the child being, as Freud puts it, *polymorphous perverse*, or sexually attracted to all types. However, an unquestionable centralization of interest upon the genital target-area of the opposite sex occurs, at least by puberty, in the male of all animals that engage in intrommittent genital acts. The human male must therefore also be assumed to respond, under normal circumstances, to this centralization on the female genitals. Why is this not so in the man who wishes to be fellated? Is he abnormal?

Normality is, of course, a very difficult concept to define, being usually considered the equivalent of statistically common and accepted acts in the society doing the defining. So understood, obviously neurotic and mentally diseased actions are regularly applauded as normal in cultures that are themselves abnormal or insane. For example, the burning of brand-new blankets and handmade axes by the Kwakiutl Indians of the Pacific Northwest at their *potlatches* or destruction-festivals, the burning off of the clitoris of female children with a red-hot stick among North African Mohammedans as their sacred ceremony of circumcision, and the burning to a crisp of all non-white human beings in the world by White

Anglo-Saxon Protestant Americans flying around in airplanes thousands of miles from home and dropping explosive bombs. This is normal. A man wanting to have his penis sucked is not normal in that sense.

It is the essential passivity of the man, during fellation, that gives the hint as to his real motives, or rather to the resuscitation in him of childhood drives that lead him to prefer the passive pleasure of fellation to the active insertion in vaginal intercourse; or to need fellation as an erotic preliminary, in order to excite him to erection. For actually, it is the male's own more-or-less violent approach to the female, and *what he does to her* in the way of preliminary sexual acts and the mastering of her body, which, in the normal animal state, create the male's excitement – with the addition, of course, of the female's specifically sexual odor. The man who engages in irrumation, forcing his penis into the woman's mouth, and dominating her body with his own during the act, may be considered to be acting in a normal and adult male fashion, though there is little biological likelihood of the woman becoming pregnant as a result of this act. But the adult male who requires that he be excited by fellation, while he remains almost entirely passive, is returning in a way to the situation of the small or nursling child, who accepts passively the (oral) gratifications offered him by the mother or other woman, in suckling him at her breasts or the bottle. Obviously, this involves an unconscious identification with the woman, since it is the man, in fellation, who is offering the substitute bottle or breast. This also means that it is the woman, in fellation, who "becomes" the man, and dominates the male. The habitual passive *need* for fellation, on the man's part, can therefore only be considered masochistic, and less than fully virile. As a technique of genital excitement, fellation is excellent. As an habitual substitute for vaginal intercourse, it is evidently abnormal.

Another unconscious return to childhood involved in fellation of the substitutive and habitual kind, is that the man is identifying intercourse with urination, and considers the flow of semen from his body as a way of "urinating into the woman." But instead of doing this in a dominant or even sadistic way, as would be the case in irrumation, he requires her to draw or suck the seminal fluid from his body, by oral friction, while he remains passive. In this sense, fellation habitually continued to the point of passive ejaculation into the woman's mouth, must be considered a far-off reminiscence of childhood urination to please the dominant mother or nurse: "*Pee for mama!*"

Often the man's need for the preliminary excitement of fellation before engaging in intercourse is an unspoken expression of the fact that he does not find the woman exciting. This does not necessarily mean that she is not beautiful or sexually attractive, but that he has for some reason not been allowed to approach her in a dominant way that will excite his virility. This is often the case in marriage, after several years, especially during the completely routine intercourse at bedtime, after the two parties undress separately and heavily at their two sides of the bed, or even in separate beds or bathrooms, sometimes chomping soapily their latest business or household troubles to each other while they brush their teeth. That will not excite any man; where tearing the woman's clothes off with his fingernails and teeth, in some unexpected time and place safe from prying eyes, would be pretty sure to excite *both* of them.

Irrumating the woman more-or-less forcibly – though one assumes she is actually willing, as she might otherwise dangerously bite the penis – and even speaking roughly to her meanwhile, to the point of erotic cursing and threats, often satisfies the man's need to dominate in what otherwise might be a routine and unexciting erotic situation. *Normal women expect and enjoy a certain amount of domination and harmless violence of this kind.* The reverse situation, where the woman practically leaps upon the man, and especially when she "talks dirty" beforehand, is generally desired by or acceptable to only very unvirile and masochistic men. It is not a symptom of some theoretically uncontrollable sexual excitement in the woman, but shows that she is imitating what she thinks of as the prerogatives of men, whom she may also very deeply envy and hate.

Fellation is particularly resorted to and requested during intercourse with prostitutes, since the man often cannot get an erection otherwise. Again, this does not mean that he is impotent. But the usual situation in the prostitute's bedroom is by no means — as people who know nothing about it imagine — that the client is violently erotic, and leaps on the prostitute before she can get her shoes and pants off. To the contrary, it is a good deal more usual for the client — who may even have been put through a humiliating preliminary of washing or inspecting of his genitals by the woman herself, to make sure he does not have a disease ("*On se lave, cheri?*") — to find that he is nervous, and repelled by the woman, has no erection, and must be excited by means of fellation in order to engage finally in intercourse. This is nowadays called "half-and-half" or "fifty-fifty" by prostitutes, and represents a large part of their trade. The less attractive the prostitute is, or makes herself by undiplomatic domineering tactics, the more likely she is to have to engage in preliminary fellation. This is also one reason why most non-homosexual men who have relations with homosexuals (often for money) will only allow themselves to be fellated, since they cannot usually get an erection with the homosexual in any other way, unless in a situation of desperate sexual starvation, as in prison, where mutual anal intercourse is common.

The emotions of normal women concerning fellation are not the same as those of homosexuals, who are often compulsive fellators. Though there are certainly many women who deeply enjoy fellation, on a frankly oral basis, it is intelligent to assist and encourage any woman with whom one is emotionally involved to a full and mature vaginal centralization of her erotic interest. Fellation then becomes an art which she can enjoy and employ, to excite or satisfy the man when this is desired, but just as much to excite herself, without fellation ever becoming either a compulsive need or a dreaded task. The approach of dread is certainly implied in the advice given in a recent sex-technique manual, signed by a woman, that: "On a wife's first attempt to stimulate her husband's genitalia orally, it might be better and easier for her if she tries it while the two take a shower together." (Or under water?) The idea here is clearly, if silently, that the woman is presumed to have neurotic and anti-sexual notions of the genitals as dirty, and of sex as the equivalent of dirt. Such notions – unfortunately – no shower-bath can ever wash away, just aside from the possibility of hidden fetichistic identification of the shower with urination.

A much more reasonable, if frankly egoistic approach to fellation, where the woman obviously does not feel any specific oral satisfaction in the act, is that quoted from a woman described as a "Sexual Sophisticate" in *The Sexually Responsive Woman*, by Drs. Phyllis and Eberhard Kronhausen (New York: Grove Press, 1964) page 167, discussing her general feelings about fellation:

> The idea of fellatio does not excite me to the extent that I have heard homosexual men rave about it, but I *find it enjoyable, if the man desires it.* To me the most pleasurable part about fellatio is the running of

> the tongue over the penis. The smooth texture of the glans against the tongue is a sensuous feeling which I enjoy. In addition, the signs of the man's excitement are more stimulating to me than my own part in the act itself.

The Kronhausens conclude, and one can only concur: "that many women do find the performance of fellatio pleasant, but not as sexually exciting as seems to be the case with that group of men who really like to perform cunnilingus . . . According to Kinsey, more men prefer to perform cunnilingus than women want to perform fellatio. This was in keeping with observations on animals, in which the male usually outdoes the female in these respects."

It is normal and desirable for a woman to enjoy fellating the man she loves, and to desire to kiss his penis and testicles before or after intercourse; also to be irrumated by him occasionally, and as violently as he pleases, she swallowing his semen. Gagging at the moment of the man's orgasm, or refusing to swallow the semen, or spitting it up into a handkerchief prepared in advance, or in such a way as to leave traces on his trousers (!) openly indicates a rejection of the man, rather than simply a rejection of the semen on the grounds of gagging at its taste or viscosity. Actually, though the semen does have a slightly salty or metallic taste, it is warm when ejaculated, and rather similar in consistency to bone-marrow – which is considered a delicacy. Many fellators express a profound fascination with the semen, and deeply desire thus to swallow or "drink" the semen during fellation, in the thought that it is the man's human quintessence or most valuable ichor, or even that it is a sort of homunculus or embryo human being in itself.

Though romantic in appearance, it is obvious that ideas like this, if insistent and habitual, are *cannibalistic* in nature, and therefore in a sense dangerous, since they involve the desire for a total oral incorporation of the fellated man. From this to unavowed ideas of biting off the man's penis during fellation, and keeping it for oneself, or swallowing it down along with the ejaculated semen, is too close for comfort. No matter under what romantic or quintessential disguise, such ideas are clearly hostile to the man, and to all men. Men respond by having an uneasy dislike for anyone who is, uniquely, a "cock-sucker," whether male or female.

At the unconscious level, both cunnilinctus and fellation equally involve primitive oral fixations, and unconscious notions of nursing at the mother's breast. That is certainly the secret of their attractiveness to the oral partner in either act. But it must not be overlooked that, in cunnilinctus, the man excites the woman with his mouth and tongue, sometimes for a considerable period of time, without actually receiving any gush of swallowable fluid at her orgasm. He therefore does not think of himself as taking anything from the woman, or as being given any repayment for his act, unless of course the woman responds by then fellating him or allowing vaginal intercourse. On the other hand, the man does deeply feel that the fellator is receiving from him the gift of his semen at orgasm – even if the semen is rejected! In fact, particularly if it is rejected, since then the man is depressed and deflated by the realization that his physical offering has been refused and his virile strength wasted.

It is important to bear this point in mind in using fellation as a form of birth-control, as is now very common among young girls anxious to retain their virginity and yet to satisfy the man "safely." Far from safeguarding the popularity – and virginity – of the girl, her preference for or insistence on fellation as birth-control will usually gain her the active dislike of the man or men she thinks she is satisfying in this way. But this is not the case when birth-control is achieved orally by the man withdrawing from the woman's vagina just before his orgasm during ordinary intercourse, and ejaculating then in the woman's mouth – a complaisance on the woman's part which the man will much appreciate.

The physical technique of fellation, its difficulties and niceties, have not often been treated in the literature of sex. It will be attempted to give here the totality of what is known to have been written on fellatory technique, before continuing with other considerations of a psychological kind. It will be observed that even the question of the *position* of the man during fellation, which is obviously crucial, is considered only by the most recent writers. All writers on the subject, in any case, invariably take the mental position that the oral partner in fellation is active, and is operating for the benefit and pleasure of the genital partner, who is conceived of as almost entirely passive. That this need not be so will be shown more fully in the section following, on Irrumation. Yet it is obvious that the idea of lying or sitting passively, while being fellated in artistic fashion, is a principal male erotic yearning or dream, however lacking in virility this dream may be.

Although all the legendary love-books of the Greek hetæræ are now lost, such as those attributed to Aspasia, Elephantis, and Astyanassa, the maid of Helen of Troy; there are still in existence ancient Greek vase illustrations showing fellation, and figured Peruvian vases of the same kind and of millennial age (reproduced in Rafael Larco-Hoyle's *Checan*, published in Geneva, 1965), as well as at least one Egyptian papyrus of earlier date, the so-called "Obscene Papyrus of Turin," which shows a caricatured sexual position for each of the astrological months, in almost all of which the woman is frankly dominant. These ancient illustrations, and the Roman satirical poets who dealt often with oragenital subjects, particularly Martial, come closer to the reality than any technical work on fellation has yet succeeded in doing. They show or describe the fellator inevitably as a violent and devouring person, acting out of a visible inner desire to perform fellation for personal satisfaction, and not really concerned with the pleasure of the genital partner, who is apparently thought of as being "pumped dry."

The erotic manuals, however, beginning with those of India – which are the oldest now existing – invariably treat of fellation as an oral manipulation or technique intended to excite the genital partner, with details of how best to please him. Whether or not we would be right in assuming that the ancient erotic illustrations still in existence were the work of women, or express their dominant fantasies and desires; it is unquestionable that the erotic manuals we have are all the work of men, and express in connection with fellation strictly passive and submissive desires.

In the very famous *Kama Sutra* or "Rules of Sexual Love," written by Mallanaga Vatsyayana, probably during the Gupta dynasty in Northern India about the fourth century A.D., an entire chapter (Part Two, chap. 9) is devoted to the *Auparishtaka* or "oral congress." (Citations here are to pages 127–8 of the translation by Dr. S. C. Upadhyaya, published in Bombay, 1961, which is superior in many ways to the earlier translation by F. F. Arbuthnot, often reprinted.) After noting that fellation is performed mostly by male homosexuals ("eunuchs") or masseurs, and by "unchaste and immoral women, quite free from any inhibitions," Vatsyayana divides the techniques mainly according to the depth of penetration of the penis into the fellator's mouth, beginning with the *Nimita or* "nominal congress," in which only the glans penis or less is taken into the mouth.

Three ways of titillating the penis orally are also indicated: kissing the tip (*Chumbitaka*), kissing and licking all sides of the penis with the tip of the tongue (*Parimrishtaka*), and the "Sucking of the mango fruit" or *Amrachushitaka*, in which the fellator "in high passion, takes in and forcibly sucks the phallus with the skin up [*i.e.* with the foreskin retracted], and after pressing it over and over again, with the lips and tongue, releases it." Beyond this there is finally the *Samgara*, or "swallowing up," in which the fellator "takes the phallus into her mouth as far as it goes, and presses it until the man's fluid falls. [She] must realise when the man's culmination is imminent, and help the man with movements of her lips and the tongue," at his orgasm. No statement is made as to the swallowing or rejecting of the semen, a fluid held – in India, as elsewhere – in mystic awe. One may assume it is swallowed.

The homosexual occultist, Aleister Crowley, in his very rare pederastic leg-pull, *Bagh-i-Muattar: The Scented Garden of Abdullah the Satirist of Shiraz* ("London" [Paris?] 1910), "translated from a rare Indian MS. by the late Major Alain Lutiy," of which only three copies are known to have escaped destruction by the British Customs authorities in 1924, annotates one of the poetic *ghazals* in which the text is cast – the last being signed in reverse acrostic form by Crowley – as follows (Note 5b, pages 110–11):

"Irrumation, with either sex, is perhaps the most popular of all the sex-perversions – or sex-refinements? – in the West.

"A well-known English peeress of American origin has kindly favoured me with a classified list of the principal methods employed by the patient [the fellator]. It will be seen that they easily surpass the crude expedients of the Kama Soutra.

1. *The Spider's Legs* [*Pattes d'araignée*]. Tickle the penis with fingers, lips, tongue, and eyelashes.

2. *The Fire-drill.* With flat palms rub the penis vigorously in a direction perpendicular to its axis. The tip of the penis is held firmly in the mouth.

3. *The Mouse-trap.* Nibble and kiss the penis all over, like a mouse at a piece of cheese. Suddenly nip hard on it and finish, like the closing of the trap.

4. *Les affaires sont les affaires* [*Business is Business*]. Swallow the penis whole, rocking the head furiously backwards and forwards.

5. *The Woodpecker.* Bite sharply with teeth upon the penis.

6. *The Limpet* (or *Barnacle*). Suck the gland hard, so as to create a vacuum (this is a rude cupping process, causes the blood to flow strongly to the part, and so is almost unfailing as a means of producing erection).

7. *The Oyster Supper.* Spit on the penis and catch the 'oysters' [pre-coital flow] until they are replaced by the 'pearls' [the semen].

8. *The Green Corn.* Suck at the penis as you do to eat green corn (i.e. all down the shaft).

9. *The Asparagus.* Suck at the penis as you do to eat asparagus (i.e. at the tip).

10. *L'éternelle idole.* Worship the penis; rub it on the forehead, and so on, according to your ideas of what a ritual should be.

11. *The Naughty Boy.* Smack the penis smartly with the hands. Afterwards make up to it, and pet it.

12. *The Sculptor.* Mould and knead with firm lips and fingers, as a sculptor models clay.

13. *The Catapult.* Pull down the penis, and let it flap back against the belly.

14. *The Metronome* (for two patients). With thumb and forefinger at the root of the penis, guide it, swinging it to and fro from mouth to mouth, one lover being on each side of the irrumator.

15. *The Whirlpool.* Swallow the penis whole, and roll the tongue round and round the gland.

16. *Parfait amour.* (Lady T – has to say that she learnt this from Mlle Marcelle of the house just off the Carrefour de l'Odéon, à Paris.) Swallow the scrotum whole, and rub the penis backwards and forwards across the nose. Excite at the same time the testes with the tongue, and the fundament with the finger."

The intention of imitating or surpassing the "crude expedients" of the *Kama Sutra* is avowed here, and the intention is equally obvious, in the title of Crowley's work, to create a confusion with the famous *Perfumed Garden* of the Sheik al-Nafzawi, first translated from the Arabic into French [by Baron Regnault] in the mid-nineteenth century, with its mnemonically-titled positions for intercourse. The "well-known English peeress of American origin . . . Lady T –" is, of course, one of Crowley's jokes, probably intended as an inappropriate dig at Lady Nancy Astor, later the first woman to sit in the British Parliament. The whole thing has somewhat the tone of a brag, like that of the literary homosexual of our own time who advertises "Personalized Blow-Jobs," in the underground press. That the list is of Crowley's own confection is made evident by No. 10, "*L'éternelle idole*," on the style of his own elaborate erotico-occult rituals. The real inspiration was probably not Oriental at all, but the popular French magazine cartoon of the 1880's, "*Comment elles mangent les asperges*" (compare Nos. 8 and 9 here), an openly symbolic illustrated typology showing how different kinds of women eat *asparagus* – or bananas, or ice-cream cones — all perfectly obvious allusions to the technique of fellation. Note the reference several times, at Nos. 2, 6, and 12, especially, to fellatory techniques of particular use in exciting the penis to erection, rather than for use after erection has taken place.

Though it might be thought that the reference, in Crowley's No. 1, to tickling the penis with the *eyelashes* is also a joke, it should be observed that this is a perfectly valid technique, especially when applied to the glans penis on its underside, at the frænum præputii (or "whang-string"), or along the corona glandis. The fluttering of the eyelashes against another person's lips, as a baroque or exquisite form of kissing, has, in fact, long been known among adolescents, being called for (when playing "Post Office", "Spin the Bottle," or other kissing-games) as "The Butterfly Kiss."

Crowley's burlesque on fellatory technique reeks of its period, the *fin-de-siècle* and the years just preceding World War I, when the doomed, decadent Europe danced itself to death in a mad splurge of erotic and materialistic nihilism — a Dance of Death just now catching on in America, after the usual fifty-year cultural lag. Very much of the same period, and style, is the extraordinary *Les Paradis Charnels* (Paris, 1903) of the erotic poet, Alphonse Gallais, under the anagrammatic pseudonym of "Doctor A.-S. Lagail," a work already quoted in the earlier section on Cunnilinctus. Gallais is actually more of a frantic romantic than a decadent, which is perhaps the definition of decadence. His treatment of fellation is placed in his tenth chapter, among the "*Folles Caresses*," as the fourteenth in his enumeration of the "*136 Extases de la Volupté*;" continuing with various forms of the *soixante-neuf* or sixty-nine, and implying that all these oral caresses are to be considered preliminaries or excitants to the hundred postures for vaginal intercourse that follow. Even so, he reserves for his 136th and final ecstasy, as the last of the well-named "Erotic Clowneries," an extravagant finale for fellation which he calls "The Judgment of Solomon," and which will be described later in its place.

Gallais considers fellation as a single or continuous act in eight numbered stages (actually nine) of excitement and oral penetration. He gives it the title, in French erotic slang, of "*Le Pompage du Dard, ou La Taille de Plume*," which means literally "The Pumping of the Dart, or the Sharpening of the Quill," terms now really only survivals, as with the archaic *pen-knife* still occasionally carried by men for sharpening the quill-pens that no longer exist. "This amiable exercise," says Gallais, "on which passionate women dote, is practised as follows:

1. Take the man's erect penis frankly in hand, and masturbate it for a moment while tickling his testicles with the other hand. Then, press it between the lips, and shake the mouth from right to left, while moving the head up and down simultaneously. [*Note well this combination.*]

2. Meanwhile, spider-claw his whole penile system, caressing him with the tips of the fingers from the anal aperture to the base of the glans penis held in the mouth; concentrating on the frænum or string of the foreskin with one hand, while tickling his testicles with the other. That is to say, caress them and squeeze them, while pressing the sides of the glans with lips and biting lightly at the corona.

3. Press the glans very tightly with the pursed lips, pushing it entirely out of the mouth and drawing it back in again a number of times, while continuing to grip and caress the phallic shaft, and to tickle the testicles now swollen with sperm.

4. Now take the penis as deeply as possible into the mouth, and, in drawing the head back for the next downward

stroke, draw the foreskin up over the glans by pulling it with the lips. Continue as though masturbating the man with one's mouth, up and down, down and up; meanwhile "postillion" him by pushing one finger briskly into and out of his anus.

5. Squeeze the testicles lightly, while devotedly kissing the hole at the tip of his penis through which the sperm will soon spurt.

6. Holding only the glans in the mouth, lick slowly all around the corona, sucking and titillating with the tongue-tip (in a flicking motion) the hole which will already be overflowing with the first drops of his love-juice.

7. Suck strongly at the penis, wildly flicking the tongue-tip over the glans, and continuing to tickle his testicles which are now hard and tight to the supreme degree.

8. Suck vigorously, continuing the motions just described and pressing the testicles madly, while postillioning the anus very deep. The man's semen spurts out violently and inundates the mouth of the fellator, who swallows it greedily, delighting in its agreeable taste of warm milk, mildly spiced . . .

[9.] When the penis is emptied of its last drop and begins to soften at the stem, the woman may, if she likes, take into her mouth the man's entire phallic system that she has just so expertly emptied. This must be done very carefully, but anyone can learn it: Both the penis and testicles are drawn together into the mouth, where, as it is expressed in the language of gallantry, one mouths them lightly like chewing-gum!"

The author, Gallais, has very well described here the simultaneous oral friction and finger manipulations that have immemorially given the art of fellation the name of "playing the flute," from ancient Greece to the present time, and in many languages. (Actually, it is closer to playing the recorder or clarinet.) As to the rest, he has hardly done justice to the subject, in concentrating in this way only on the final or crucial activity. Another French writer of the same period, this time unidentified but probably a physician during the First World War, has left a brief monograph of the entire art, again taken from the point of view of the entirely passive man being fellated by the active woman, but in much greater detail.

This has never been published in English. A typewritten manuscript twenty-five pages long, meticulously done on square-ruled paper in purple ink, I found it recently in Paris in a group of manuscript songs and printed broadsides, of the type known as "*Chansons de Salles de Garde*": the erotic and satirical songs that are the favorites of French students, especially in the faculties of medicine and of art. The collection had been made by a French army officer attached to the medical corps during World War I, and was discovered at the sale of his library after his death. I assume that he was the author, as there are manuscript corrections throughout in the same handwriting as some of the songs. The rest of the material contained dates as late as 1915, which is probably close to the date of the manuscript as well.

This is a real manuscript, and not the usual polite literary mystification or stalking-horse disguise. By this I mean that I am not the author of the following "Treatise," but only its translator – more faithful than free. Other than the translation of French colloquialisms into their nearest English equivalents, I have added only a few *scholia* in parentheses. The first two pages are omitted, containing a somewhat mannered preface saying little more than that this is an enlargement of a private lecture the author had given, probably to a medical club, considering the technical medical terms used.

He calls it – using the same popular French term for fellation as does Gallais above, "*tailler une plume*": to sharpen a quill – "*Traité didactique de la Plume*: *Ses avantages*: *Ses inconvénients*": "A Practical Treatise on Fellation: Its Advantages and Inconveniences." The translation does not attempt to retain the author's continual word-plays involving the title-phrase. It must also be obvious that I do not share a number of the author's male-dominant preconceptions. But I have preferred to leave his "Treatise" without revision, as the document it is:

A PRACTICAL TREATISE

"It should be clearly understood that our intention here is by no means to write an amusing, libertine, or bawdy work. To the contrary, this is a serious didactic study, without so much as a single improper word. Our whole intention is to attempt to revive, among the few persons we can influence, the classic art of erotics now fallen into decadence. God willing, this and future generations will not rush into coitus, like the brutal fecundation of a stud-bull, but will know how to express their erotic emotions in nuances, to refine their reflexes, and to augment with new and harmonious tones the gamut of eroticism.

Fellation (*la taille de plume*) is an art essentially French in nature. It consists of provoking seminal ejaculation in the man, accompanied by a more or less prolonged voluptuous prelude, by using only the soft parts of the mouth: lips, tongue, the soft palate, uvula, and cheeks. The teeth and fingers should be used only exceptionally, and always in an accessory and fleeting way.

The synonymy of fellation is extremely rich. Leaving aside purely technical or religious terms, such as *inosculation*, we will note only some of the more usual colloquial synonyms. Schoolboys, still at the lollipop stage, use the very inexact terms *suck* or *suck off;* highschool girls say *eat*, or more prudishly *kiss;* the middle-class says *go down;* the less elegant refer to *head*, or *blow*, or *a blow-job;* the vulgar say frankly *to suck a cock* or *lick a dick*, or even *blowing the meat-whistle*, *playing the skin-flute*, or *chewing* (*or chomping*) *mickeys;* young ladies of culture *know more tricks on a limber prick than a monkey on a rope*. Would-be sophisticates aspire to the low Latinity of *fellatio* (but privately say *to do*); the priest makes use of *the sin against nature;* prostitutes offer to *take it in the mouth*, or *the French way;* showgirls refer laughingly to *kissing* or *nibbling the worm*, or *inhaling the oyster;* the criminal element say crudely *cop-a-jock*, *gobble-de-goop*, or *swing* or *scarf a joint;* the gourmet speaks of *tasting*, or *sword-swallowing*, or *liking bananas;* the romantic of *kneeling at the altar;* the French speak of *trimming a quill*, or *giving one a fantasy;* Greeks and other nations say *tooting the flute;* the British say *gam* (for *gamahuche*); Americans say flatly *to French*. Physicians, as disciples of Aesculapius, forbid themselves all such fantastic nomenclature, and employ the elevated expression *coitus ab ore*, which sounds false indeed to the ear of any voluptuary.

[The actual French terms of the manuscript include: *sucer*, *travailler*, *scalper le mohican*, *extrêmonctier le Père François*, *faire dégorger la sangsue*, *titiller la gluante*, *savourer la banane*, *téter* or *travailler à la française* (Spanish), *jouer de la flûte*, *faire des fantaisies sur la tringle*, and *tailler une plume*. Many others exist, both in French and other languages. It might be mentioned that the last phrase, literally "to sharpen or trim a quill," preferred by this author, really refers to pressing back the foreskin with the lips, as one turns and moistens a pen or pencil-point in the mouth.]

Of all these terms we will retain only the first, *fellation*. It is the most classic, and has also the advantage of being understood everywhere, while its elegant and equivocal Latin derivation, which is both polite and agreeable to the most sensitive spirit, permits it to be employed without inconvenience on the lecture platform or in the most formal parlor conversation. Let us now consider what are the most favorable conditions for the development of the fellatory art, in all its perfection.

It is obvious, for example, that an experienced man, whether of calm or of passionate temperament, but knowing how to master himself, will be an incomparably better subject than a nervous beginner, overexcited, probably ticklish, and unable to stand much contact. However, a good fellator or artist should be capable of creating masterpieces even with defective tools. If such a specialist possesses to the proper degree the qualities we will enumerate below, she will always be able – at first contact, and after a rapid glance – to grasp her subject's character completely, and thus know how to graduate and vary her caresses according to his condition.

Everything, in both her physical and emotional attitude and in her movements, should inspire confidence and provoke erotic abandon on the man's part. She must be languorous and silent with the nervous or brutal individual; but, in the contrary case, she will be energetic, smiling, and rapid with the apathetic or sexually fatigued. To the beginner she must be friendly and encouraging; to the married man she must present herself not too highly perfumed, but full of consideration and of little hygienic services. Attentive and daughterly with the Dirty Old Man, she will show herself, with members of the clergy, discreet, worthy of confidence, and free of evil thoughts.

Let us now consider the capital question of the choice of a *place*. It would be a grievous error to imagine that a room destined for coition is perfectly suited for fellation. Each requires comfort of a different sort. A room fitted out as a fuckery should be cool, spacious, furnished with a vast bed and warm but light covers, decorated with curtains and other hangings of cheerful colors, ornamented with charming bric-à-brac and bright flowers, and lit by diffused white light that is not too dim. A room for fellation, on the other hand, should be moderately small, well-heated by steam or hot air to 70°F. or more. The light – ranging from rose-mauve to violet – should be diffused and very dim, coming from one lamp or two as desired, but in either case at the head of the bed and no closer than two feet from the pillow. The furniture, curtains, and carpet should be restrained in taste and few in number: one might almost say official in style, rather resembling the banqueting halls of the more fashionable restaurants. Everyone is of course aware that the former President of the French Republic, the venerated Félix Faure, who was nothing if not refined, preferred for fellation just such a chamber in the Elysée where, unfortunately, he died of a heart-attack in the heat of action – a martyr to the Art!

The woodwork of the bed and its covering should be dark in color, preferably red. There should be neither jutting-out corners nor useless objects nearby: no screens, nor any voluminous objects near the middle of the room. In one or two vases, a few simple flowers of single color, such as lilies, camellias, or violets. The orchid, with its obvious and indecent symbolism, is to be reserved for the fuckery. Finally, a small, thick and springy rug should be placed at the entering side of the bed. An adjoining bathroom is essential, or, at the very least, some simple toilet accessories placed in the least-well lighted corner of the room: warm water, towels, perfume, and *eau de cologne* of good quality. On the side-table should be prepared a strengthening collation of port, sherry, or madeira, with biscuits of any desired kind, except those too allegorically cylindrical and long.

A moment, now, of thought, before attacking the important question that follows: *the choice of the artist, or fellator*, a matter requiring unusually close attention. As to the sex, I will say without hesitation that the feminine sex is to be preferred, while admitting of course that this is not an indispensable condition. Her age should not be over thirty-five; the most capable fellators are from twenty-two to twenty-eight years of age. (Younger than that they are generally very enthusiastic, but worthless. – *Editor's Note.*)

The body-type is of no real importance, as there are fellatresses who, though tiny, are past-mistresses of the art. However, all other things being equal, the true connoisseur will always prefer a well-developed woman with a thoroughbred body, to any tiny pocket-Venus. The hips must be quite supple and of only moderate corpulence. A slender woman is to be preferred, for fellation, to one who is too fat, who may be lacking in mobility, and who will assume only with difficulty – or get quite red in the face attempting – the twists and bendings that fellation requires.

The bosom need be only slightly developed, but the neck and shoulders supple and well-articulated; the arms full, round, and firm; the hands soft and fine, the fingers well cared-for, and the fingernails short. The skin, even without cosmetics, should be velvety, and the face youthful, lit up by laughing eyes and an affable smile. The hair is best if blonde and fine, or in natural curls. If straight, this drawback to the work must be remedied by artistic coiffure, lightly curling the front and sides, and fluffing or aerating them later by teasing with a comb. Though necessarily curled and out of the way at the front and sides, the fellator's hair may be long and flowing in back. But in this case, if her hair is pretty and she wants to keep it long, she must learn the art of tossing it charmingly or holding it out of the way, so that it will not be an annoyance or an embarrassment during the work. When her hair is not one of her good points, or if she is not perfect at the technique of keeping it out of the way, it would be best for her to fix it in a loose bun at the base of the neck, which will best allow the diverse motions of her head. (This is very ancient. Compare the woman "which was a sinner," in *Luke,*

7:37–47, usually considered to be Mary Magdalene, kissing and washing the feet of Jesus with her tears, and then "did wipe them with the hairs of her head.")

The voice should be fresh, well-modulated, and of a pleasant tone. The mouth merits special discussion. It need not be too large, but should be sufficiently hospitable, ornamented with red, fleshy lips; the teeth white and regular – preferably small. A woman completely without teeth, or with teeth in the upper or lower jaw only, would be acceptable in an emergency. But under no pretext may one accept for this work a woman lacking one or more of the sixteen front teeth, or having any of these broken or snaggle-toothed! If, by chance, the fellator wears false teeth, she can retain them the whole time if they are perfectly well-attached, adaptable, and mobile. If not, she should remove them, bringing her case back to that already noted as to defective dentitions.

The tongue and lips should be humid and supple. The tongue in particular will have undergone special training in rapid vibration (similar to the "double-stops" used in playing the flute). The *test* is to be able to pierce with the tip of the tongue, and without touching with the lips, a round hole ⅜ths of an inch in diameter in a visiting-card of normal thickness, in less than one minute. This precious muscular organ must also be able to be stiffened or to remain soft at will, even while engaged in the most rapid motions.

So much for the physical qualities of the fellator. Those of her character are no less important. The fellator should be trustworthy, loyal, helpful, friendly, courteous, kind, obedient, cheerful, thrifty, brave, clean, and reverent. Beyond that, she should be courageous, attentive, devoted, philosophical, persistent (but without personal bias), both a physiologist and psychologist, intelligent, broadly comprehensive, cultivated, supremely tactful, reserved, sweet in character, and animated by the sacred fire of passion, without which she can never arrive at perfection in this art, nor merit the title of "priestess" with which the ancients honored her.

Technique of Fellation. Reuniting in herself all the above virtues, the fellator joins the man or accompanies him to the specially-prepared bedroom already described. The voluptuary has dined well. He undresses, and stretches himself out completely naked on the open bed. Or, if he is in a hurry, he can take off only his shoes and trousers, drop his underdrawers below his knees, and lift his shirt as high as possible, perhaps holding it in his teeth so as to leave his hands free. The priestess, who has also taken off her clothes, has not yet said a single word. This is now the moment for her to lavish on the man affectionate names and endearments, but these to be charming and respectful in nature and completely exempt from ridicule. She should ask if he has any special recommendations to make as to how he wants her to proceed; whether the light and the warmth of the room are as he likes, and so forth. Then, while continuing these mild and ingratiating remarks, she should place under the man's hips – if he agrees to it – a rather hard pillow which, after being flattened by the weight of his body, will still bulk six to eight inches thick. This pillow, intended to lift the pelvis and the genital parts, should reach from the small of his back to the bottom edge of his buttocks. This done, the work itself begins.

The reader will have observed, in what precedes, that there has been no discussion of washing or ablutions of any sort. This is intentional, for it is assumed that the habitual cleanliness of the man is not in doubt. The *amateur* of fellation is in general too refined to allow the noblest and most precious parts of his person to be mortified by filth. If, by chance, the case should be otherwise, it cannot be denied that this is an unpleasant circumstance, but one to which the fellatress — and it is precisely here that the philosophical side of her character is called upon — should pay no attention whatever. Aside from the fact that any preliminary contact with water at this time, however warm, is necessarily astringent and will retract the genital parts disastrously; washing will obviously require drying. Then, however soft, silky, or gauze-like may be the towel employed, it will be found that, owing to the friction of the towel, the genital area here concentrated upon will temporarily lose a good deal of its exquisite sensitivity. It is a far more favorable sort of preparation to keep the genitals in the warm and even temperature of the trousers till the last minute. This will also protect these sensitive parts from any external irritation.

While undressing, the fellator should continue to chat affectionately, but without venturing any obscene jests or remarks — even if flattering — as to the size of the man's organs, or his apparent religion; and especially without any provocative political or patriotic allusions, or other observations in doubtful taste, such as prayers or murmured invocations to one's mother, father, or other member of the family, human or divine. The fellator will then climb gracefully and promptly into bed with the man, but without bouncing in grossly with excessive enthusiasm.

She may be completely naked or may retain a short night-gown or chemise, preferably white and transparent, and perhaps ornamented with shoulder-strap ribbons of light blue, coffee-cream, violet, or delicate green, but in any case of very light tint to avoid distracting her partner's attention. She may also wear black or very dark silk stockings, of lace net or otherwise. (As it may well excite the man's imagination, a narrow black garter-belt, *without* panties, or decorative garters often add a delightful touch. Many men like the woman to wear fine high-heeled shoes as well, however impractical these may be in bed, as the sight of bare feet is not always attractive or exciting unless these are slender and well-shaped.) These preparations accomplished, fellation proper begins:

It is permissible for the fellator to adopt, at the very beginning, one of two positions. The better (No. 1) consists of kneeling or lying at either side of the man, with her head facing the foot of the bed. Her soft and rounded buttocks, belly, thighs, and genitals thus fall at the man's fingertips for him to manipulate and caress meanwhile, as it may excite him (and her) to do. This position gives the best contact of the two bodies, and thus the illusion of physical possession, which is precisely what is lacking in fellation: the one main weakness of the art. In the other position (No. 2), the fellator places herself in the same direction as the man, her head facing his head, and presses her body against one of his legs or lies between them, her torso stretched out downward on the bed and her knees bent. (This is similar to the position in which the woman kneels before the standing man. It therefore lacks, similarly, any exciting bodily intimacy with her, except touching and holding her head or hair, which will in general be found to inconvenience her necessary motions.)

Embracing the man then with her arms, one of which passes underneath his loins, she should begin by testing the man's excitability by touching his penis lightly with her cheeks and hair, and by a few light kisses on his lower abdomen. (The pubic hair can also be seized lightly and pulled with the lips and teeth.) If these methods prove too mild, and without effect, as may be the case with a man somewhat tired by sexual excess, she should bite him lightly and briefly on the inner surfaces of his thighs, to see if he stands this well;

continuing with similar light biting all around his umbilicus and at both sides of his lower abdomen. In biting in this way, she should employ the lips more than the teeth. This sort of *oral pinching* will generally have the effect of arousing the man, exciting his muscular reflexes, and provoking erection.

"AROUND THE WORLD." The work of the tongue, in this famous specialty, is both the longest and the most demanding of the preparations for fellation. The fellator leaves the genital area (unless she has found the man to be so excitable that it is necessary to finish him off orally at once), and begins at his nipples. The nipples are brushed with the mouth a few times, and sucked lightly with the inner side of the lips. The tongue-tip meanwhile turns slowly in circles around the areola, or medallion of the nipple, each in turn. Finally, letting go with the lips, the tongue vibrates rapidly against the nipple, though without insistence, for the sensitivity of the nipples is rapidly lost. In passing from one to the other, it is a good idea to brush the lips caressingly over the hair of the chest and the upper part of the abdomen. This elliptical caressing of the body-hair should be quite brief, and simply a transitional maneuvre, which can also be repeated at every necessary change of position. It should always be done over a rather broad surface of the skin, with full strokes of the head.

From the nipples, the fellator descends, trailing kisses of her lips either diagonally across and down the man's abdomen or straight down one of his sides, tracing a series of overlapping curves or scallops that might best be described geometrically as the oblique projection of a spiral on its vertical axis. She will arrive in this way at the pelvic angle known anatomically as the anterior-superior iliac crest – vulgarly, the hip. From this point she proceeds obliquely downward and inward toward the fold of the groin, simultaneously shaking her head from side to side (stroke of no more than three inches) while *trilling* or vibrating her tongue-tip rapidly from side to side against the man's flesh. This is known in slang as "tongue-lashing" or "zigzagging." The fellator can repeat this whole maneuvre several more times, up and down, and down and up, approaching the crotch and diminishing the sidewise motions of her head the lower she goes.

Her tongue has by now reached the lowest part of the groin, and enters the groove or furrow of the crotch itself where this separates the testicles from the thigh at either side, the tongue now vibrating at maximum speed. To make matters easier, the fellator can now lift outward the man's nearer thigh, holding it up with her arm in order not to require any physical effort of him, particularly not at this moment. In the groove, two or three trips of the tongue up and down should be sufficient, working principally at the point of insertion of the powerful tendon of the thigh, which is easy to recognize.

"The Rose-Petal" (*Rimming*). Until now the tongue has remained supple and rather soft. Now it stiffens, instead, and becomes firm and pointed when passing to the perinæum, of which the thicker skin and the underlying muscles make it less flexible and sensitive. The tongue-tip passes, therefore, rapidly and quite stiffly along the crevice of the perinæum, from behind the testicles to the anus. It is for this titillation of the anus that position No. 1, in which the fellator's head faces the foot of the bed, shows itself incomparably superior to any other. One might even say that it is the only position to be used for this, since it is the only one that allows the action to be done properly. Otherwise the man must change his own position considerably, or lift his legs very high, which would generally cause him to lose a good deal of the excitement created by what has already been done.

Her cheeks between his thighs, and the top of her head quite touching the bed, it is here that one sees the true value of the fellator's hair being kept low at the nape of her neck, and of the cushion under the man's buttocks, thus allowing her convenient entry. She now performs against the delicate mucous lining of the anal border the titillation known in French as "*the rose-petal*" (in English: "rimming" or "reaming"), a short and expressive term which is by no means unpoetic, but which is neither very precise nor complete for what can be described physiologically only as a sort of gyratory and plunging lingual movement at the anus, somewhat like a corkscrew, combined and alternated with a light vibratory or fluttering motion of the tongue-tip at the anal border.

Slipping, then, from the perinæum to the anus, the tongue-tip enters deftly, retaining a certain rigidity, though less than when used on the perinæum itself. The tongue-tip now executes several circular movements, while varying slightly the depth of penetration in and out. Then it withdraws, and the lips, which have until now remained inactive and open, are brought together. The fellator blows out through her pursed lips a light but energetic stream of air, and presses them at the same time very lightly to the rim of the anus. This produces a rapid and unexpectedly pleasant vibration, and an amusing sound similar to the buzzing of a large fly, known irreverently as a "Flutterblast", "Raspberry Tart," or "Playing the Bazooka." (French: "*trompette au chocolat*," or "*frelon volant*.") It is one of the charms of anilinctus.

Both the reaming with the tongue-tip and the rimming with the lips should be continued only rather briefly, as the surprise element and the sensitivity of the anus diminish rapidly after a minute or so. Also, prolonged labial vibrations of this kind would inconveniently numb the tactile sensitivity of the fellator's lips, thus reducing her aptitude for the remaining phases of the work. Leaving the anus, therefore, the tongue passes back along the perinæum and comes up through the crevice of the crotch, between the testicles and thigh. The side chosen is the one opposite to that used in descending, and all the same titillations are engaged in now as during the earlier descent, but in reverse order.

SCROTILINCTUS. The licking of the sensitive scrotum, in which the testicles are contained, requires all the art of the fellator. It will well repay all the long hours she may have spent training herself in what might be called the musical or calligraphic figurations of the Art of the Tongue. (Note, in particular: the "Telegraph Key," or "Woodpecker," a rapid vertical tapping or lapping motion with the tongue-tip; "Figure-eights," endlessly tracing the mathematical sign of *infinity*, as in ice-skating; and especially the "double-tonguing" and even "triple-tonguing" at alternate sides and the centre of the lips, well known in playing trills on the transverse flute, as in cunnilinctus.)

If the testicles hang quite low, and press against the perinæum, as is sometimes the case with older men or when the man is sexually fatigued, the fellator must lift the scrotum in order to work on its lower surface closest to the body. This she should do with dignity, and not by seizing the whole packet brusquely or roughly and hoisting it high, perhaps casually pinching a bit of the skin between thumb and forefinger as though pullyhawlying a sail or pinning up damp laundry. Her actions at this point show the refinement of her character. She should observe the true æsthetics of eroticism, and should delicately slide the tips of four fingers or the side of her whole hand underneath, to cradle the testicles and lift them carefully.

She will now be able to operate with the tip of her tongue not only along the front and the lower edge of the scrotum, but also on its underside facing the thighs. This particular area of the body, being always lightly moist and protected from contact with the clothing, retains an incomparable softness and sensitivity to any touch. It is also the area where properly-applied lingual titillations can be continued for the longest time without any fading or diminution of the sensitivity of the nerves. It is here, therefore, that the most delicate labial touches and brushings with the lips should be practiced, as also the most refined lingual vibrations. The latter should not be too rapid (no more than four oscillations per second), to avoid agitating or bruising the testicles. The tongue-tip should exercise hardly any pressure at all, and the flat of the tongue should remain quite supple and soft, and absolutely without rigidity or roughness.

The center of operations of this labio-lingual massage should be the lower edge of the scrotum. From here the fellator's lips venture occasionally toward the front or back, but less often to the front and there staying at the centre line of the scrotum, or "puckering-string." In any case, these sallies should never last very long, and are essentially only to allow of prolonging the subtle titillation of the lower edge of the scrotum, by avoiding the fatiguing or anæsthetizing of its nerves too rapidly.

A word of warning may be added: Certain fellators attempt a pleasantry in dubious taste, wishing no doubt to show themselves superior to the classic maneuvres of the art. They draw one or the other of the testicles into the mouth (sometimes even both together), and agitate this orally for a moment – or hum! This they call "chewing gum." Though acceptable as a caress after ejaculation will have taken place, it is quite useless as an excitant beforehand, when the testicles are swollen and engorged, and is sometimes very painful.

FELLATION: 1. *External.* Leaving the testicles, the fellator draws back the man's foreskin, if necessary, holding it lightly between the thumb and forefinger of one hand, and completely denudes the glans, leaving clear the balano-preputial groove that separates the glans from the foreskin. (This can also be done entirely without the use of the hands, pressing the foreskin back with the pursed lips. However, this abbreviates the external caresses, now to be described, and may also spoil the man's mounting anticipation of his ultimate entry between the fellator's lips.)

The fellator now changes nimbly from position No. 1, where her head faced the foot of the bed, to position No. 2, where she faces the head of the bed. Meanwhile, her lips engage the shaft and skin of the penis – a comparatively insensitive area, and one on which refined and prolonged caressses would be wasted – with a rapid buzzing maneuvre, the "Flutterblast" already described. This serves to disguise her necessary change of position with an amusing touch, and to keep the man's excitement from losing velocity while she changes. (The penis can also be nuzzled with the nose.)

All the preparatory activities that have gone before, and now the fellatory act itself, should be done in a continuous and uninterrupted way, without any long pauses that might break the mood for the man. The fellator should take particular care not to get any of the man's pubic hairs into her mouth, which might require her to stop in order to get rid of these. In any case, she has no reason to deal orally now with the hairy region of the man's pubis, which is sensitive only to powerful pressure (as of another person's pubis or hand), and where she is likely to take up a loose hair with the active tip of her tongue.

Now, without using her hands in any way, neither to direct the penis and certainly not to support or twist it in any way – a manipulation hardly worthy of an amateur prostitute or chambermaid – the fellator passes her tongue deftly but firmly around the entire corona of the man's glans penis.

In doing so she will pay no attention to any preliminary secretion of the man's pre-coital fluid, nor to any possible particles of preputial smegma that might accidentally be present under the foreskin. These last are regrettable, no doubt, but should be overlooked. She will also not hesitate, in making the complete tongue-tour of the *corona glandis*, to rest first one of her cheeks and then the other flat against the man's abdomen. This tour completed, her tongue becomes soft and enveloping, and acts on the glans over a large area at a time, using lapping and massaging motions rather than stiffening or pointing or performing any violent vibrations, which would make the penis bounce around ridiculously like a rubber ball. This lingual massage or envelopment should last a certain amount of time, and must be done with great delicacy and with a very wet tongue.

To complete the external phase of fellation, a few rapid vibrations with the partly-stiffened tongue are performed at the opening or meatus of the penis, which is sometimes an aperture large enough for the tongue-tip to enter it very slightly. This is followed by a complete tour or lingual caressing of the entire ridge of the *corona glandis*, concentrating especially on the point of attachment of the frænulum or "draw-string" of the prepuce on the underside of the penis. (Note well that this undersurface of the corona, and the lower side of the shaft of the penis itself, toward its tip, where it connects with the frænulum, is the most sensitive square inch of the male genital anatomy, irrespective of whether or not the man is uncircumcised. Lingual caresses at this point, just above and below the frænulum or draw-string, are the most exciting to the man and the most appreciated. They are most effective when the penis is already erect, and the skin well-stretched and taut. The inside of the foreskin is also very sensitive, and it is unfortunate that it is so often removed owing to vulgar superstition. If long enough, the entire foreskin can be drawn forward by the fellator's lips, or by her fingertips – even during erection – thus imprisoning her pointed tongue-tip, which is then vibrated against the glans penis or even circles around it inside the foreskin. A high-point of the art.)

2. *Inosculation.* Now, without haste, with a slow and continuous motion of the mouth – and always, of course, without the use of the hands to support or direct the penis – the fellator seizes or, rather, envelops with her mouth all the contours of the male organ in turn: the glans with its curving ridge and the spongy external corona, the balano-preputial groove all around the glans beneath the corona, and the shaft of the penis itself, to a depth of no more than about three inches, depending upon the oral capacity of the fellator. (Deeper penetration at this moment is useless, from the point of view of exciting the penis and glans. There is also the inconvenient likelihood of creating a gagging-reflex in the fellator, if the penis is allowed to strike suddenly against the back of the mouth and palate. The oral inosculation of the penis should therefore be done smoothly, without pausing but also without haste, the whole movement taking not less than about five seconds – the fellator counting the seconds mentally: "*One big rhinoceros, two big rhinoceroses,*" and so forth, and savoring the oral impaling of herself in this way on the fully erect penis. If the man's rhinoceros is not, actually, so very big, it would be kind of her to use the same metaphor anyhow, out of a spirit of good-fellowship.)

It should be clearly understood that the only parts of the mouth to be used now are the inner surfaces of the lips and the cheeks, the soft palate, and the tongue curved into a long groove, somewhat like a shoehorn and for the same purpose. *The teeth are under no circumstances to come in contact with the penis.* Once the penis is fully drawn into the mouth, the fellator can rest one cheek and her hair on the man's abdomen, but not so heavily as to diminish the rotary motility of her head. She now draws back her tongue, retracting it to the base of her mouth, where it remains supple and helpful as need be, performing continuous motions of envelopment and an exciting circular massage, all around the glans penis. This movement of the tongue is more easily effected when the penis is partly drawn out of the mouth at every simili-coital stroke, than when it is being pressed all the way in. Most fellators, even the most experienced, find it necessary to liberate an inch or two of the imprisoned penis in order to engage in this lingual manipulation with the desired dexterity and circular sweep. It is essential that the mouth be opened wide, while the lips are drawn as far forward as possible, making a tight oval. The penis rests on the tongue, the cheeks being drawn inward to grip the glans penis at the sides.

3. *Oral Friction, or the "sucking" of the penis.* (The true and effective action in fellation is not that of sucking – despite this name being given to it in many languages – but *oral friction,* in which the mouth and tongue of the fellator attempt to imitate the reciprocating motion and kneading action of the vagina during ordinary intercourse. If any actual sucking takes place during fellation, it is at the moment of inosculation, at the entry of the penis into the mouth, and then only as a nicety or brief caress; also at the moment of the man's ejaculation, as will be seen below.) All the lingual titillations that have preceded the complete taking of the penis into the mouth have naturally been done with a wet tongue and with the mouth thoroughly moistened. But it is now, at the final stage, that the salivary glands must come in very strongly and do their part, so that an appreciable layer of saliva is in evidence between the glans penis and the inner surfaces of the fellator's cheeks. One might say without either exaggeration or error that fellation must be performed *wet.*

The fellator continues to rest her cheek against the man's belly, thus allowing the penis to remain in its normally erect position. It is very undesirable for her to take any such position during the final oral friction as will pull the penis downward: its own natural erect position must be respected. Meanwhile she begins to move her mouth back & forth, that is to say, up & down on the shaft of the penis, her motions becoming deeper and faster as she proceeds. She usually begins quite slowly, and builds up speed imperceptibly at every forward stroke, until finally she is taking the largest possible amount of penis into her mouth. (To protract the man's pleasure she can also vary the speed of the up-&-down motions, going down quite fast but drawing up slowly and languorously with the mouth held lasciviously, almost gluttonously tight around the shaft and glans; nearly letting it slip out of the mouth, but then driving down fast again for the next stroke, and so repeating with continuing speed.)

The maximum amount of the penis that can usually be taken orally is only from 3 ½ to 4 inches, which is hardly more than half of the length of the average penis. Care must be taken to prevent the tip of the glans from coming too close to the fellator's tonsils, or striking too hard against the back of the palate, as this might automatically provoke the gagging reflex or even nausea – which is obviously undesirable during fellation and will seem to the man a form of insult or rejection, and all the more wounding in that it is beyond the fellator's conscious control. I might add, however, that experience with fellation will, after a certain number of séances, so exercise the pharyngeal vault of the upper throat that it becomes indifferent to thrusts and shocks, and the gagging-reflex no longer takes place. (It is also an important point, necessarily overlooked by this writer who is essentially dealing with fellation by a professional or prostitute, that when the fellator is herself very excited sexually by the man and by the act, the gagging-reflex that might otherwise take place will be quite absent, and this even during extremely deep thrusting of the penis into the mouth and upper throat. This is similar to the relaxing and opening of the tight vagina during intercourse. – *Editor's Note.*)

During the whole period of the oral friction, or salivary oral masturbation of the penis, the glans is at all times more or less deeply inserted into the mouth, and should at no time be allowed to slip out so far as to come into contact with the air, which would certainly cool it. Simultaneously, and as an accessory maneuvre, the fingers of the fellator's hand should be curled into a sort of basket, and should lightly envelop and lift the man's testicles, agitating first one and then the other by means of rather mild finger-motions of twiddling and dropping. This special manipulation, which is always much appreciated by the man during fellation, is commonly called "Spider-clawing." It should be distinguished carefully from anal digitation, or "Postillioning," the insertion of the fore-finger or middle-finger into the man's rectum to massage his prostate gland, which should not be done until it is desired to cause his ejaculation to take place, when the well-moistened finger should be agitated rapidly back & forth in the anus – and deep.

It should be obvious, from what has gone before, that the fellator does not and will not engage seriously in any sort of *sucking* or *blowing* (despite the slang phrases for fellation using these terms). This would only cause a congestion of the blood in the glans penis, which would greatly diminish its sensitivity, and which often causes a definite and sharp sensation of penile pain – not to mention the unwelcome psychological ideas of being harmed phallically, or of having the penis bitten or eaten off by the voracious fellator. Not only such ideas would dampen the man's ardor, and waste all the art and labor that have gone into fellating him, but sucking or biting the penis have also been known to make many a man give up being fellated at all, and to return strictly to coition, to the great detriment of his repertoire in the sexual art, or palette of erotic possibilities. Such is the unfortunate result of inexperienced enthusiasm, or thoughtless voracity, on the fellator's part. (In the words of the slang admonition, in all its simple folk-crudity, "*Suck, damn you! 'Blow' is just a figure of speech!*" As has been shown above, the effective action in fellation is really oral friction, and is neither sucking *nor* blowing; so that "suck" is also really "just a figure of speech.")

4. *Ejaculation.* This oral friction, or – as it is worth insisting – salivary masturbation, need seldom be continued very long, if the man has been properly excited beforehand by lingual caresses. After only a limited number of oral strokes – from forty to fifty strokes are usually sufficient: often far less – the man's desired seminal ejaculation should take place. The fellator then closes her eyes (if they are not already closed), and receives the sacred liquor without resistance, without even fluttering her eyelids. She waits until all the main spurts of the man's ejaculation have ceased, and then, *without either hesitation or gluttony, swallows the semen.* Then, opening her lips slightly, she permits the beatific penis to withdraw.

In exceptional cases, where the fellator has much work to do, or if her stomach actually cannot assimilate the spermatic fluid without causing gastritis, it is permissible for her to reject it rather than swallow it. But it is essential that this should be done, if at all, quietly and with the greatest discretion, without running to the bathroom nor making sounds of noisy hawking, gargling, splashing water, flushing the toilet, or incipient retching. These inelegant charades of rejection, worthy only of a low-class and somewhat inexperienced whore, are disagreeable to listen to, and can only shock the man's self-esteem. (That is perhaps their purpose.) In all cases, I would insist, swallowing the semen is preferable. For though, admittedly, it adds no particular physical pleasure for the man – the fellator, for her part, may adore swallowing the semen – it does involve a very real psychological satisfaction for him, which is well worth taking into account.

The act of fellation being now fully accomplished, the fellator should slip into an elegant dressing gown of light blue or cream color, and bring the man – who is slowly coming back from his ecstasy – water and a towel with which to sponge off and refresh his genital apparatus. Then, putting away the sponge and towel, she should engage in very light conversation with him, murmuring or talking by herself if he does not seem to care to reply, or maintaining a pleasant silence if he indicates his preference for that. The conversation, if any, should be limited to superficialities: the weather, the latest plays, political elections and assassinations, and other matters of no importance, and should not in any case make the slightest allusion to the act of fellation just accomplished.

The fellator should exert herself, at this moment, when the man is otherwise likely to feel somewhat depressed or even morose, to show herself charming, comforting, witty, and as helpful as possible. She should find the man's lost socks for him, if he must dress and leave; helping him on with his trousers, tying his shoelaces, holding him up a mirror as he readjusts his toilette, knotting his necktie for him, straightening the collar of his jacket and overcoat, and, if necessary, brushing up the crown of his hat a bit with the side of her bare arm. Finally, to say goodbye, a gentle but polite farewell, pressing the man's hands with her own, and urging him to return soon; offering her cheek, neck, or shoulder to be kissed by him, but not attempting to kiss the man herself, and especially not on the mouth. [!!! – *Editor's Note.*]

Specialties. The least serious difficulty encountered in fellation is an excessive nervousness or excitability in the man. This is generally easy to remedy, by employing only those manipulations which the man can stand, and carefully avoiding any light and unintentional caresses with the fellator's hair or fingers, or her nightgown or chemise if she is wearing one. The main essential is to do only one thing to the man at any one time, so that he can concentrate erotically and not become flustered and overwhelmed.

On the other hand, the fellator may have to deal with a man who is sexually fatigued, whether temporarily or really almost burnt-out erotically, owing to age or sexual excess. It is precisely here that she should make use of all the accessory maneuvres and specialties that act strongly on the man's reflexes and are capable of bringing him more easily and quickly to ejaculation. A primary point to observe is that if the fellator begins to realize, after the act of fellation is well along, that the man is able to muster only very little ejaculatory power, she should by no means go desperately at her various arts of lingual excitation. These are her best and last resource, and should instead be saved for the culminating moment. She should fall back to further and longer preliminary preparations, stopping all lingual excitation and going back to her earlier and milder manipulations, particularly on the man's testicles, coming back to the intended finale again only after a relatively long while.

If, however, she realizes early during fellation that the man is fatigued sexually before he even begins, and that it may be long and arduous to bring him to his ejaculation by oral means only, she should begin at once with some or all of the series of special and accessory maneuvres that follow. All of these combine excellently with fellation, though they are not listed in any special order of increasing effectiveness:

The Palm Leaf. This consists of passing the fingers through the hair of the man's head, the fingernails drawing lightly against his scalp, in a motion from front to back and back to front, and concentrating especially on the back hair and on massaging the nape of the neck. (This is very relaxing to the nerves, yet has an unmistakable undertone of sexual approach and readying.)

Salty Dog, or *Shrimping.* Consists of lingual tickling and licking of the instep of the foot, the arch and sole, and between the toes. (If the man is very ticklish this is still possible if it is begun without suddenness over the instep, and with *firm* rather than light touches of the tongue and lips on the sole of the foot. Ticklishness is always much reduced if unexpected and apparently threatening gestures are not involved, thus avoiding unconscious fear and tenseness in the person being tickled.)

Around the World, or *Tongue-Bathing.* Rapid licking and lingual vibrations over the entire body. (A modern homosexual glossary, *The Guild Dictionary,* Washington, D.C. 1965, at "Trip around the world," suggests the following itinerary as a build-up or preliminary to oragenitalism. Obviously, many other possible sequences exist. Note the omission here of any reference to kissing: "Begin with the face, then behind the ear(s), and progressing under the chin, over the throat, then to the chest and nipples, under the armpits. Turn the subject over at this point, and tongue the shoulders, down the back, along the sides, over the small of the back, over and between the buttocks, down the thighs, calves, ankles and heels, over the soles of the feet (eyelashes may be employed here, and fluttered to tickle). The subject is turned over, toes sucked, licking up the legs, then anilinctus (*rimming*) is performed, legs high, and ending with fellation (male) or cunnilinctus (female). Note: The pattern can certainly be used in part, or added to as the situation calls for, *i.e.* with those who are very ticklish or become aroused too quickly, etc.")

The Butterfly Kiss. The eyelashes are fluttered against the most sensitive parts of the man's torso, especially at his nipples and the sides of his abdomen under the arms.

The Persian Kiss. Lingual titillation of the inside surface of the ear. Very effective. This can be accompanied by the "buzzing-bee" maneuvre of the lips, and can finish with sucking against the inside of the ear. Both of these should be done carefully, and without too much force.

Tit-kissing. This does not refer, in the present context, to the classic kissing of the woman's breasts by the man, but to the "kissing" of the man's body by the woman's breasts: promenading her nipples up & down all over his torso and thighs, and directing her breasts without the use of her hands, simply by swaying motions of her chest. (She can also, of course, excite the penis with her breasts in the same way, slapping it delicately back & forth with her nipples, and finally imprisoning the penis between both her breasts – pressed together by her hands, this time – to imprint a kiss on its tip.)

Ice-skating, or *Kitten-on-the-keys.* A rapid stroking sideways or vertical drumming with the fingertips all over the man's lower torso and thighs, especially at the line under his ribs in front, and at the sides of his abdomen under the arms. (The stroking or skating motion of the fingers is like that of the rapid playing of the harp. The drumming is similar to the "Devil's tattoo" of the fingertips on a tabletop, or to a trill on the piano. The man is not slapped with the fingers.)

These are the main preliminaries with which the fellator can begin. And though others may suggest themselves to her imagination, I would repeat that the best results will be achieved by devoting her main effort and principal study to the classical maneuvres of the fellatory art to which she must eventually come. It is to the description of these maneuvres, and the true and complete technique of the fellatory art, that the present brief treatise has been dedicated. But before ending, mention should perhaps be made of at least two "erotic clowneries" connected with fellation, though having little to do with the fundamental maneuvres. These are admittedly not specially exciting in themselves, but they can add an air of fun, or of luxurious voluptuousness, to the proceedings, which need not, after all, be taken solemnly:

The Indian Chief. The fellator takes advantage of a momentary pause, to pluck a few feathers out of the pillow. These she sets vertically in a circle between the man's foreskin and his glans penis, thus forming the war-bonnet of an Indian chief.

Hammocking, or *Coconut Roulette*. This exotic form of fellation is doubtless practised mostly in tropical climates such as Africa, lower Mexico, and the South Seas. I owe the description to the obligingness of an explorer friend: "The man lies face down on a coconut-fibre hammock, allowing his penis to protrude down through the centre meshes of the hammock, which is suspended on long cords so that its centre is only about a foot above the ground. Underneath the hammock, face up, lies the woman – generally a captive – with her mouth just at the level of the man's protruding penis. She starts the hammock swinging, and every time the man's penis passes the lowest point of the arc she gives it a lick, tickling it as fast as possible with her tongue. As the oscillations of the hammock slow down and diminish, the vibrations of the woman's tongue speed up, and the depth of penetration of the penis into her mouth increases. At the climax, the hammock is stopped, the woman turns her body so as to allow the greatest possible penetration into her mouth, and the penis is sucked uninterruptedly, just as in our own country."

The advantages and disadvantages of fellation can of course be argued. I have tried, in this brief pioneering study, to give simple but complete details, without either prejudice or prudery, adhering to the scientific principle of telling the plain truth and avoiding ornamentation, however attractive this latter might be. In concluding, however, I should like to deal fairly with a completely unmerited reproach often made against fellation. Many believe that fellation is far more exhausting to the man than ordinary coitus. This is completely false, and the idea perhaps results from clever but secret propaganda by specialists (of both sexes) in fellation. It may also stem from imprudently repeated experiences with over-enthusiastic amateurs at fellation, who, among other habits, such as "milking" the man with the fingers at his orgasm, both along the penis and inside the anus, often require or allow the man to make violent pelvic movements or physical efforts of concentration. Though the quality of the orgasm thus achieved is doubtless more intense, the least taxing results, for the man, are achieved instead by his remaining entirely motionless and inert under the fellator's manipulations.

Another disadvantage, and one that is perhaps more serious, is that fellation, to be properly performed, requires intelligent training and a certain amount of experience. In general, real experts in the art will therefore usually be found only in large cities – where prostitutes and pederasts abound. It is precisely this problem that the present treatise, which is the first ever written on the subject in modern times, is intended to solve, by making it possible for chaste and faithful mistresses to learn the art in all its ramifications. Any man who will study this treatise carefully, and then explain the details to his mistress – not as an Art, but simply as something that it would please him for her to do for him – should be able to bring her to quite a pitch of proficiency in only a few lessons, using either his penis or a mannequin for her to practice on.

For the lingual vibrations, which are so important a part of expert fellation, yet so little understood and so seldom expertly performed, I would recommend frankly practising on a mannequin or dummy formed simply of a well-inflated condom. If the woman is intelligent, and especially if she is herself passionate and affectionate, and really wants to learn, she will soon become quite expert. Though it may take a good deal of practice and experience before she can give immediate satisfaction to a fresh penis of unknown form or unusual size, she will nevertheless be quite well adapted to the man from whom she has learned, and to whom she will thus be capable of affording the most exquisite erotic sensations."

Essentially, the art of fellation consists of everything described in the "Practical Treatise" preceding, but especially the opening of the mouth as far as possible, while *drawing together the lips over the teeth as tight as possible*, the lips forming a tight oval as in a profferred kiss. Fellation is, however, neither kissing the penis nor sucking it, but oral friction, the head moving up-&-down and side-to-side at the same time, rhythmically. It is just as important to rise high at the end of every up-stroke, so that the lips *and tongue* can titillate the corona of the glans, as to drive deep at every down-stroke. The glans can also be sucked or pumped in-&-out of the mouth strongly and slowly several times. But the important activity must be the oral friction on the penis inside the lips, which remain curled over the teeth, thus creating a simulacrum of vaginal coitus, to bring the man to orgasm.

It does not really need demonstrating that the "Practical Treatise" is written entirely from the point of view of the customer of a prostitute, being fellated for pay by a woman having no visible emotion about the matter one way or the other. One almost expects the anonymous author to end with a careful discussion of how much to pay her: whether to pay before or after, and in varying amounts according to the *expertise* the fellator has been called upon to show, no doubt with a final admonition about paying in the elegant gold coins of the turn of this century, rather than vulgar paper money. In fact it is surprising, considering the author's open insistence on a total lack of emotion in both parties – as is necessary in dealing with prostitutes, unless the whole scene is to descend to play-acting and bathos – that he simultaneously insists so hard on *the right to be passive* under the oral ministrations of the fellator. (The entirely opposite point of view will be considered in the following section, "Irrumation.") This is by no means unique to this anonymous author. Many men feel exactly the same way, and one may venture the psychological guess that all such men unconsciously consider fellation to be a sort of glorious continuation of, or halcyon return to, their own infancy, with the hovering and nutritious mother anxiously coaxing the urine out of their recalcitrant little penes.

The ejaculated semen is thought of by such men as a *flow* to be excited by external manipulation, rather than an *eruption* coming from uncontrollable inner forces. Often they consciously consider that they are thus losing their virile "strength" at the moment of ejaculation, and that fellation is therefore specially "exhausting" – a superstition the anonymous author weakly attempts to combat toward the end. The unspoken idea here is, of course, that in fellation the semen is somehow sucked out by the woman, rather than spurting or emerging naturally, and that only by a careful passivity can the man keep the *succuba* or Delilah (that the fellator is thought somehow to be) from thus weakening and emptying him, as with Samson and the strength residing in the expurgated virility of his hair.

That this involves an emotional as well as a physical passivity is also made clear, in the insistence on the prostitutory and unemotional sexual situation. Many neurotics also consider that *any* emotions of love or concern that they are called upon to feel or – perish the thought! – express, will somehow "weaken" them. The having of such emotions is therefore, if unavoidable, the duty or rôle of the *other* party (in this case the woman, representing the loving mother), while the man will remain the surly and resistful little boy all his life. This is of course a large element in the current pose of being "cool," or unemotional and uninvolved, modelled largely on the homosexual and emotionless detectives of murder-fiction and spy-fantasies, at least since Sherlock Holmes.

On the other hand, it would be unfair to discuss the man's position in all this, without considering that of the woman, and how far she may or may not be responsible for the hidden fears men feel in connection with fellation, no matterly how eagerly they seek it. The day is now past when a woman publicly accused of fellation in a divorce case, would learn that when, thereafter, it would be necessary to receive her socially in the homes of her peer-group, any cup or glass out of which she might drink would then be immediately taken away and broken! Washing or sterilizing the glass would not be enough: it would have to be destroyed – sacrificed, as it were, to redeem or wipe out the guilty and sinful touch of the fellator's lips. Negroes taking advantage of their legal right to be served in restaurants or saloons in white-master Southern states have also had similar experiences.

It is also now unusual, except at the very lowest social levels, for such superstitions and pathetic confusions to be expressed as that which the present writer once heard described by the man involved (a tobacco-shop clerk), who had, by means of long persuasion and extravagant promises, convinced his girl-friend to fellate him in his automobile one night. Afterward, she sat up in the moonlight, with his semen glistening on her lips, which she was wiping with her hair. "Well," he said, "I was just so *disgusted*, I punched her right in the mouth as hard as I could." "But what for?" I asked in astonishment. "*Ahhh, for being a cocksucker!*"

Scenes like this are now becoming a thing of the past, even in the notably sexually-repressed Anglo-Saxon culture, which never shows the evil results of its repression so glaringly as on its increasingly frequent "moral holidays," with prostitutes (by preference in foreign countries) and with other men's "swapped" wives, when it wallows piggishly in everything it really considers sinful and forbidden. Nevertheless, however free of repression men consider themselves to be, there is often a clear unconscious fear of the fellator — whether a woman or a homosexual — which can easily break into expression in violent scenes such as that described above . . . and worse. These fears doubtless rise in large part from the castratory fantasies sometimes aroused by the idea of putting one's penis inside the grip of another person's *teeth*, and the remarks passed about "women with buck-teeth" and fellation, at the folklore level, make this very clear. The more willing, or even anxious, the fellator shows herself to perform fellation, the more likely the man is to feel such fear.

Very many women feel powerfully moved toward fellation, sometimes without ever having heard of it, nor seen it, even among household animals, simply as an unconscious survival of memories of feeding at the mother's breast — or of having been deprived of this. But they will still find, surprisingly often, that their unstudied attempts in this direction, or candid requests, will be met by a certain resentment on the man's part, even though he may be more than willing. That is to say, he wants her to agree to fellation when he suggests it: he does not want her to want it herself. Essentially this involves a certain normal desire to "rape" the modest and unwilling woman, and it is not always wise to deprive a man of this fantasy. Certainly no woman of cultivation really imagines it excites any but the most masochistic kind of male for her to grate out in passionate vulgarity such an invitation (or threat?) as I also once heard: "Oh honey, I can't wait to get your cock in my *jawr!*" There are still certain things that are better said by gestures, and certain prerogatives that should be left to the man.

The modern French dadaist writer, Isidore Isou, is credited with the authorship of a rare little pamphlet on sex technique, *Les 32 Positions*, signed "Docteur Pieli," and published in Paris about 1958 under the rubric, "Editions F.O.B., Mexico." This pamphlet is unfortunately cast in a satirical and sardonic tone throughout, and is therefore much inferior – as the technical manual it pretends to be – to its obvious model, *Les Paradis Charnels* of Alphonse Gallais, fifty years earlier, which has already been quoted. At no other point does the author, "Pieli" (Isou?), who is obviously deeply versed in his subject, express the contempt and resentment that suddenly break through in his brief chapter on fellatory technique, when he discusses the technique which he calls "*College-girl style, or Dirty Mary*":

"College-girls are instinctive creatures. Virgins both in front and in back . . . not knowing what to do with a penis, and not daring to put it into either their anus or vagina, it is perhaps only normal that they put their mouth to the instrument of which they dream. Men who have been fellated by college-girls, and women who have had the opportunity of seeing how these little bitches go about it, agree that their method can only be called the lowest and the most humiliating . . .

"Girls like this throw themselves on the penis with a rare voracity, and pump at it wildly without the slightest sense. A woman who had the occasion, during a private party, to observe a college-girl in fellation, described it as follows:

"With her eyes bulging out of her head, she approached the man, whose penis, valiantly erect, indicated his unequivocal desire. The bitch flung herself on her knees, and, the moment she had his penis in her mouth, began pumping nervously. She worked at it with everything all at once – lips, tongue, and teeth – with all the incoherent avidity of a bloodsucking leech. Before the first minute was over the little glutton was out of breath, in her rage to get it all into her mouth. With her fingers clawing at the man's balls, she choked and panted without ever stopping pumping! And, when the man finally did erupt his load of semen, the slut tried to swallow it, but, incompetent and greedy as she was, she lost all the good juice of his loins. Her mouth was smeared all over with it, and her chin was dripping. She dirtied both my carpet, her dress, and the trousers of her generous partner."

No one is expected to believe, of course, that this is an authentic quotation from the hostess at an elegant sex-party, though such parties certainly do take place – and have for centuries – in both France and other countries. The author is simply expressing his animosity against a certain kind of too-enthusiastic fellator, whom he here assimilates to the hated social equal of the educated woman, or "college-girl." Observe the closeness of even some of the images used, such as that of the "smeared mouth," in this presumably super-sophisticated complaint, to the similar complaint – expressed physically rather than verbally – of the uneducated tobacco-shop clerk, who punches his girl-friend in the face with all his strength after she has fellated him at his own request. Neither the sophisticate nor the shop-clerk can state his grievance clearly, yet it is certain that what is troubling both of them is *fear*.

Though it is not to our purpose in the present work to discuss homosexuality in connection with oragenital acts, it should be mentioned that despite the relative relaxation of the taboo against fellation by women in the Anglo-Saxon culture, there has been no matching relaxation of the animosity against the homosexual. Homosexual men – of whom a very large percentage are lifelong compulsive fellators, searching for "fresh meat" at all times – are particularly exposed to a dangerous kind of panicky fear and resentment on the part of the men they fellate. There even exists a special type of male prostitute, known to homosexuals as "*dirt*," whose whole activity is to lead homosexuals on to perform fellation, after which the male prostitute or "dirt" beats and often robs the homosexual, on the self-righteous pretext of hating and despising him for being a fellator!

There is also a matching belief, actually a superstition, that homosexuals can perform fellation much better than any woman (because they do it for their own pleasure, and therefore have more experience), and also in a way which particularly exhausts the virility of the fellated man. Meaning, of course, that he is thought to be somehow in danger of becoming (or being considered) homosexual himself, as a result of being fellated by a man. Other than the perfect if unconscious logic here, this is again the *succubus* or *succuba* idea, which always surfaces when faced with the compulsive fellator, of whichever sex. What is involved is a lack of recognition of the basic fact concerning oragenitalism, already discussed at the opening of this volume in the section on "Cunnilinctus," that *oragenital acts are* NOT *essentially a special type of sex technique, intended to satisfy the erotic needs of the* genital *partner; but are the expression of a profound emotional urge, intended to satisfy the erotic needs of the* oral *partner.*

Where this is made too transparently clear, by the overt eagerness of the compulsive fellator or cunnilinctor (who may even be searching for genital partners by means of toilet-room graffiti, or the precisely matching classified advertisements in the "underground" press), the genital partner will generally respond with the uneasy realization that he or she is not really being caressed, but is being *used*. The result is naturally anger and resentment, reinforced in the case of men by unconscious fears of being castrated by the dangerous mouth and teeth (the myth of the *vagina dentata*) of the over-eager and compulsive fellator. Though many women are powerfully drawn to fellation, to express their affection for the man, the biological primacy of their vaginal need makes the compulsive female fellator rather rare; where the compulsive homosexual fellator is the most frequent or, at any rate, the most ostentatious type.

The *using* of the genital partner, in oragenital acts, is often more serious than just for purposes of the sexual relief of the oral partner, whose pleasure also seems rather mysterious, since his or her genitals may not even be involved in the sexual act, nor be masturbated manually to orgasm, yet some kind of satisfaction (or even spontaneous orgasm) is obviously felt. The solution of the mystery is this: The spontaneous orgasm or satisfaction of the compulsive fellator represents not a sexual relief, but a relief from *anxiety*. All homosexuals suffer from unconscious ideas of having been castrated, or of being in danger of being castrated, by some superior authority-figure, especially by the father, for their incestuous desires for the mother, sister, or other desirable female-figure, who is thought of as part of the father's forbidden harem, and about whom the homosexual often gravitates sexlessly for a lifetime. It is this fear of castration which makes men homosexual (*i.e.* impotent with women), along with a panic dread of the female genitals, which they take as visual "proof" that castrated beings can exist!

Homosexuals also over-react massively against their imaginary fears about being castrated, by wishing in turn, and consciously in many cases, to castrate, harm, disgrace, imprison, destroy in business or in love, or plainly to kill as many other men, or even lower animals, as possible – sometimes even themselves. (*You Can't Fire Me, I Quit!*) In forcible pedication or anal intercourse with boys or young men, which is thought of as "effeminizing" the pedicant, and in compulsive fellation of hundreds or thousands of men in the course of a lifetime, homosexuals act out in a partial way their hidden desire to cut or bite off the penis, and thus to make the other person suffer the castration that they themselves so much fear. Only when faced by the "evidence" of this imaginary castration – for example, the swallowed semen of the fellated man, which is sometimes fantasied as being blood, or "better than blood" – can this type of homosexual feel relief from his anxiety about having been castrated himself, and experience orgasm. The type of homosexual who accepts the passive position in anal intercourse, compulsively and with hundreds of partners, expresses in a somewhat less hostile way the same ideas, since it is he himself who accepts the fantasy castration of being pedicated again and again, yet is somehow *not* castrated by it, as his achieved orgasm shows.

(*Say It Isn't So!*) This is the truth about homosexuality: the truth that the propagandists for this unfortunate neurosis never tell, and would prefer not to understand.

In the case of women who are compulsive fellators, or who plainly prefer fellation to any other sexual act (very commonly the case with prostitutes), the situation is very similar, though rather transparently veiled behind some hygienic, virginal, or birth-control excuse. These are generally women who hate men and are jealous of the penis, which they would like to bite off and keep. Their choice of fellation as a preferred sexual act is intended to prevent themselves from being faced by the enemy-penis in any situation except one in which they are dominant over it, and could harm it if they liked. In vaginal coitus, the man is too obviously dominant for his phallic dominance to be denied, and almost any excuse is taken to avoid such coitus; the hand, mouth, or anus being offered desperately as substitutes. Such women are also often unconscious Lesbians, avoiding normal sex out of fear of their mothers, precisely as homosexuals fear their fathers.

It is an inner overwhelming by, and the fear of being found out in, these castratory and hateful fantasies that makes compulsive fellators, both homosexuals and women, dislike having relations with any one person more than once. This is the Don Juan complex, less romantically known at the slang level as "*oncing*." Such persons suffer intensely from emotional strangulation – the pose of being tough, emotionless, or "cool" – and are stricken with enormous unconscious guilt for the hostile fantasies they continuously act out wholesale in their sexual life, and by fear of retaliation. Not retaliation of the sexual acts engaged in, which they would often welcome, but retaliation of the imagined oral castration of the partner, which they imagine as the climax of the sexual act, with the partner's ejaculated semen representing the swallowed blood. (This is often admitted to frankly by homosexuals under psychoanalysis.) Such persons must therefore continue their "oncing" for a lifetime, moving on hastily to some new partner or prostitute the next morning or the next week. This is also the truth about homosexuality, and is equally true – with obvious modifications – about anally-directed homosexuality, including those types in which the homosexual takes the part of the pedicant or victim himself, with self-directed castratory notions.

The heterosexual Don Juan (of either sex) generally has similar problems, and is almost invariably unconsciously homosexual as well, since the principal activity of the Don Juan is not the desiring or seducing of the present partner, but the hating and *running away* from the hundreds or thousands of partners preceding! (Most Don Juans are great travellers.) Thus, the daily or nightly "conquest" of some new sexual partner is really only a panic flight from the partner of the day or night before, of whom the presumed sexual conquest has really only been a dismal and repetitive failure. Among both homosexuals and women, the *oral Don Juan* is by far the commonest type (including sexual braggarts!) It is therefore in no way surprising that the partner or conquest of the compulsive fellator, or oral Don Juan, of either sex, so often feels resentful and depressed after fellation, and conscious that he has been *used*.

Women of this kind often "telegraph" their hostility against men by a particular pose of toughness, and by habitual obscene talk, often without even the pretext of "low" social origin to explain this, or the pretense that it is supposed to excite the man sexually – something it can only do with very neurotic or masochistic men. Obscene and insulting speech of a compulsive kind, especially in leading up to, during, *or replacing* sexual intimacy (quarrelling), is psychologically known as *coprolalia* ("talking dirty"), and is very common among the insane, both male and female, in whom social repressions have broken down. The new term, *erotolalia,* has recently been suggested, to replace this, with the clear intention of directing emphasis away from the self-evident hostility involved, and of implying that it is only another kind of oral sexuality or endearing speech.

Actually, it does not take too much sophistication to distinguish which is the endearment and which is the insult, as between: "*Get down on your knees and suck that, before I slap your ears off, you bitch!*" and "*I love you, dearest.*" Take your pick. It is certain, in any case, that the pose of emotional and verbal toughness (oral sadism) in women is *not* sexual or social equality or freedom, but is a hostile way of mocking and imitating men, exactly as homosexuals similarly express their overt hostility against women by mocking and imitating women's mannerisms of speech, dress, and bodily motion, generally in an excessive and obviously caricatured way called "*camping.*" Dirty-talking toughness in women—often combined with an open preference for fellation—is, therefore, hostile female "camp."

Rather than leave standing the absurd idea that homosexuals are necessarily better fellators than an affectionate and willing woman can ever be, the space may be taken here to quote the only homosexual manual of erotic technique known to me, *The Gay Girl's Guide*, a very rare mimeographed pamphlet privately issued, probably in Boston or Cambridge, Mass., in 1949, with imprint: "A Phallus Press Publication." The tone and vocabulary vacillate between the technical and vulgar in a rather uncharming fashion, in obvious self-applied coprolalia, as just discussed, but no falsification of this authentic document will be made. Sandwiched between a glossary of homosexual slang, and a directory of "gay" bars and parks in the U.S.A., are the following notes, entirely concerned with methods of giving pleasure to the genital partner:

"TECHNIQUE. – There are three main groups of [homosexual] techniques. They are the oral, the anal, and the miscellaneous, which we will arbitrarily call mutual masturbatory. In the various possible combinations, quite a large number of relationships can be evolved from these basic groups.

"To some extent, it is possible to predict to which technique a certain person is partial by his general characteristics and behavior, but such predictions are notoriously subject to exceptions.

"For instance, generally speaking, the orally-minded [homosexuals] are the most concerned with the factors of youth, looks, and genital dimensions. Conversely, the ones who show no great interest in the genital dimensions, age or looks of their potential partners are very likely to be anally-minded, assuming they are not commercial [*i.e.* male prostitutes].

"In general, cocksucking talent is directly proportional to age. The very young have usually neither desire nor talent, and if they have desire, their talent is very mediocre. Talent and desire seem to both increase with age, and whether it is due to psychological or physiological reasons, there are very few really top-notch cocksuckers far short of thirty.

"It is also worth noting that among youthful cocksuckers, talent is in inverse proportion to swishiness ["*camping*"]. Almost always, the more obvious, the less talent; the least obvious, the most talented.

"ORAL. – This is the technique which has become most generally associated with homosexuality (at least where bathing facilities are available on a mass basis), though it may be that only about half of all homosexual affairs center around it. . . There are two primary factors that determine the good cocksucker. They may be summed up as DEPTH and SPEED.

"*Depth* refers to the necessity of taking at least half of the length of the erect penis, and preferably more. *Speed* refers to the necessity of matching, orally, the rhythm and tempo which naturally precedes an orgasm, whether in heterosexual, anal, oral or masturbatory activity (slightly over one per second).

"The novice tends to violate both these important rules, by taking only the head of the penis into his mouth, and moving his mouth very slowly, which is often partially explained by his initial repulsion. These two points are most important of all at the time of orgasm, and it is at just this time that the novice tends, because of his anxiety about the disposition of the ensuing flow of semen, to slow down his movements and have the minimum phallic content in his mouth. The result is invariably highly unsatisfactory to his partner.

"Two secondary factors that also play their part are worth a brief note. The ability to produce a great deal of saliva at the time is obviously most helpful. (The amount of saliva will generally be in direct proportion to the sex appeal of the one being "done" [*fellated*], there being a substantial amount of truth in the expression "drool over.") And of equally obvious benefit is a fairly large mouth.

"If he has a sufficiently large mouth, and has mastered the factors of speed, depth and saliva, the novice has become a good cocksucker. Only a great natural aptitude will enable him to pass beyond this rating to attain a truly superb status."

A few further paragraphs in *The Gay Girl's Guide* (which will be quoted elsewhere) discuss the matters of irrumation, body-kissing and anilinctus, and the question of the disposition of the ejaculated semen. If this is the best that the homosexual contingent has so far produced, in the way of an exposé of the presumably superior secrets of homosexual fellation, no woman who seriously wants to hold her man need ever worry about the homosexual "competition," at the level of pure technique.

An Oriental form of fellation, of great interest and effectiveness, is described in "Docteur Pieli's" *Les 32 Positions* under the title "*La blanchisseuse de tuyau de pipe*" (The Pipe-Stem Polisher), which would refer it to Chinese opium-dens. This method is also mentioned in passing in an American work as having been encountered by a sailor in Yokohama, as the specialty of the "Number One expert" in fellation among the Japanese prostitutes during the First World War. "Docteur Pieli" (Isou?) describes it as follows:

"The woman straddles her partner at the level of his chest or shoulders, pressing down on his face with her buttocks. She is facing his feet, in such a way as to be able to reach his penis with her mouth when bending far forward. Once she takes his penis into her mouth, she sucks it in rhythm, matching the strokes of her tongue with those of her whole body. The movements of her body are like those of a washerwoman, doing her laundry in a river. The motions back and forth of her head and shoulders give the penis the sensation of *oral masturbation*. It is neither her lower jaw nor her cheeks that pump the man, but her entire body which masturbates him through the medium of her puckered lips."

The American work, Dr. W. F. Robie's *The Art of Love* (Boston, 1921), a work which was half a century ahead of its time in the English-speaking world, as to candor and detail in the matter of oragenitalism, uses the same metaphor or comparison, of "oral masturbation" in describing this method. In this Japanese form, however, the woman faced the man's head and not his feet, kneeling between his legs "at the proper distance for moving up and down from the hips and thus causing her mouth to masturbate me, so to speak. She went into action energetically, and never tired, flying up and down faster and faster, after first bathing me in saliva with her darting, snake-like tongue." The man describing this states that he relaxed meanwhile, as much as possible, to prevent his orgasm from coming too soon, and was left gasping for air when it came. He states also that even the (visual) memory of the woman in this rapid action was particularly stimulating, but that – warning note! – "a sore, where one of her teeth had grazed me, remained on my penis." He adds ruefully that if he were ever to become rich he would hire a talent-scout to find him a girl like that, "preferably with removable false teeth, to employ as a secretary."

It was apparently on this suggestion – taken much more seriously than can be the animadversions on fellators with false teeth, in the "Practical Treatise" above – that a private American sex-researcher during the 1940's, known as "S. W. Regius," or "K. S. Grien" (an anagram), discovered or developed a form of fellation which he called "*The Flying Fuck*," stating that it involves the most powerful possible orgasm for the man. The rather strange or strained position that the man must take, in this, is not intended to be fantastic, but is quite essential to the violence of the orgasm achieved. This is based on the important but seldom considered fact that the achieving of orgasm in both sexes involves, first, a *relaxation* of the nerves and repressions, to allow sexual excitement to take place; then an intense concentration of nervous and physical *tension*, increasing to a crescendo at orgasm. If these are reversed – if the man or woman is too tense at the beginning, or too relaxed when orgasm approaches – the orgasm will come either too soon or, more likely, not at all.

Grien's method, which he described in a personal communication to me — never before made public — as achieving "the true summit of sexual sensation" for the man involved, makes use of the important subsidiary techniques of anal digitation, and the striking (in intercourse: the kicking or spurring) of the man over the loins by the woman, as his orgasm approaches. But the particular intensity of the orgasm achieved by this method is merely enhanced by these means, and they will not by themselves have the same result. The main effect actually rises from the peculiar and particularly *strained or tense* position the man is forced to take, rather similar to some of the Yoga positions sculptured on the Hindu love-temples, which also probably had a similar intention of somehow increasing the man's erotic pleasure.

In Grien's method, or "The Flying Fuck," an armchair or rocking-chair, with flat arms at the elbow height of the person sitting in it, is placed in a doorway, such as that of a parlor, across the top of which there is a strong rod or bar, intended to hold a curtain, the curtain being pushed out of the way. In this chair sits the woman, who, according to Grien, is to have "a complete set of false teeth, upper and lower, *which she has removed*." (The method is not actually premissed on finding such a woman, who might well be old or ugly; and normal women with all their own teeth can use this method just as well.) The man then stands on the arms of the chair, facing the woman, holding the curtain-rod with his uplifted hands to steady himself — especially if a rocking-chair is used.

Fellation is then begun, not in the ordinary way, but by the woman *rocking* back and forth with her whole body, either against the padded back of the armchair, or by means of the rockers, holding her mouth steady and engaging meanwhile in tongue-caresses of the penis at every stroke. The similarity is obvious to the Oriental method ("The Pipe-

Stem Polisher") described earlier. However, the extraordinary difference takes place here just before, and at the moment of, the man's orgasm. Then – and this is not possible in the Oriental method – the woman simultaneously continues her fellatory rocking, also digitates the man anally with the middle finger or thumb of one hand, and strikes or hammers him over the loins with the palm or clenched fist of the other hand. All this, of course, matching the rhythm of her fellation of him, which he may also second, until orgasm, by rocking himself on the arms of the rocking chair (steadying himself with the curtain-rod, to avoid falling), or by flexing and unflexing his knees and tightening his buttocks at every stroke, if an armchair is used. The crucial point now follows.

Whether attempted on an armchair or a rocker, the essential gesture is this: As his orgasm approaches, *the man draws himself up into the air* by pulling on the bar or curtain-rod with both hands. This is simply the ordinary gymnastic exercise of "chinning," but it is unnecessary for the man to lift himself any farther than just enough to be off his feet. In this way, with his entire weight pulling on his flexed arms, and his knees drawn up at both sides of the woman's head, there is created *the most powerful possible physical tension of the man's whole body*. The "chinning" should not be done until the man realizes that his orgasm is close (unless he is a gymnast), and he should then attempt to maintain himself in the air until his orgasm is completed, or at least the first several spurts, which are usually the most poignant. He then slowly lowers himself to a steady position on his feet, on the arms of the chair, when his orgasm is ended.

Very few people have ever tried Grien's method, as he disappeared mysteriously in the American southwest shortly after communicating it to me. Those who have tried it are all agreed that it is everything claimed for it, as to absolutely shattering intensity of the resultant orgasm for the man. The woman is, as can be seen, left completely to her own resources or devices. The main difficulty found is to avoid falling on top of the woman at the moment of orgasm, knocking both her, oneself, and the rocking-chair to the floor. It has even been suggested that the woman assisting did not have false teeth until the second time it was tried. This is the opposite of the fantasy of the *vagina dentata,* or teeth that hurt the penis, for here it can easily be the penis that hurts the teeth. It is therefore a good idea to strew several sofa-pillows at both sides of, and particularly behind the chair, beforehand, to soften any possible crash.

The search for exotic novelties in connection with fellation largely descends to the bathos of erotic jokes and "clowneries," which Grien's method most emphatically is not. For example, the use of a feather to tickle the penis meanwhile, as will be discussed below, an idea usually presumed to be taken to the point of almost torturing the subject or victim, as in the 1900's sado-pornographicum, *The Way of a Man with a Maid* (recently reprinted), and in Norman Mailer's short story of 1952, "The Man Who Studied Yoga," where middle-class couples are watching an erotic moving-picture in which this device is used. A humorous broadside entitled "*Catalogue des Prix d'Amour* de Mademoiselle Marcelle LAPOMPE, 69 Rue du Chat-Noir, 69" (Paris, about 1915), notes as its final listed specialty: "*Suçage à la Menthe:* Before having your asparagus gargled (*glouglouter le poireau*), have the operatress suck a mint candy. Delicious little burning sensation." This is to be compared, of course, to the inserting of a mouthful of wine or brandy into the vagina during cunnilinctus, discussed at some length above, which is at least as old as the *Satyricon* of Petronius Arbiter (about 65 A.D.) and probably much older.

Similarly, in a well-known modern French recitation, "Madame Furina" (printed in the students' erotic song collection, *Trois Orfèvres à la Saint-Eloi*, 1930), the whole humor turns on the professional fellatress' table of "specialties," as recited by her excessively officious husband or pimp, who also offers to *prepare* the unready client! Another such farce, "La Ventriloque" – first printed in the extravagantly rare original collection of French students' erotic songs, *Anthologie Hospitalière & Latinesque* (Paris, 1911–13), anonymously compiled by "Dr." Edmond Dardenne Bernard, vol. 1, page 423 – laments the impossibility of finding a fellatress who will also be a ventriloquist, so that she may intone the "Marseillaise" and other national anthems while fellating the poet! This problem, of the necessary *muteness* of the oral partner during fellation, will be returned to again in the following section on Irrumation, in connection with the so-called "Hum-job." The ventriloquial poem is an evident students' recitation, intended humorously, but has been attributed to Guy de Maupassant, whose own authentic and perfectly serious oragenital poems or pæans appear in the final edition of *Le Nouveau Parnasse Satyrique du XIXe. Siècle* (Bruxelles: Henry Kistemaeckers, 1881): "Ma Source," in praise of cunnilinctus, "*69*," and "La Femme à Barbe," this last doubtless the inspiration of "La Ventriloque," but itself a masterpiece and clearly Maupassant's own neurotic fantasy-confession of his making love – as a woman – to the Bearded Lady in the circus dressed as a man. This actually sums up his own tortured relationship with his final dominant mistress, who did not, however, have a beard.

The preceding pages by no means exhaust all that is known or could be said concerning the art of fellation. A good deal is left to the reader's own erotic imagination and spontaneity, especially as to movements of the heads and bodies of the participants, and for special cases or even minor fetiches. But the main lines have, I feel, been laid down. The whole matter of *positions* used in fellation, of places convenient and inconvenient, of the woman's erotic satisfaction meanwhile, by means of the man's or her own subsidiary actions during fellation, and of the disposition of the ejaculated semen, have been left for the following main section, "Irrumation," where they are perhaps of greater importance. Other elements will be treated even further along, in the final section, "The Sixty-Nine."

As a closing example of what must be considered subsidiary or even fantastic fellatory techniques, might be mentioned the various ways of *tickling* the penis, with the mouth or otherwise, either before or in connection with fellation. All such tickling is to be concentrated on the frænum of the penis, the so-called "whang-string," and the area surrounding this on the lower side of the penis, including the bottom or ends of the corona glandis, where these rise to a point precisely where the frænum connects. It is understood, of course, that the prepuce – if present – has been retracted. For it is the frænal area which is the most sensitive part of the penis (and actually, therefore, of the male body), and capable of appreciating so delicate a sensation as that created by tickling, as differentiated from simple caressing.

The standard appurtenance used for tickling is, of course, the feather. When used in connection with fellation, the feather should be held in the mouth, not in the hand, and the motions of the tip of the feather are directed not so much by the motions of the fellator's head, as by the motions of her tongue-tip hidden behind her teeth, operating like the tiller of a boat on the naked or quill-end of the feather held between the teeth or lips. The charm of this sort of *erotic clownery* is that the penis is really being tickled and titillated by the fellator's mouth and tongue, but at a coquettish distance, through the intermediacy of the feather. The more obvious it is made that it is really the tongue that is directing the swinging motions of the feather, on the swivel-point of the notch between the front teeth or lips where it is held, the more amusing such tickling becomes, and the more laughter it creates.

Not too long a feather should be used, as the leverage required of the tongue becomes too great if a very long feather, such as the oft-mentioned peacock's tail-feather (the erectile organ of the fowl) is employed. Actually, the penis can be very handsomely tickled and caressed by nothing more exotic, nor far to seek, than the woman's own long hair or nipples, simply by her moving her head and shoulders swayingly from side to side. This is really the most natural and romantic way, and is often used as the first gesture in fellation – other than the suggestive promise of touching one's own half-open lips with the tongue-tip, at top and bottom or in figure-eights – by sophisticated and imaginative women.

It is rather far, yet only a step, from such simple and natural methods to the elaborate tickling of the man's frænum with a violin bow, handled by a voluptuous woman, as shown in the drawing "*Andante con fantasia*" in the rococo series, *Fleurettens Purpurschnecke* (1905) by Franz von Bayros, showing the man falling backward with his eyes shut and fingers clutching, in mannered ecstasy. Actually to be effective, this would require a good deal of rosin on the bow, and might not be very pleasant at all. The same is true of an even more complicated sexual mechanism or *succedaneum technologicum*, reported as used in China in combination with fellation, but probably only an elaborate joke. (Something very like it also appears in one of the grotesque paintings of the sixteenth-century Flemish master, Hieronymous Bosch.) In this, the man who is being fellated from below, while on his hands and knees, has introduced into his anus a sort of wide-mouthed wooden funnel, across the open end of which are strung several fiddle-strings, or a woman's pubic hairs, the whole being played with a bow or plucked with the teeth. The instrument is called a "Swinette." As anyone who has ever heard Chinese music can understand, this would be more excruciating than enjoyable.

Except for such musica exotica and other baroque coadjuvants, nothing of this is really new, and many more details as to fellation and its permutations will be found in some of the principal poetic collections of antiquity, such as the *Greek Anthology*, the *Priapeia*, and the Roman satirists, Martial in particular. The beautiful and astonishing Peruvian erotic pottery of the Mochica cultures, dating from about the first century A.D., and showing all the known sexual acts with great humor and fantasy, represent with particular frequency both pedication (anal intercourse) and a form of fellation in which the man is lying on his side, his legs tangled with those of the woman, who is also on her side facing him, and who is clearly being dominated by the grip of the man's hands on her head. This is even more clear in the vases showing oragenital acts with the man standing over the kneeling or sitting oral partner. See the vases illustrated in color in Dr. Rafael Larco-Hoyle's magistral study of the Peruvian erotic art, *Checan* (Love!), published in both French and English versions by Éditions Nagel in Geneva, 1965, plates 30–33 and 133–135. These materials show clearly that the Peruvians thought of oragenital acts involving the penis as a domination of the oral partner, and not as an erotic maneuvre with the oral partner dominant. The action should really therefore be considered *irrumation*, not fellation, a difference that will be made more precise in the section, "Irrumation," following.

This includes all positions in which the genital partner is clearly dominant in oragenital acts involving the penis and the mouth. For it is obvious that in a position in which, for example, the man is on all-fours, kneeling over the woman who is lying supine on her back, it does not in any way diminish his dominance over her if his phallic entry and thrusting are made orally rather than into her vagina. Just as the woman would assist him vaginally – one assumes – with motions of her hips, both back & forth to meet his strokes and in circles to grind against him, and with purposeful vaginal contractions at the deepest point of each stroke; just so the woman lying beneath the man whose entrance is made orally will assist him with whatever motions she can of her lips, tongue, cheeks, head, and even her torso. But this does not in any way take over the directing of the action from him, when he lies, sits, or stands above her; and all such positions for oragenitalism are therefore grouped in the section following, as irrumation.

Mixed positions also exist, in which it is difficult to know which party is dominant. Fellation being the easiest of all sexual acts – except for mutual masturbation – to engage in almost without preamble, or in cramped quarters; some very unlikely locales are sometimes employed, whether at the man's desire or the woman's. For instance, in adjoining theatre-seats in the dark, in a telephone-booth or other semi-public place, or even in a toilet-compartment! Most famous, nowadays, and most dangerous of all such unexpected places, is the masturbating or fellating of a man in an automobile . . . while he is driving at high speed. At one time it was possible for the woman to curl at the man's feet to do this, though there is now the added difficulty, in the fake-virile "sports cars" in which the man actually imagines himself as *becoming the automobile*, or it as being his motorized penis;

that the passengers may be kept purposely alienated and separate, as though in two buckets, by a massive gear-box — really a hollow shelf — between the two front seats: a separation now generally furbished with knobs, gadgets, coffee and liquor-dispensers, as well as an electric clock, shaving machine (with suggestively foaming cream), radio-telephone and bootleg television.

Obviously, it is difficult for any woman, even the most passionate, to lean conveniently — let alone passionately — over such hurdles, to fellate the would-be sport in the driver's seat, who may also be drunk or high on the latest drugs while they hurtle through the dark. *Cool!* Nevertheless, this is still occasionally achieved, though the folklore insists that the man will then usually lose control of the car at his orgasm, and both partners will be killed in the wreck, sometimes with extravagant mutilations only possible during fellation. The revenge of the *vagina dentata.*

This is clearly a modern dream-version of the Love-Death of *Tristan & Isolde,* or perhaps the even cruder and more ancient Scandinavian form, in which the dying hero requires that his horse (in this case the automobile, not the woman) also be sacrificed on his grave. Love and sex being the opposite of death, and, in fact, nature's riposte and reply to death, most normal and sensible people do not require the sick masochistic fillip of mortal danger and sudden death to attune them properly to their sexual lives, and prefer to engage erotically with each other on the ground or in bed, where this can also be done much better. When it seems absolutely necessary to have sexual relations of any kind in a moving vehicle, such as an automobile, airplane, spaceship, Ferris-wheel, or hovercraft, it is wise to have someone else do the driving.

III
IRRUMATION

ORAGENITALISM

III. IRRUMATION

THE ESSENTIAL passivity of the man during fellation is both its greatest charm to a certain kind of man, and its most undesirable quality to the more virile. The "Practical Treatise" preceding has made very clear the extreme bent toward sexual passivity that many men feel, which finds its fullest expression in coitus with the man lying on his back and the woman kneeling above him, or in fellation by the active and even dominant woman. This feature of fellation is taken to the point of absurdity in the notorious "medical chair" of a famous Paris brothel of the 1900's, stated to have been kept specially for use by the then Prince of Wales, in which a semicircular hole is cut in the seat – rather like the childbirth stool of primitive races – so that the woman fellating the Prince could kneel comfortably on the carpeted floor between his legs, despite his protuberant abdomen. This must have served for more than one overstuffed statesman, since there is a very persistent tradition that the President of the French Republic, Félix Faure, died suddenly in 1899 in this same Paris brothel, of a heart-attack, while being fellated. The "medical chair," or sexual mechanism itself, halfway between torture-chamber furniture and Victorian high-*kitsch*, was displayed publicly some years later at the auction-sale of the furnishings of the brothel in question, when legal prostitution was outlawed in France by the Marthe Richard law after World War II, and a photograph of it *in situ* has been published.

A far nobler expression of this same passivity, and centuries more ancient, is to be seen in the *Papyrus Ani* of the Egyptian *Book of the Dead*, in which the goddess Isis is shown kneeling before the mummified god, Osiris – supported by the jackal-headed god of the dead, Anubis – resuscitating him from death by means of fellation: the classic identification of impotence or castration as the equivalent of death. (Reproduced in Giuseppe Lo Duca's *Dictionnaire de Sexologie*, Paris, 1962, vol. I: at page 160, article "Fellatio.") According to the Egyptian myth, Osiris had been killed and dismembered by his brother and enemy, the demonic Typhon or Set, representing the sea. Isis has found thirteen of the parts of Osiris' body, but he cannot be brought back to life until the final part, which is the sacred penis, is also found, and is restored to his body in erect or living form, as the key of life. While there are probably few readers whose religion extends to believing, still, in the myth of Isis and Osiris – in which, in any case, Isis' ability to find the missing penis at all is very suspect: could she have hidden it herself? – the message of male sexual passivity under the ministering lips of the female goddess in the late Egyptian matriarchate is unmistakable.

As is well known, nursemaids and often young mothers in many cultures – including our own – will suck the penis of boy babies in their care, on the excuse that this quiets the child when crying, or with the frank idea of "strengthening" the immature organ, which, in fact, it will not do. Actually, the fellation of infants is really intended to satisfy the oral urges of the maid or mother, and not the genital needs or emotional calming of the infant, and must be considered simply a form of erotic domination. When this is continued to an age where the boy-child can actually remember such incidents or habits (anywhere after his second year), an abnormal propensity toward sexual subservience and masochism with regard to women is likely to develop later, along with a confusion between urination and sex. This is all the more certain in that women who will not hesitate to express their sexual domineering in this usually-taboo way on an infant, are very likely to continue their domineering by other, less overtly sexual, methods and tactics all through the child's early life and adolescence, until he finally manages to get away from home – if ever.

Childhood experimentation with the sexual organs of one's own and one's siblings' or little friends' bodies, of either sex, is obviously a harmless and necessary part of growing up and of "testing reality." It is a kind of spontaneous sexual education, and in many ways the *best* kind, to which only dangerous prudes could object, whether achieved by oral, anal, or eventually genital means, as the child develops through these progressive stages. But as to the seduction of children by adults, the moral position on fellation should really be, as with all other sexual acts, the simple sporting principle: "*Pick on somebody your own size!*" It is essential that the modern recognition of the sexual rights of children should not become a protective cover for perverted scoutmasters and oral-neurotic mothers, nor end up as mere propaganda for the "right" of adults to seduce infants, to exploit children, and to prostitute adolescents, heterosexually or otherwise, and thus fixate them neurotically on parent-figures for life. It is not "modern parenthood" to masturbate or fellate one's own children, on the excuse of strengthening their penises or making sure that their foreskins don't bind. Let them find playmates of their own to do this. *Pick on somebody your own size!*

The normal adult male will generally enjoy fellation being performed on him by a woman, as part of their love-play and as a preliminary to intercourse, but it is seldom his preferred method for reaching orgasm. It is also much less likely to excite his imagination erotically in the way that he is excited by, and powerfully attracted to, performing cunnilinctus on the woman – an attraction he shares with all male animals of the mammalian order, almost all of whom approach the female first with their nose and tongue. This is also true of all the higher apes, who cannot be presumed to be held to naso-oral sexual preliminaries by the inconvenience of having clawed paws or hooves instead of hands.

It is the visible and palpable difference, that in cunnilinctus the male is active rather than passive, while in fellation he is passive rather than active, that makes fellation only a sort of second string to the erotic bow, for most normal men, nor is actual fellation common among other mammals. In fact, it is also not common for the females to make the physical overtures to the males, and those who do – certainly among human beings – are not often psychologically desirable partners, and will generally be found to be rotted with hatred of the male and with jealousy of both his genital organs and his sexual prerogatives. Normal men do not ever search compulsively for fellation, in the way that they often deeply desire cunnilinctus, and the author of the "Practical Treatise," preceding, is judged by that fact. On the other hand, normal men also do not react with anger or horror if the woman feels the urge toward performing fellation, and will often ask her to do so during erotic foreplay. This is seldom enjoyed by the man after intercourse is completed, when women will sometimes wish at least to kiss the penis or lick up the remaining drops or traces of the semen on the glans, in a spontaneous gesture of gratitude and adoration of the male principle. To the normal man, ordinary fellation is a pleasant sexual preliminary or caress, but it will not compare with vaginal intercourse for the creation of a powerful orgasm in him, since it goes entirely counter to the unconscious virile urge to be *active and penetrating* in the sexual act, matching the normal female urge to be sexually *passive and receptive:* the man rapid and violent, the woman slow and accepting.

It is an important biological principle and erotic rule, never to be overlooked or lost sight of, that basically *the male is excited by* WHAT HE DOES *to the female, not by what the female does to him; while the female is excited by* WHAT THE MALE DOES TO HER, *not by what she does to him.* These predispositions obviously match, and are true of mouth-kissing, caressing of the limbs and body, pressing of the breasts and buttocks, and direct approaches to the genitals, both manually, orally, and with the penis. They are equally true of general and powerful *hugging*, which is really a sort of pre-coital dominating of the female's body by that of the male, with more than a hint of rape. Women who are normal are thrilled by being strongly embraced and held helplessly in the arms of a man to whom they are attracted, and enjoy pretending that they are being dragged off by a cave-man and being *forced* to do what they want to do very much. They don't really want to be forced, but the idea excites them. And women are likely to close their eyes, when the man goes on to a more intimate exploration of their bodies with his own, and to feel – like the sweet old lady explaining to the young girl what to expect on her wedding-night – "*It's all beautiful, beautiful, beautiful!*"

That is not the way a man feels at all, and his perfectly normal approach to the woman he wants to make love to may partake of an extremely powerful psychological undercurrent of wanting sadistically to dominate and overwhelm her, even to hurt her – nor will she often object. Women sometimes waste a good deal of their erotic activity and attention in trying to caress a man's body or genitals in trick ways they think will excite him specially, while he is simultaneously caressing them. Actually, this tends to siphon off much of the psychological concentration which the woman would better spend on feeling and enjoying intensely what is happening to her, and thus preparing herself for intercourse and orgasm. As has already been observed, orgasm cannot be achieved at all without, first, a *relaxation* of the nerves and body, and particularly of the repressions, so that excitement can take place, and second, the creation of the most extreme possible *tension*, both physical and psychic, of which orgasm is the final dissolving or explosion.

No real man wants a woman to bear-hug him, nor to lie on top during anything from a kiss to total intercourse, except as an occasional amusing changeover – a sort of Slave Rebellion or Feast of Fools, if the truth is to be told, similar to the exchanging of clothes and sexual privileges at Hallowe'en, Twelfth Night, or Carnival – and not always then. The most virile men and womanly women never feel the slightest urge toward any such transvestism or swapping of sexes, an activity principally attractive to the half-sexed creatures surrounding us nowadays, who do not themselves know whether they are women or men, as their interchanged hairstyles and clothing are intended to show.

Feminist propagandists do not like being reminded of the basic biological predispositions and natural sexual rôles, in their urge to castrate men and reduce them to impotence under the banner of "sexual equality" (except when it comes to paying the bills). And they greet with squeals of delight the tendentious statistical frauds and veiled propaganda for homosexuality of such outrageous fakers as the late Professor Alfred Kinsey, and other con-men, who would reduce "male" and "female" to sliding and indefinable graph-points or a one-to-ten scale, of which the real intention is to sneak across the idea that everybody is *really* homosexual – which is fortunately false. Meanwhile the visible and unchangeable matching functions of the penetrating penis and the ensheathing vagina, throughout the mammalian order, leave absolutely no doubt as to what are the biologically true and natural sexual characters of male and female, in a state of physical and psychological health.

"Irrumation" is a classical Latin term, meaning "to give suck, as a mother gives the breast," which I revived and clarified in the first edition of the present monograph, and introduced to sexology in my glossary, "The Slang of Homosexuality": a supplement to Dr. George Henry's *Sex Variants* (New York: Hoeber, 1941), omitted pudibundly in later reprints. The term is very common in the poetry of the Roman sexual satirists, such as Martial, where *irrumation*, as the action of the dominant genital partner in oral sexuality involving the penis, is carefully distinguished from *fellation*, as the action of the dominant oral partner. To the Romans, the irrumator was considered powerfully male; the fellator – especially if himself a man – obviously homosexual. The whole question of whether any given oragenital act involving the penis is, in fact, irrumation or fellation, turns entirely on the crucial point – essentially psychological rather than physical – *which partner is dominant and active, and which partner is passive and receptive?* Where the genital partner is dominant, the action is irrumation. Where the oral partner is dominant, it is fellation.

As can be seen from the considerations just above, as to the natural sexual rôles of men and women, this really amounts to deciding which partner in oragenitalism is acting the male part, and which the female. A large element in the uneasiness that many men feel about being fellated, and their distrust or even hatred of the too-willing or compulsive fellator — whether male or female — derives from the almost-conscious assessment that, in being passively fellated by an active oral partner, they are giving up the normal male rôle, and are therefore somehow being "castrated" emotionally, or effeminized, by the fellator. Since, as has been discussed earlier in considering homosexual fellation, this is exactly the unconscious feeling and motivation of the compulsive fellator as well — but from the opposite point of view — the uneasy fear of allowing fellation by such compulsive fellators, as being somehow freighted with danger, is very solidly based in psychological fact. Most men are similarly unwilling to engage in what is otherwise a remarkable erotic combination, in which the man sits astraddle the woman's lap facing her, while she pedicates him with a dildo and fellates him *at the same time*. The reversal of sexes is too clear for comfort.

This is quite similar to the manly code of honor as to cowardice. Men want to survive, in conditions of mortal danger, the urge to survival being biologically anchored. But the more civilized and psychologically-determined that men's background and youthful training becomes, the less likely it is that they will care to survive at the cost of cowardly expedients that would involve giving up their image of themselves as *men*. It was from this code of *machismo*, or "maleness," and its resistance to unmanliness — and with perhaps more than a nod to the oragenital (and anilingual!) implications involved — that the motto of the woman-leader, "La Pasionaria," in the Spanish Revolution of the 1930's took its heroic force: "*It is better to die on your feet than to live on your knees!*" The opposite of the crudely cynical motto now gaining ground in America: "*If you can't lick 'em,* JOIN *'em and cash in!*" which is an obvious adaptation to the current weakly-acceding males of the earlier advice to women: "*When rape is unavoidable, relax and enjoy it.*" What man really wants to "join" and be raped? And in what part of his anatomy is this rape going to take place? Think it over.

From all the foregoing discussion of normal sexual rôles, and of what it really means to be a *man*, it becomes clear that the most natural and satisfactory form of oragenital relations involving the penis is not fellation but irrumation, and that irrumation will also give the deepest possible psychic satisfactions possible in this act to both the man and woman involved. This is all the more true if irrumation is not always continued to the point of the man's orgasm in the woman's mouth, but is used as part of the lovers' ritual, as a partial sexual approach, preceding and finally culminating in vaginal intercourse: the so-called "half-&-half," but undertaken for the exactly opposite reason than that of prostitutes. The same is also true of cunnilinctus, which is most effective as a preliminary to vaginal intercourse, and not as an attempt to bring the woman to her ultimate orgasm by this means.

The psychic satisfactions involved in any sexual act are, for human beings, at least as important as the physical sensations. Many experienced lovers agree, in fact, that it is the psychic factors in sexual excitement that are the most important, and in a way the only ones that are really *exciting* to the imagination. It is these psychic or emotional elements that are being overlooked in the frantic search for some acme or "true summit of sexual sensation," such as the quasi-*flying* motions and tensions of Grien's Method, described at the end of the section on Fellation preceding, where even the physical sexual satisfaction of the woman is also completely overlooked. In irrumation, the man will find himself acting the part of a man, being active and penetrating, not passive and engulphed; and the woman will be excited by being dominated and penetrated – *by what the man is doing to her*, as already discussed, rather than trying to find her excitement, as she seldom will, in *what she is doing to the man*, in the merely maternal pleasure she is giving him by means of her oral manipulations, only to have him finally arrive at his orgasm without her!

The man should not hesitate to be rough and demanding in irrumation, though it is most unwise to build up the habit of doing this *verbally:* insulting and dominating the woman sadistically, or insisting with curses and insults that she "go down on" the man's penis. That is not a love-act. It is not even something a woman can perhaps enjoy as "oral rape." It is a coprolalic charade of hatred, disguising itself as an act of love, and is to be avoided. The man's maleness and roughness should express themselves, instead, by a self-assured physical (rather than verbal) insistence, pressing the woman on the back of her head or neck, or even taking her by the ears or hair – without actually hurting her – and pushing her head down to the penis, to indicate to her what she is to do.

If words seem necessary, one will get a lot farther with any woman with a decent amount of self-respect, by such firm but endearing demands or invitations as "Take it!" or "Kiss it, sweetheart!" than by obscene insults in which the woman is made to understand that she is being asked or forced to do something that the man himself feels will soil and degrade her as a human being, and reduce her to dirt. There is also the matter of the woman's urges toward *revenge*, if the action is all one of sex-hatred, as will be seen. A woman fellating a man can, at all times, inflict terrible damage upon him. The male rôle of domination should not be over-emphasized either physically or verbally to the point where she is tempted to do just that.

Possible positions for irrumation will be discussed more in detail at the end of the present paragraph and section. What is being emphasized here is, rather, the expression of active and passive rôles, for the man and woman respectively, by the choice of position. The man can, at all events, so arrange his body that, if not actually over the woman, at least he is not lying passively on the flat of his back while she kneels or crouches over or above him, ministering to his erotic needs as though he were a baby having his diapers changed. The positions of choice in irrumation are those in which the man stands or leans against some object, indoors or out-of-doors, while the woman kneels (or sits on some low support such as a hassock or fence) before him; or in which the man kneels while the woman sits or lies before him on the bed or ground, either on her back or on her belly, in a way emotionally reminiscent, to both partners, of vaginal intercourse. Even if the man must – owing to the location, such as on a sofa or in a parked automobile – be sitting or lying down, he can turn somewhat on his side, and rise as high as possible, so that his penis enters the woman's mouth from a sidewise position or from above, rather than require her to bring her mouth down upon it from on top.

It may seem that too much insistence is being made here on the status-symbol of physical position – top & bottom; high & low – but that is precisely the point about irrumation, and the real difference between its male-dominant character and the male-passive character accepted in fellation. The man should also not lose his dominant position at any time during the action, and should in particular pay very little attention to the woman's possible objections that he is "too big" (which may just be intended as a compliment), or that he should go slower, etc. Resistances of this kind are biologically-toned, and are intended to be overcome, at the risk of the man's losing the sexual respect of any woman to whose delaying or objecting tactics he accedes, which would mean turning the dominance in the situation (and in their relationship) over to her. Many women, especially nowadays, seem to want to dominate the man in just this way. Those who really do want this are to be avoided. The others are just teasing and testing the man, and are willing – even aching – to be mastered sexually.

There is an important difference between being firm and manly, and being brutal and unpleasant, especially in sex. Every man must learn to walk the narrow line between the two in his own way. Many men never learn, just as many women never learn the difference between being sexually complaisant, as is their biological heritage; and charmingly feminine, as is their civilized right; and being damn fools and doormats, laying down to be walked on by some cruel and pre-psychotic sadist who is looking for a matchingly masochistic wife or victim. This problem, which is essentially that of the *limits* to which male dominance and female acceptance can be pressed without becoming unpleasant or abnormal, often arises in ordinary intercourse as well as oral, especially during seductions and on wedding-nights.

It may be stated as axiomatic that *it is much better, for both partners, for the man to err on the side of too much violence and virility, in all sexual situations* – whether social, vaginal, or oral, or simply in struggling for a kiss – than to show himself too cautious and too politely considerate. All female mammals, from lionesses on down, know how to back up to, and piss upon males who do not show themselves sufficiently male in the sexual encounter. This is not a joke but a fact. Women may not express themselves in such simple pantomimes, but their real emotions are generally identical. The standard "marriage manuals" take the opposite point of view about all this, I know; but they are wrong. Terribly wrong, and intent on brainwashing their male readers. Truth to tell, a woman who will angrily refuse or sulkily spoil a man's further sexual company, on the grounds that he seduced her a little too roughly (or tore a hole in her stockings, or mussed her hair!) possibly on their own wedding-night or similar, is the type of reclamatory bitch that *any* man is better off without. Conversely, no woman worthy of the name really wants as sexual consort a man who treats her in bed as though he were a white-clad anæsthetician with an ether-mask, trying to slip it to her so delicately that she will not know whether she has been made love to or has made *pipi*. Sex is, or should be, a matter of male penetration and female ensheathing: of violence and acceptance, of sweat and semen, of tangled limbs and hair. It is worthless when it is anything less, when it is really just masturbation *à deux*.

Irrumation has its greatest value, perhaps, as an expression of male dominance in the sexual situation, quite aside from the sexual pleasure the man expects in the act, and which the woman may very well share. A woman should, of course, be free to take an intramural sexual holiday whenever she wants it — a sort of exchange of sexual clothing during Carnival — by such reversals as lying on top of the man during intercourse, or fellating him in as dominant or maternal a way as she may wish. ("Maternal" in the sense of ministering to his sexual needs, while he remains passive and a child.) But the whole intention of the present paragraphs is to indicate that it *is not wise* for what should be an occasional holiday of reversed sexual rôles to become the lovers' habitual ritual. If this happens, they seriously risk losing each other's sexual respect and confidence. Or else they may be suspected of simply expressing in this way, in what is only an erotic charade, their underlying and matching neuroses or their hopeless immaturity. An encapturing — as has already been noted in connection with cunnilinctus — of what may be considered the normal oral-erotic body kisses or foreplay of the mammalian sexual approach, often to serve very ugly neurotic needs.

Any insistence, for example, on the urinary function of the sex organs during oragenitalism (the so-called "Golden Shower" of urine-fetichists), or on protracted anilinctus — whether active or passive, and whether or not this continues to its obvious perverted extreme, either in fantasy or in fact — can certainly be considered such a neurotic encapturing, and should be firmly rejected and refused, along with the partner having such tastes. Children are occasionally known, in honest ignorance of the real mechanism of sexual intercourse and its various adjuncts, to attempt to urinate on each other's bodies (often reciprocally), as a quasi-sexual game, or even into each other's mouths. This is more likely an innocent blunder or experiment, than premature vice or an attempted degrading of the other child. But such physiological ignorance — and certainly any such attempted degrading — is neither acceptable nor desirable in adults. Not even once, "Just for fun!" In sex, as in everything else, there are limits, and it is important to have the intelligence and character to know where to draw the line, whether drunk, drugged, or cold sober. It should be unnecessary to add that the attempted combination of oragenital acts with flagellation or other sadistic perversions is extremely dangerous, both physically and emotionally, and that persons habitually attempting such combinations generally end — and belong — in jail.

The woman's possible hostility against, or her biting or scratching of, the man's genitals during irrumation may simply be commensurate with some excess of violence in his domination of her at that time. Or it may be (and usually is) an expression of her general hostility toward him, and her envy of men and of male prerogatives, culminating in her desire — unconsciously felt, or perhaps consciously repressed — to bite off the man's penis and keep it for herself. This unspoken urge is very common in the sexual relations with men of girls and women who are really or unconsciously Lesbians, and who therefore refuse vaginal intercourse, usually on some excuse of birth-control, "convenience," necessary haste, or the like. During actual *oral rape* of a woman by a man (and sometimes of one man by another, as in prisons, or in homosexual sado-masochistic situations), the orally-raped individual seldom responds by biting the penis of the irrumator, who may be very much on the alert against this defense, and may warn the other person that any such attempt will be met by tearing at the hair, beating of the head, or choking. The victim of oral rape is more likely, therefore, to respond with the gesture that is the exact opposite of biting: holding the mouth so far open that there is no oral friction of the lips and inside of the cheeks to bring the rapist to orgasm.

Intimidation of the oral partner in irrumation is actually more common than would appear likely, and it is here that what are merely male gestures of normal domination of the female, in the usual sexual situation, become nothing other than oral rape. This is also a common form of homosexual ordeal or initiation, as in fraternities, armies, prisons, and juvenile gangs. It is of ancient lineage, being known throughout the Middle East and having been brought to Europe at least by the time of the Knights Templars, in their secret initiations during the thirteenth century, as I discuss in *The Guilt of the Templars* (1966) Part XII. The most extreme form of such intimidation or oral rape does not involve irrumating the victim against his or her will. Rather it consists of forcing the victim to perform active fellation, which also thus involves a crushing of the victim's will and integrity. I myself know of an informal teen-age gang, in Queens, New York, not too long ago, which "elected" a pretty young girl to the group without her knowledge or consent, had her decoyed into an automobile by another girl, in broad daylight in the corner of a public park on Christmas Eve, and there forced her to give a "blow job" to the leader of the group, mocking her meanwhile for being inexpert. Stories like this are common and are authentic, and the victims generally bear the traumatic wounds for life.

As to who is the victim and who is the rapist, in oral rape, things are not always as might be imagined. Dr. Eugene Schoenfeld, a young California physician imitating the late Albert Schweitzer and Father Damien, by bringing his medical knowledge and advice to the drug-addicted American "hippies" in the new Molokai or lepers' colony of the so-called Underground Press, has published two perfectly extraordinary letters (in his "Dr. Hippocrates" column in the *Los Angeles Free Press*, October 18th, 1968, page 29), both from erotically-minded young men who can, at best, only be called naïve. One of them – whose account must be read to be believed; and even then! – allowed his girl-friend, as a prelude to intercourse, to *cut a hole* in his scrotum with her fingernail-clippers, and to fill the scrotum with air by blowing through a plastic straw, then closing up the hole with a piece of adhesive tape to keep the air in; later practically cauterizing the hole with alcohol. (As can be seen, this particular sadist came with her paraphernalia all prepared . . . Most of them do.) The other young man, who is in no doubt as to his own masochism, writes:

> Dear Dr. Hippocrates:
>
> My girl friend was experimenting and blew a large quantity of air into my urethra. Well, she says it feels great to her to feel that balloon strike bottom. I do get a thrill from it, albeit a masochistic one because, God, it hurts. Can this form of fun in any way injure me?
>
> Write soon, cause I don't want to stop unless it might really hurt me.

In giving these kooky communications far greater publicity, in the national Underground Press, than the present modest monograph need expect or fear, Dr. Schoenfeld was attempting very rightly to put a stop to such lunatic sadistic practices. He notes:

> I hesitated for a long time before deciding to print the above letters about very literal "blow" jobs. They appear in print only to point out that pleasurable sensations should be weighed against potential dangers. [*A discussion follows of the danger in the use of drugs, such as amphetamine and heroin, ending:*] Nineteen known deaths have been caused in the last year by inhalation of freon gases from glass chiller ærosol cans. [*What next?*]
>
> If any readers doubt that the practices mentioned in the letters are harmful, I should point out firstly that more bacteria exist in the mouth than in any other body orifice. Our skin is a natural barrier to bacteria and other micro-organisms which are not nomally found in the bladder or scrotum. Infections of the bladder (cystitis) may continue up the urethra to the kidneys. Infections of the scrotum? Not a pleasant prospect. Even more dangerous is the possibility of an air embolism. Air forced into a closed tissue space may enter the blood stream, go to the heart, lungs or brain, and cause sudden death or a stroke.

(Dr. Schoenfeld has already been quoted, earlier, as to precisely such sudden death caused by blowing air into a woman's vagina, when she "had just stopped menstruating and her vascular system was therefore directly vulnerable.")

The hostilities aroused in the woman during irrumation — if, in fact, she does not actually enjoy the man's passionate domination of her – are seldom so repellent and horrible as the two "literal blow jobs" just cited. Observe in both of these that their particular vengefulness rises specifically from the unknown "girl-friends'" attempting to turn the tables on the man during oragenital acts, and *to blow something into the man's body*, via their mouths, rather than accept that something should be intruded or ejaculated into them. In a far milder resistance to oragenital domination, it happened to me in Paris, in 1955, to mention to a young Dutch-Sumatran girl very proud of her erotic abilities and independence, that the Latin satirists often observed that the oral partner in fellation *cannot speak;* the Latin slang term *tacere* (to be silent) therefore being applied to the act. She responded, without even a moment's thought, by HUMMING the opening bars of Strauss' "Beautiful Blue Danube" (a kitsch-plagiarism of the opening of the slow movement of Mozart's first Flute Concerto, K.313).

This response to the idea of enforced silence during fellation was certainly original with this girl, yet it must often have been invented by others spontaneously, since even nursing babies can be observed to hum and mumble while their mouths are fastened to the teat. More folklore, perhaps, than fact, in the *Berkeley Barb*, December 22nd, 1967, Dr. Schoenfeld quotes a letter from an unnamed reader calling fellation in this way a "hum-job." In an attempted topper (in *Dear Dr. Hip-pocrates*, 1968, page 14), another correspondent re-invents the fellatory "Flutterblast" earlier described in the "Practical Treatise on Fellation," above, calling it a "Razzberry job," and noting that: "It is similar to the 'Hum-job' . . . it is important to maintain good contact while 'razzing,' so that the vibrations are not all lost to the air." Babies also adore this when done to them on their bellies or midriff.

Obviously relevant at this point is the very well-known joke, taking the idea to the *n*th degree, in which *A sybaritic millionaire or Indian prince offers a thousand dollars in a brothel for a girl who must be beautiful, blonde, no more than five feet, two inches tall, and able to fellate him while standing on her head and* humming *the coloratura air, "Listen to the Mocking-Bird," at the same time. The girl becomes confused by the multiplicity of the demands on her, stops completely just at the man's orgasm, and explains that she has forgotten the next few notes. "Fake it!" the man screams; "Improvise!"* Note here that it is the girl's silence itself that is her hostile riposte.

I have also encountered this trick of the woman's stopping during fellation, when the man least wants her to stop, with the explanation that a *hair* (his or hers?) had got into her mouth. Actually, it is much more common for the man to find after fellation that there are hairs of the woman's head – especially if she wears her hair long – tangled into his pubic hair. This is a standard guilty evidence of "cheating" on the part of married men, if the mistress' hair is not the same color as that of the wife, on the style of unexplainable lipstick-stains on the husband's shirt – or underwear. Such traces are sometimes left purposely by the mistress, in order to hurt and embarrass both the husband and wife. A similar trick is the leaving of a single hairpin of the mistress' hair-color mixed in with the wife's hairpins (if of a different color), when the mistress has been smuggled into the man's home during his wife's absence.

One degenerate female harpy encountered in recent years – the secretary to the head of the philosophy department in a California university, and herself an aging divorcée – would assure any man who made sexual approaches to her that she had "nothing to give," which was only too true; but, if the man did *not* make approaches to her, she would curl up seductively on the floor at his feet, when in private, and insist unexpectedly on fellating him while both remained fully dressed. When she had brought the man to ejaculation in her mouth, she would suddenly *spit the semen* virulently on the fly of his trousers, and hiss: "Now let's see you explain THAT to your wife!" A visiting professor who had been apprised of her tricks, and came prepared, simply pulled out an extra pair of pants from his brief-case, changed, bowed, and spat back at her with a polite smile.

Another such harpy, but this one young and heartbreakingly beautiful, told as positively true an obvious wish-fulfillment folktale or fantasy concerning *A girl's revenge on the detective who had sent her gangster-brother to jail, by having a protracted affair with him, ending one Sunday afternoon, after fellating the detective in his apartment, by stabbing into his glans penis the tip of a burning cigarette she had left in an ashtray nearby; his foreskin then being drawn up over the glans and cigarette together by her long and evil fingers* [sic], *and the girl rising to her feet and leaving the apartment before the man was even able to scream!* Though obviously folklore and not fact, note well that these are the fantasies some people have, and the games they would play if they dared. YOU HAVE BEEN WARNED.

The usual expression of female hostility to the man, in connection with fellation or irrumation, is not in such extremes as the biting or burning of the penis, nor in fantasies to this effect, nor in exotic practices – such as those, earlier, with fingernail-clippers and drinking-straws! – adding up to the classic *vagina dentata* or "toothed vagina" motif in folklore. The usual expression of such hostility, even in fellation undertaken of the fellator's own presumable free will, is in the matter of the disposition of the ejaculated semen. In order to see this in full perspective, it is necessary to consider again the actual physiological technique of the man's arriving at orgasm and ejaculation during oragenital acts, particularly during irrumation. This is not as simple as it might seem.

The point has already been made that a very definite amount of *emotional release*, coupled with and followed by *physical tension*, is necessary before most men (or women) can come to orgasm at all. It is for this reason that the anonymous French author of the "Practical Treatise on Fellation," translated above, who is so visibly anxious to get every *centime's* worth from the prostitutes he was obviously accustomed to frequent, insists so absurdly that the man should never be under any tension at all during fellation, and that his orgasm is to be brought on strictly by the fellator's oral ministrations, while the "client" remains entirely passive: that is to say, takes as long about the matter as possible. From the exactly opposite point of view, of searching for the "ultimate orgasm," it is for the same reason that Grien's Method, described toward the end of the section on Fellation, involves and demands the man's increasing his physical tension almost to the breaking point, by chinning himself on a horizontal bar during fellation by the woman rocking in a chair below. Whether this is or is not the "ultimate orgasm," it is certainly on the right track – physically at least.

In irrumation, as differentiated from fellation, the amount of physical tension the man can develop, and thus the speed or slowness and the satisfyingness with which he reaches his orgasm, largely depends on the physical position he takes. It is assumed that, in irrumation, the man is active and to some degree physically *over* the woman or her head, just as, in fellation, it is assumed that he is passive and to some degree physically *under* her body or head. There is thus little possibility of physical tension for the man, during fellation, unless he is standing or in some other strained position not usually taken, such as kneeling while leaning or arching backward to rest his weight on his hands against a wall or pillow. *Les Paradis Charnels* (1903), as the next-to-last of its "136 Extases de la Volupté," has the man assume the gymnastic pose called "The Wrestler's Bridge," pressing his body face-up from the floor or bed with his hands and feet, to create the most extreme tension and sensation while being fellated. At orgasm, this "human bridge" collapses, but in fact a man being fellated while lying on his back will often arch himself up into a low wrestler's bridge just at orgasm, to increase his tension and pleasure, and can easily hold himself thus by jamming his fists under his waist.

Most of the positions the woman can take in cunnilinctus can also be taken by the man being fellated, and for this reason no special discussion of positions for fellation has been made, the reader being referred instead to the final section on Cunnilinctus. The passivity of the man is in general so great, during fellation, that even that classic position for the woman in coitus or cunnilinctus may be used, where the genital partner lies on his-or-her back with the legs uplifted and bent back at the hips, the knees being pressed down toward the chest by the arm of the oral partner, who may also be capturing both of the other's feet (held sole-to-sole) with one hand. In this position, just as the woman's vulva – when the action is cunnilinctus – is wholly lifted and exposed to the man's oral caresses (or to his phallic penetration, if he prefers); just so – when the action is fellation – the man's erect penis and testicles appear between and *below* his uplifted legs, and are there accepted orally by the woman. Passivity can hardly be taken further than this.

In irrumation, to the contrary, the man will almost invariably be pressing himself tensely against the woman's head and mouth, and driving his penis in & out by his own effort, precisely as in vaginal coitus (except not quite so violently). The woman remains passive to a degree, assisting him with the soft, sucking surfaces of her lips, tongue, and the inside of her cheeks as much as she can – sometimes also with her hands – but without actually making any except reciprocating motions with her head. Her head is also likely to be immobilized, flat against a pillow, or vertical against the head-rest of a chair, sofa, or car-seat – even against a wall, but in this case the man should gallantly place one or both of his hands behind her head, with the palm cupping her hair, so as to take the "strike" of the wall against the back of his hand, and also to show him how much to temper the violence of his stroke. For it is only the emotional feeling and physical semblance of domination of the woman by the man that is desired – as much in irrumation as in vaginal intercourse. The man is not really raping the woman, at any rate not as an habitual act.

In irrumation, in particular, the overmastering of the woman should not be allowed to become more than she can bear, and slight pauses between the in-driving strokes by the man will usually make it easier for her to accept even his most violent thrusts. Both parties must bear somewhere in mind that they are engaging in a love-act, and not in a charade of violence. Their responses must therefore be suitably cushioned against actually harming each other: the man against harming the woman's mouth with his penis and the thrust of his pelvic bone over the pubis; the woman against harming the man's penis with her fingers or teeth.

A very simple method of preventing the thrusts of the man's penis from hurting the woman's mouth or choking her, is for the woman (or the man himself) to wrap one hand around the penis, allowing only a reasonable amount to enter at every thrust. This is almost obligatory during irrumation when the penis is very long, as otherwise the strike of the head of the penis against the back of the woman's palate at every stroke will often cause a gagging-reflex, though this is much diminished when the woman is very excited sexually, by the whole act and by the man's violence and his visible passion which the woman realizes she has aroused.

This holding or fisting of the penis during irrumation — as also during fellation — develops naturally enough from motions of helping the man to his erection, if necessary, by masturbatory gestures at the beginning of the oral act. The author of the "Practical Treatise," above, expresses himself as very contemptuous of such manual assists, but they are often an assistance indeed, especially when the man feels any nervousness. The hand which has helped the penis to erection at the beginning of the oral act, by any of the usual titillations of moistened palm or fingertips, is then simply left in place throughout the act, the fist forming a sort of "sword-guard" to prevent too deep an entry. If the man feels any shame about the woman's hand helping or holding him in this way, during an act in which he is ostensibly dominating her, he may take pride rather than consolation in the thought that the hand is really necessary to protect the woman from his virile strength and the length of his penis.

In the same way, and for the same reason, the man can also hold his penis in his own fist during oral entry in irrumation, if he is already erect, thus protecting the woman from his thrusts and violence. Whichever of the partners does this, it has the added and very important advantage of striking or causing pressure against the man's mons pubis, by resisting the drive of his hips with the bones and flesh of the enclosing fist. *It is of paramount importance that some simili-coital pressure or striking of this kind be exerted against the pubis,* if the individual is to achieve orgasm easily and profoundly.

This is as true of women as it is of men. *The quality of the orgasm* is the thing! Not the mere fact of arriving at it. Yet, obviously, in irrumation, the woman can hardly accept such violent striking of the man's pubis against her lips and teeth. Pubic pressure or striking of this kind is the normal action for both partners in vaginal intercourse, when violently engaged, the man driving deeply in. His pubis then strikes against the woman's pelvic bones through the flesh and hair of her own pubis, or vulva (or buttocks, in coitus from behind), thus also exciting and gripping her clitoris in face-to-face positions, and in all cases exciting his own passions in a physical way.

This is likewise true during male masturbation, the bottom edge of the hand generally striking the pubis at every stroke. It is for this reason that many men find – though few ever dare say it aloud – that masturbation was (or is!) more satisfactory to them, in *the quality of the orgasm* achieved, than the kind of intercourse they usually engage in, which is often far too mild and of superficial vaginal entry. That is also why the orgasm they achieve in fellation of the very artistic, but wholly lingual and fritillatory kind, is not by any means as physically pleasurable and erotically satisfactory as they had expected, and may instead leave them with a feeling of unsatisfied or incomplete ejaculation: what has been graphically called "pelvic retching."

As it is necessary to have the courage to say – and to do – what is authentic and true, I will add here that the situation sometimes arises where irrumation must be frankly combined with a sort of masturbation of the man. In this, the woman excites the man manually along the shaft of his penis, holding it quite tightly and *striking outward or down against his pubis* at his every irrumatory stroke, while the man, for his part, enters her mouth simultaneously only with his glans and the top half or less of his shaft. At his orgasm in this way the man sometimes will, if he can, tear the woman's hand away, so that he may enter her mouth and upper throat deeply at his final thrust; or the woman may simply have removed her hand from his penis some time before, and is taking it all orally when the man's orgasm comes. There is no question, of course, in such situations, that the woman must be and is willing to swallow the semen at the moment of ejaculation. It is even sometimes the case that the man must masturbate his own penis, generally by means of his moistened palm pumping and rotating on the glans penis, then simply presenting the penis to the woman's vagina or mouth, and pressing inward, when he feels his orgasm approaching.

Both these quasi-masturbatory maneuvres have their use and may be necessary when the woman, for reasons of age or of health – that is to say, for reasons of weakness – actually *cannot* engage in violent intercourse or irrumation, but nevertheless very much wants to "satisfy her man." Such situations are self-evidently pathetic, and the real reason it is necessary for the man to be masturbated in part, whether by the woman or by himself, as a preliminary to ejaculation in her vagina or mouth, is that her physical weakness makes him unable to be sensually excited by her body (as is also the case when the woman is simply a prostitute, or for some other reason unappealing). When the woman in this situation is loved by the man, what he is really trying to do is not so much to arrive at orgasm for his own pleasure, as to prove to the woman, by means of his achieved ejaculation, the truth and validity of *her self-image as a woman*, and to allow her to express and fulfill the love toward him that makes her wish to act out her sexual rôle even at such a time.

Without, perhaps, rising to the tragic intensity of the love-deaths of *Tristan & Isolde* or *Romeo & Juliet*, such moments – which can arrive to anyone, and very unexpectedly, as after an accident, during hurried leave-takings, and especially in old age — are very much like O. Henry's tragic little story about *The man who sells his heirloom-watch to buy his wife the expensive combs she longs to have for her lovely hair, only to find that she has meanwhile cut off and sold her hair to buy him a watch-chain.* Women understand, of course, that no man can have an erection at will, and especially not at moments of crisis or anxiety (though this does seem to excite some simple natures). But women can be just as hurt and just as disappointed, at what is to them this crushing proof of the undesirability and inadequacy of their own bodies — for that is how they unerringly see it — as if the man had purposely rejected them. In the same way, what really hurts a woman in a man's actual impotence is not her sexual starvation, but the insult to her feminity! *Noblesse oblige.* The penis may be mightier than the sword, but the possession of a penis is sometimes more of a problem than a privilege.

The satisfaction of the woman during the man's erotic satisfaction in oragenitalism is fortunately not always a problem. Though cunnilinctus is usually really engaged in for the emotional pleasure of the orally-active party (in this context, the man), it is the woman who receives the specifically genital excitement or satisfaction. In the same way, in fellation, it is also often possible for the supine man to reach *from behind* between the buttocks or thighs of the woman, who is perhaps kneeling over him or sitting at his side, facing his knees, and to titillate her clitoris while she fellates him, so that they both may reach orgasm together or thereabouts. This is seldom possible in the usual postures for irrumation, where the man's head and torso are generally high up over the woman's head, and his hands far from her genitals. Her breasts, however, can usually be reached, the man's hands being turned to face and grip them, and to knead deeply at the base of her nipples.

Two positions for irrumation nevertheless exist in which the woman can be very satisfactorily excited genitally by the man, at the same time, and brought to orgasm. Where the man kneels, with the woman kneeling on all fours on her hands & knees facing him, to fellate him, her head and body being turned somewhat to one side; the man can then bend forward at that same side, over the woman's back, to reach her genitals with his hands. This he can do either by reaching up underneath her body, pausing at her breasts, or down from between her thighs in back; or – if he has long arms – with both hands simultaneously, one from above and behind, and the other from below and in front. He can, in this way, excite her vaginal opening or her clitoris, or both together with his two facing hands, while irrumating her at the same time. The woman can seldom engage in any fellatory motions of her head in this position (though she is, of course, quite free to perform any desired maneuvres of her lips and tongue), for the man's torso and shoulders will generally immobilize her head as he bends over her back to reach her genitals with his hands.

Another position, which is in fact one of the most common for irrumation, is that in which the woman lies back on the bed, or sits up partly with her head supported on a pillow, and the man straddles her chest, with his knees supporting him on the bed just under each of the woman's armpits, while he irrumates her. As the man's arms will be halfway up the head of the bed or against the wall, supporting his torso (or he may be pressing against the head of the bed with his chest and shoulders), he cannot reach the woman's genitals with his hands. However, without disturbing the support of his knees under the woman's armpits, he can – if his legs are long, and her torso rather short – so bring his lower legs and feet diagonally together over her belly, that both his big *toes* lie between the lips of the woman's vulva, and she can rub herself on these, while he wriggles them helpfully, simultaneously irrumating her. This charmingly entangled position is shown in one of the drawings in Michael Zichy's famous erotic series, "Love," the masterpiece of nineteenth-century sexual art in the West.

Although we are not really accustomed in the West to the erotic use of the toes in this way, it is common among all peoples who go barefoot, or who commonly remove their shoes in their homes. A well-known Japanese erotic print, for example, shows a woman reading a romantic (*i.e.*, to a woman, erotic) novel while nursing her baby, and unconsciously rubbing her vulva with the baby's foot held in her hand like a dildo. In another Japanese print, this time more humorous than tender, a man is shown tickling the genitals of a woman across the table from him, by means of his foot and toe, unseen by the other people at the table with them. This is of course the real meaning and implication of the Western seduction game or technique of under-the-table "footie," though it is seldom taken so unequivocally far.

Before leaving the subject of the genital excitement of the woman by the man, during irrumation, one other unusual position should be mentioned. In this the woman simply lies on her back across a bed, or at the edge of a sofa or the back seat of an automobile, with her head *hanging down backwards* over the edge, and her mouth open, while the man kneels on the floor before her face and irrumates her – upside-down, as it were. The man can then easily bend or reach forward to titillate the woman's clitoris and vagina with his fingers, with a complete freedom allowed by almost no other position for irrumation or fellation. On the other hand, there are two real disadvantages to this position, despite its ornamental charm. First, the woman's head hanging downward lower than her shoulders will usually make the blood flow to her head, and she may become giddy, though this will not necessarily decrease the pleasure she feels, curiously enough — something like being drunk during sexual intercourse. Second, and often more importantly, with her head upside-down in this way, the woman's tongue lies along the top side of the man's penis, when inserted in this position, rather than along its more sensitive underside. This is also one of the main objections formulated to mutual, simultaneous oragenitalism, in the classic position of the "Sixty-Nine," as will be discussed in the following section devoted to this.

In describing as "one of the most common positions for irrumation" the exactly opposite position to the above, in which the kneeling man straddles the shoulders of the supine woman (lying on her back facing him), it was not meant to imply that the form is common in which the man reaches back with his feet and toes to tickle the woman's genitals with these. In the actually common or "family" form, the position used is without any toe-work, and is that in which irrumation is really used as a form of birth-control, involving the Biblical withdrawal or "sin of Onan." (*Genesis*, 38:9.)

In this form, the man engages in ordinary vaginal intercourse with the woman, lying on top of her face-to-face; but withdraws just as his orgasm approaches. Instead of ejaculating then against the woman's lower belly, or downward between her thighs — the usual maneuvres in withdrawal (*coitus interruptus*) — he rises up over the woman's body, to ejaculate into her mouth at the last moment. In this way he achieves for himself at least a sensation of moist ensheathing not very different from what would be the sensation during ejaculation inside the vagina. As it is rather difficult to scramble upward, at such a moment, from the usual face-to-face position in which the man's legs are *between* those of the woman, this irrumatory conclusion of vaginal intercourse for birth-control purposes — or when the woman particularly desires to taste and experience the man's ejaculation in this way — is perhaps better undertaken when, at some point during intercourse, the man has removed his legs, one at a time, from between the woman's thighs, which he is then straddling thereafter, ready to rise upward at the end.

Another extremely simple irrumatory conclusion for vaginal intercourse in the face-to-face, man-superior position, is for the man simply to rise up on his knees when his orgasm approaches, and sit back on his heels. The woman then sits up quickly, pulling on the man's waist, or he pulling on her shoulders to help bring her torso vertical, and she takes the man's penis into her mouth just before the moment of ejaculation. This maneuvre can be done very rapidly and flowingly, when the couple have had experience with it together, and it has become part of their ritual, thus allowing the man to continue intercourse almost to the instant of ejaculation. These extra moments of intercourse are often precisely those necessary to bring the woman to her orgasm just before the man. They are also the most likely to make her pregnant.

Occasionally the couple will miscalculate the amount of time still remaining before the man's orgasm, and the woman will arrive at the vertical position, accepting the man orally, only to find that the shifting and the delay have broken his rhythm and that he cannot yet ejaculate. The woman is seldom able, in this sitting position, partly under the man, to make proper fellatory motions of her head; but the man can easily rock both of them back and forth, in an irrumatory way, sometimes pitching forward heavily upon her when his orgasm does come. He should then roll to one side with her, as soon as possible thereafter, to avoid letting her feel suffocated or choked by his penis.

It can also happen that the miscalculation is the other way 'round, and that the man has been much closer to his orgasm than either of them thought when he withdrew. In such case, there will often not be time for the woman to accept the penis orally as the intended conclusion, and the man's ejaculate will strike or fall upon the woman's breasts or lips, or into her open eyes. Women accustomed to this irrumatory conclusion of intercourse, and who enjoy and are excited by the taste of semen and by the idea that they are in this way "drinking" their lover, will of course consider such a miscalculation or contretemps a waste of semen. But they will also often admit that the *idea* of the semen striking their breasts, body, face, or open eyes, or even their cupping hands reaching forward as a last resort, is also very exciting: like *bathing in semen*, as I have heard it expressed.

The disposition of the ejaculated semen should never be a problem. It should be swallowed by the oral partner, and any other conclusion to either fellation or irrumation can only be considered vulgar. To refuse to swallow the semen is always a rejection of the man, and is always so understood even when this rejection does not go to such hateful lengths as spitting the semen against the man's trouser-fly, as described earlier. Women sometimes express their resistance to fellation or irrumation by extreme gagging-reflexes at the moment of the man's ejaculation, even though they may not have gagged at all during the driving of the penis deep into the back of the mouth against the palate, when this physiological reflex actually would be more logical to expect.

Prostitutes in the Mohammedan countries, who are not allowed by their religion — the prohibition against "despoiling nature" — to swallow the semen, though fellation is perfectly permissible, will spit the ejaculated semen into a special handkerchief or scarf, used for that purpose throughout a whole working-day . . . or night. The religious consideration no doubt makes this understandable, or at any rate unavoidable. But this is not the case with Western women and girls — particularly in America and England — who may similarly spit the semen into a handkerchief, a towel, a liquor-glass or even a nearby ashtray; on the ground, behind the sofa, in the fireplace, or into a potted plant; or dash madly into the bathroom with bulging cheeks or paroxysmically gaping mouth, to dribble the semen into the toilet-bowl or sink. One would imagine rather that the man had infected them with leprosy, than that he had offered up to the ministration of their mouths the precious fluid on which the continuity of the human race depends, and which, even at the folklore level, is considered to be condensed and refined drop by drop from sixty times its volume of blood. For the most extreme such rejection — with antiseptic mouthwash! — see the French manual, *Pratique Sexuelle* (1968), quoted later.

It does not take much perception on the man's part, under such circumstances, to realize that he has been erotically insulted and personally rejected by the woman who refuses to swallow his semen, or who does so with evident bad grace and with gargling sounds of difficulty in getting it down or, flatly phrased, incipient vomiting. What woman would feel anything *but* insulted if a man went through the same comedy after engaging in cunnilinctus with her? When it is an unsophisticated girl or young woman who rejects the semen in this way, no purpose will be served by the man's reacting with anger, or attempting to force her to swallow after she has already withdrawn her mouth from his penis. However, if the relationship is to continue at all, he must make it perfectly clear to her that spitting out, with open manifestations of disgust, the semen that is after all the purest essence of his body and of his manhood, is not an acceptable gesture, and also that it suggests low rather than high social class. By means of a certain restraint, at first, as to deep thrusts during irrumation — or by diplomatically allowing himself, instead, to be fellated by the girl while he remains more or less passive, during their early relationship — it is sometimes possible to help the girl to overcome her notions of disgust and motions of rejection before these become a grained-in part of her or their erotic ritual, and a matter of unpleasant contention between them.

In any case, the man should, during every oragenital act, at least require the girl to keep the penis inside her mouth until he has completely ejaculated. This is an indispensable minimum. Attempting to bring the girl slowly to accept the ejaculation, by starting with incomplete fellation, shifting to vaginal coitus before ejaculation takes place – the so-called "half & half" – will often be rejected on a birth-control basis, and will also seldom have the desired effect as fellatory training. It is much more likely to set up precisely this "half & half" as part of the couple's sexual ritual. Actually, the exactly opposite type of "half & half" – where the man begins with vaginal coitus and ends with oral ejaculation – is a far better sort of training. The girl being highly excited after protracted intercourse, during which she should of course be brought to orgasm before the man attempts to rise to her mouth, she is not then so likely to refuse to swallow the semen, and may very well not know what she is doing at all.

Another, and rather more virile approach is also possible, and one which will often win the respect of young women who might only be made all the more finicky and difficult by the man's attempting to be over-solicitous and "reasonable." When irrumation is continued to the point of orgasm, the man should simply under no circumstances allow the woman to pull her head away and to refuse or reject the seminal ejaculation. She must swallow it. All gestures of withdrawal, refusal, rejection, gagging, choking, etc., are merely to be overlooked, or ridden over roughshod if necessary. *Swallow, or die!* This may seem like acting the Lord High-Riding Pego indeed, but it is probably the best way. If the slightest attention is paid to the woman's attempts to struggle away and to reject the semen, a pattern of seminal (and sexual) rejection will be set up that will later prove almost impossible for that man and that woman to abandon with each other. Also, as in similar rejections of ordinary intercourse, the *next* man – who plainly forces her – may have no difficulty with her at all, and will instead earn her appreciation for this evidence of his overmastering passion which, after all, she realizes has been excited by her sexual charms.

Probably to be considered more a rejection of the semen than the florid acceptance that it pretends, is an erotic "clownery" saved for the very last in what is the most remarkable and complete of all Western manuals of sex technique, *Les Paradis Charnels* ("Priapeville," 1903), signed "Doctor A.-S. Lagail," an evident anagram of the name of a writer of sex books at the period, Alphonse Gallais. I have already discussed this extraordinary work above, and in *Rationale of the Dirty Joke*, pages 547–8, particularly as to its final section of erotic "clowneries," mostly exotic spinning- or flying-postures for intercourse, such as the ever-famous "Whirling Basket Trick," the "Wheel-Barrow," and Gallais' version of the mysterious "Diligence de Lyon."

The final "clownery," and, in fact, the last of the *136 Extases de la Volupté* promised in the book's subtitle, is "The Judgment of Solomon," addressed as a final *bonne-bouche* to the author's lady readers, whom he apostrophizes as follows:

"Say to your lover – whether him or me, as you may choose – 'Would you like to see me *cut a baby in two*, by a far less sanguinary method than that invented by King Solomon the Just?' The lover so addressed (unless it be me . . .) will doubtless exclaim that the idea is mad. But he will be wrong, very wrong. And here is the proof:

"You suck off your lover, as artistically as you know how, meanwhile postillioning his anus deeply with your finger. He spends, he seizes you . . . and he ejaculates, while you accept deep in your throat every drop of his semen, but without swallowing it. Then – and this is the hard part – you *snort* it into the air, still warm, through both your nostrils! The baby that your lover's life-juice, poured into you during his orgasm, might well have given you, is in this way neatly divided into two halves, one through each nostril of your roguish nose." (This is still done, as a joke or "specialty," by French prostitutes, who also attempt to catch the divided ejaculate on their tongue. It is only a joke, of course; otherwise it would be disgusting. This has to be seen in profile.)

The point has already been made, in the citation from the homosexual manual, *The Gay Girl's Guide* (Boston? 1949), in the section on "Fellation," earlier, that the two most important elements in oragenital acts involving the penis are *depth* of entry into the back of the mouth and upper throat, and *speed* of the stroke, especially at the man's orgasm. "The novice," says this author – his masculine pronouns referring of course to homosexuals – "tends to violate both these important rules, by taking only the head of the penis into his mouth, and moving his mouth very slowly, which is often partially explained by his initial repulsion. These two points are most important of all at the time of orgasm, and it is at just this time that the novice tends, because of his anxiety about the disposition of the ensuing flow of semen, to slow down his movements and have the minimum phallic content in his mouth. The result is invariably highly unsatisfactory . . ."

In irrumation, no such problem is encountered. Both the depth of entry into the oral partner's mouth, and the speed of the stroke or thrust, both at the beginning of the act and certainly at the moment of the genital partner's orgasm, are almost entirely under his own control. Even if the woman's hand (or the man's own) is left in place, encircling the lower half of the penis, to prevent too deep an entry or to assure the sensation of striking against the man's pubis for his own erotic need, both the speed of the stroke and – depending on the position taken – the depth of thrust, up to the blocking-point of the "sword-guard" hand, are still entirely under the man's control at orgasm.

The author of *The Gay Girl's Guide* also makes the following interesting statement as to resistance to swallowing the semen, even among homosexuals! "There is sometimes an issue over whether to swallow or eject the semen. Sometimes the most ardent of cocksuckers profess an inability to swallow it and the necessity to eject it. This must be viewed on a psychological basis . . . where there is genuine repulsion, it must be because of the taste. Yet the taste remains longer when the semen is retained for those few additional seconds before a decent manner of ejecting it can be resorted to; when swallowed at once, the taste remains for a much shorter period. By this defense mechanism, they give due compensation to the disgust they feel they should have, and don't."

He adds: "The taste will, of course, vary surprisingly from person to person, sometimes very mild, sometimes very tangy. But in each and every case, the faster it is swallowed, the less time the taste remains. It is doubtful that there is any genuine allergy to semen." Women, and others, worried about their figures, have also attempted to calculate how many calories a mouthful of semen may contain! Actually, it contains very few calories, being – as its inseminatory biological function would lead one to expect – almost entirely composed of active elements: protein and minerals, like the white of an egg. It is the minerals contained that give the semen its curious and powerful taste, which most women who experiment with fellation find both fascinating and sexually exciting.

IV

THE SIXTY-NINE

O R A G E N I T A L I S M

IV. THE SIXTY-NINE

Mutual simultaneous oragenitalism is usually referred to in English under the euphemistic French numerical form, "*soixante-neuf*." As there is, in fact, no precise classical or scientific term for this practice – though it dates from immemorial antiquity – the English colloquial term "sixty-nine" will be employed in this monograph, as both noun and verb. In both English and French, the term is derived from and alludes to the similar appearance to the numerals *69* of two human bodies engaged in mutual oragenitalism, the circles in the numerals *6* and *9* representing the participants' heads, and the tails of the numerals representing their torsi and legs. The ancient Chinese Yang & Yin (male-female) symbol is identical. The Zodiacal sign of Cancer, the Crab, is also very similar, and has been used as a scarf- and tie-pattern among homosexuals and members of fast society: what would be called "swingers" in current American slang. The term "*soixante-neuf*" has not been traced any earlier than certain *Whore's Catechisms* published in the 1790's in France, usually attributed to the Lesbian demigoddess and early leader of the French Revolution, Mlle. Théroigne de Méricourt.

It would be idle to attempt to discover the origin of the sixty-nine, since – like all sexual acts – it must be of very great antiquity, though its first documentary and artistic evidences are relatively recent. It does not seem to be specifically shown in the Egyptian murals or papyri, though the position is very clearly indicated or implied in the famous depiction of the Egyptian god of the Earth and goddess of Heaven, Nût, she as a starry vault arched over him, and the two lying head-to-foot and touching each other's toes, while the god of the Air (standing between them like their child and, as it were, joining them) excites simultaneously the goddess' breast and vulva.

The earliest unequivocal representation of the sixty-nine appears to be that on an oil-lamp preserved in the Munich Museum, and first reproduced in Dr. Gaston Vorberg's courageous and superb portfolio, *Die Erotik der Antike in Kleinkunst und Keramik* (Munich, 1921) plate 58, showing the woman lying on top of the man. Dr. Vorberg gives this in a group of erotically-decorated lamps, stated to be of the period of the Roman Cæsars, showing various coital postures and practices. However, another oil-lamp of the same kind, showing the sixty-nine almost identically – down to the very knobs on the legs of the bed – is more recently reproduced as a full-color plate, in Prof. Jean Marcadé's *Eros Kalos* (English-language edition, Geneva: Nagel, 1965) facing page 58, in a large group of other such lamps, again showing various positions of intercourse, lamps preserved in the Heracleion Museum in Greece.

It seems unquestionable, therefore, that these lamps were ancient Greek folk-artifacts, probably dedicated as votives to Aphrodite, goddess of Love, and produced in quantity, dating at the latest from the fifth century B.C. They are extraordinarily similar, especially in their intentional humor and fantasy, to the Egyptian posture-drawings of the famous Turin Papyrus – probably the oldest known depiction of human intercourse in various positions: the woman being dominant in all of them – and possibly are derived from Egyptian inspiration. They are themselves perhaps the source of the more artistic posture-drawings and orgiastic scenes on the

Greek figured vases of the classical period, none of which (so far as can be seen on those which have miraculously survived) specifically show the sixty-nine.

Essentially, it is unnecessary to continue these speculations based on erotic art, since all erotic acts except the most refined and contortionistic are ancient and immemorial. In fact, most erotic acts known can occasionally be observed among the other animals, some of which preceded human beings on earth. I myself have, for example, observed kittens sixty-nining as part of their erotic play, and remember this well since it came as a great shock to me: I had until that time – I was very young – imagined that I had invented the sixty-nine myself! The writing of the present work, which was the first ever printed on these subjects, was doubtless unconsciously intended to redeem this early disappointment. Actually, I need have felt no such chagrin. The sixty-nine may well be the most ancient of all erotic acts, since *twins in the womb* almost invariably take that position long before birth, as X-ray photographs have shown, though of course without any erotic engagement.

Very little can or need be said as to the physical technique of the sixty-nine, since only three main positions exist in which it is possible. Two of these are, in fact, almost identical. Either the woman kneels on her hands & knees over the man, who is lying supine facing her, but head-to-foot – or, rather, head-to-groin. (This is the most usual position, as shown on the ancient oil-lamp mentioned above.) Or else the man kneels over the supine woman in the same way. This is less commonly employed, as the woman cannot as easily control the depth of the man's phallic penetration into her mouth, as she can in the classic sixty-nine position.

When the man is on top the action is, to all intents and purposes, *irrumation*, with the man lying forward to excite the woman's genitals with his mouth. When the woman is on top the action is *fellation*, with the man simultaneously engaging in cunnilinctus with the woman astraddle his face. These differences are very real, and by no means merely terminological, as has been shown in the preceding chapters. In the sixty-nine the question of the dominant partner does not seem to be raised, yet it is always present or immanent, as is felt immediately if the two partners roll over sideways ("barrel-roll") without letting go of the others' genitals orally. This is an easy maneuvre, for persons of almost any physique, though it is seldom done. Perhaps this is due precisely to the desired dominance or subdominance of each partner in the form they usually or ritually prefer, which is then suddenly reversed when they barrel-roll to the opposite form of the sixty-nine, bringing the other partner on top.

No matter how passionately transported the partners may be, care must be taken, during this barrel-roll maneuvre, for the woman's legs not to crush or even press too hard upon the head of the man which is deeply engaged between her thighs, and ends up suddenly imprisoned below or unexpectedly delivered above. It is for this reason that the question of dominance in the act is seen to be so essential, as in all oragenital acts. For it is one thing for a man to lie over a woman, irrumating her in a head-to-heels position, while leaning forward to tongue her clitoris as though in reward for her complaisance. But it is another thing for a man to lie on his back passively beneath a woman who is fellating him, with her body and thighs sometimes quite overwhelming him, and his head meanwhile fairly imprisoned underneath – though required to be highly active and motile at the same time. The masochistic element in the latter situation, for the man, is perfectly evident. The classic sixty-nine, with the woman astride, is for that reason one of the favorite sexual activities of outright male masochists, as their public advertisements for cunnilinctus – and, even more so, their letters to the persons who reply – make very clear.

That the woman lying beneath the man in a sixty-nine is even more powerfully dominated, sometimes thinking of herself as pinned to the bed or impaled by his penis, is even more clear. However, as this is the normal situation in face-to-face intercourse, with the man on top, a position which millions of women accept with great satisfaction in many cultures, it is possible – without attempting to posit any "natural masochism" in women, though their sexual rôle does seem to suggest this – that women do not necessarily object to the constraint and domination of the man lying on top, whether during vaginal coitus, irrumation, or the sixty-nine. It may be observed, nevertheless, that the immobilization of the *head* of the underlying partner in any oragenital act, and particularly in the sixty-nine, where the genital partner's whole weight may be felt pressing down or likely to do so, is of a quite different order of constraint than that merely of the woman's or man's pelvis constrained in the underlying position in intercourse. The uniquely powerful "personalness" of the head, as the seat of the main physical sensations and expressions, which is of such central importance in all oragenital acts, leaves a very great difference here as to the constraint that the individual of either sex can accept, when it is the head and not the pelvis that is being constricted. The wisest course, and in fact the motto of all oragenital acts, is that suggested in the Golden Rule in the Sermon on the Mount: "*And as ye would that others should do to you, do ye also to them likewise.*" (Luke, 6:31.)

More as an entertainment than as an actual erotic act, the sixty-nine can also be engaged in with the partners vertical: that is to say, with the man standing up on his feet, and the woman clasped to his torso in the embrace of his arms, while they bring their mouths to each other's genitals. Theoretically, the woman too could stand in this way, while clasping the man upside-down against her body, but owing to the usual disparity between the man's size and strength, and that of the woman, the vertical sixty-nine is assumed to be with the man standing. If the woman's torso is long enough, she can also let her legs fall down behind the standing man's back, thus helping to support herself in the curve of her hips, and taking much of her weight off the man's arms. Practically, however, though the woman can engage in fellation on the man as long as he can hold both of them vertical in this way, cunnilinctus with the woman held vertical is not likely to succeed or to be very profound. Also, the man may well have a tendency to sink or fall to the ground at his orgasm, his knees buckling under him, and care must then be taken that the woman does not then strike on her head, even against his thighs, which might also cause her to bite the man's penis with the whole weight of her body behind the bite. The vertical sixty-nine is really therefore only an erotic "clownery," when the relative length of the partners' torsos make it possible at all, and it is not recommended to continue it to the man's orgasm.

This matter of the relative lengths of the partners' torsos is of the greatest importance in the sixty-nine, in all positions. Many couples find to their surprise that they cannot engage in the sixty-nine at all, owing to the excessive shortness of either the woman's or the man's torso, when that of the other partner is particularly long. This refers strictly to the length of the torso itself, not to that of the whole body. The sexual matching of the bodies of the partners – as well for vaginal coitus as for the sixty-nine – involves a proper matching of the lengths of the two torsos, which is not always reflected in their relative body-heights. There are, for example, couples in which the woman seems quite tall when standing, and the man quite short; whereas, when they are lying down, it turns out that the woman has a short upper body, but long legs and large hips, while the man may have an enormous torso, but short legs. Their body-sizes will thus be entirely reversed when they are sitting or lying down, the "short" man turning out to be much taller than the "tall" woman, and experiencing no difficulty whatsoever as to their erotic body-matching. This is often seen, for instance, among London Cockneys and the Japanese, where the torso is generally exceptionally long, but the legs comparatively short.

In the average European or American couple – which we will assume involves a slightly taller man and a somewhat shorter woman, or, at least, both of the same height – the extra length of the man's torso is taken up, during the classic woman-superior sixty-nine, by the necessity under which he then operates, of entering his head deeply between the woman's thighs, actually to appose his mouth to her vulva. The woman, for her part, simply leans forward to accept his penis into her mouth. When her torso is also long, this merely means that she must arch her back slightly at the same time, which poses no problem. But where the man is really very long in the torso, and the woman very short, it will often be found that either his mouth will reach to her vulva during the sixty-nine, but only at the expense of pulling her head back and away from his penis; or else the reverse, she being able to fellate him, but he then not being able to reach forward far enough toward her hips, as measured from his own, to reach her vulva with his mouth. This problem sometimes arises quite unexpectedly – the apparent body sizes not giving any reason to expect it – when the torso and leg sizes of the partners are of an unusual match, and the result can be quite a

Tragi-comedy of Errors. Although such couples can make use of the sixty-nine posture, it is really only possible for them to use it for one-way fellation or cunnilinctus, the other partner finding himself or herself tantalizingly close, but *not quite there*, unable to reciprocate orally and forced to bring the other person to orgasm strictly by the use of the hands.

The vertical sixty-nine, mentioned just above, is far from being in any way merely a joke, and has in fact quite a long history, though in the politely disguised and presumably non-sexual form of the children's game known as the "Elephant Walk." This game is really nothing but a series of combinations and progressions of various postures of the sixty-nine, particularly concentrating on the "barrel-roll," by means of which the partners suddenly reverse positions, top & bottom. The two then alternately lumber along in opposite directions (the Elephant's walk) as best they can, which involves the upper partner at any one moment dragging along the lower partner, who is clinging to his or her underbody with arms and legs. As carrying-methods of precisely this kind—whether face-to-face or head-to-feet—are common among the entire monkey and ape kingdom, to which human beings belong, for the carrying of the young by the mother, it is likely that this game, and, in fact, the sixty-nine itself, can be traced to such carrying-methods, independent of and preceding the development of human beings. Many female animals can be observed licking and cleaning the anus or genitals of their young, while nursing, in just this way, often in a close approximation of the sixty-nine position. I would guess that this is the real mammalian origin of the sixty-nine. It is observable that such carrying positions are also strikingly similar to the eroticized mother-&-child pose of the anthropomorphized Heaven & Earth, in the ancient Egyptian depiction described earlier.

As to the vertical sixty-nine, parallel to and preceding the occurrence of the "Elephant Walk" as a children's game, it was and still is a common *tour-de-force* of acrobats and jugglers of the comedy sort once to be seen at country fairs in all countries. A rather confused drawing of the Elephant Walk, being done by two street comedians precisely in the vertical sixty-nine position, is reproduced from a scatological "four-winds" painting, in Du Tilliot's study of the Feast of Fools celebrations, *Mémoires pour servir à l'histoire de la Fête des Foux* (Lausanne, 1741) plate 7, reprinted in smaller format a decade later, with the engraved plate impossibly showing both partners' buttocks on the same side facing the reader! This painting appeared on the back of the banner carried by the Dijon Infantry at that time, during the procession of the Feast of Fools, the front side having a more polite reference to the same scatological farting-games, showing "La Mère-folle," or Mother of Fools (the burlesque anti-goddess of the feast) contending against the four winds with bellows in her hands and feet.

During the 1930's, a well-known vaudeville and circus pair of clowns in America did a beautifully synchronized "Elephant Walk" act, in all positions, especially vertical, with the added and perfectly unmistakable erotic allusion or fillip that both wore extremely baggy pants, gaping at the waist and held up by suspenders, into which pants the other man's head would repeatedly disappear during the act, then emerging with obvious gestures of repugnance, "cleaning it up" by implying that the other man had farted! The erotic implications of the sixty-nine were heavily stressed, especially when the top-man or rider would actually *dive* into the standing man's pants head-first, and their act kept the audience in hysterics. This is no doubt the circus-transmitted full form of the street-comedy act of the Feast of Fools at Dijon, in France, two centuries earlier. I have also seen, much more recently, an Italian nightclub comedy act – composed of one very large and pretendedly stupid man, the other man very short and pert – in which much the same acrobatic act (but without the baggy pants) was combined with a further anal-sadistic symbolization of the implied erotic act, in which the little man wears himself completely out kicking the big man's arse, in punishment for some mistake in their acrobatic opening; the big man finally having to crouch down, like a helpful mother, to bring his arse closer to the almost-collapsed, but still kicking, child.

Whether the sixty-nine is engaged in with the man on top, or the woman on top, or with the man standing and holding the woman upside-down against him (or the reverse); the position of the two bodies in regard to each other is always more or less the same. Only the practically irrelevant position of the legs can change. Those of the kneeling partner usually are bent back to pass under the armpits of the supine partner, who may in turn clasp his or her legs over the other's neck and head at orgasm, thus immobilizing the other's head and signalling that no more oral excitation can be endured. During coitus in face-to-face positions, and even during oragenitalism when the expressions of the other's face can be seen – even if verbal requests are not possible without stopping the oral action – couples often signal to each other their needs and the moment of their approach to orgasm. In the sixty-nine, such signals are not possible facially nor with words, and pre-arranged bodily signals – such as the pats on the small of the back used in the same way by wrestlers – must be resorted to for such communication.

One of the most convenient positions for the sixty-nine, and perhaps the least fatiguing, is that in which the partners both lie on their sides, head-to-groin. This position requires the woman to lift her upper knee very high, resting the toes of that foot on the ankle of the other foot, for leverage, in order to spread her thighs sufficiently for the man's head to enter between them. The main disadvantage of this position is that cunnilinctus cannot be very profound, though the tongue-tip can usually engage at least the clitoris, if that is a sufficient excitation to the woman.

It is also possible for the partners to abandon their side-lying position, by rocking and then half-rolling sideways in either direction, thus arriving at the more classical sixty-nine pose, with either the man or woman on top. It is a charming opportunity for pretended combat, in so rolling from the side-lying position, the couple wrestling and rocking back & forth in mock struggle to decide which one will end up on top. "Barrel-rolling" in this way can also be continued beyond a half-turn, and in fact beyond a full turn, the couple rolling continuously over and over each other, the whole width of a lawn or carpet. It is not suggested to try this on a bed, unless it is *very* low, with a thick carpet nearby to catch the couple as they fall. The caution expressed earlier, as to the care necessary during such rolling maneuvres, to avoid crushing the man's head between the woman's thighs, and for the woman to avoid biting the man's penis, is of particular importance when engaging in this way in a series of barrel-rolls: practically what is known in æronautical stunting as the "Immelmann Turn."

The final sixty-nine position that will be discussed here, in a practical way, is that in which one of the partners – usually the man – sits with his legs stretched out before him, while the woman stands facing away from him with her thighs spread, astraddle and in front of his shoulders, to allow him to engage orally at her vulva, and then bends all the way forward to fellate him at the same time. This position can also be achieved, both more naturally and without the unattractive gesture of presenting the buttocks backward to the man's face – a classic gesture of contempt – by the woman moving her hips and body up and backwards from a position in which she is simply fellating the man, lying or kneeling at one side of him. However reached, the final position is very similar to the vertical sixty-nine, but there is far less strain on the man in holding the woman up: first, because he is sitting and not standing, and thus does not have to support his own weight also; and second, because the woman's feet can usually rest on the bed, at each side of the man's hips, taking much of the rest of her weight. The reverse position is also possible, with the woman sitting below the man, but is seldom used.

What is evidently a further development of this type of vertical sixty-nine is considered too acrobatic or contortionistic for most couples even to attempt. Yet, as it is by no means impossible when the woman's torso is sufficiently supple and long, it should not be omitted here. This may be called the "cross-back" sixty-nine, for the woman's body does not face the man's except at the upper part of her chest and head, which she twists or *crosses-back* to engage in fellation with him. The position is similar to the vertical sixty-nine as described earlier, or may be achieved more conveniently from the vertical form with the man sitting, as just described. But instead of the woman turning her buttocks toward the man's chest, she sits down on his shoulders face-to-face, straddling his neck with her thighs, her vulva being presented directly to his mouth. She then leans all the way backwards, while he holds her at the waist and under the knees to prevent her from falling. As she leans backwards, *she turns her upper body as she goes,* so that her head twists 'round to one side to face the man's waist, thus enabling her to engage in fellation with him. As noted, this can only be done when the woman is very supple and has a sufficiently long torso.

A Hindu temple-sculpture from the sacred caverns of the island of Elephanta, near Bombay in India, showing this position with the man actually standing, and holding the woman hanging down in this way from his shoulders, was vandalized and brought to England in the late eighteenth century on the man-o'-war *Cumberland*, entering then the private museum of antiquities of a Mr. Townley. All trace of this sculptured fragment has since disappeared, but very fortunately it is both discussed and illustrated in Richard Payne Knight's *A Discourse on the Worship of Priapus*, privately issued for the Dilettanti Society of London in 1786 (and withdrawn and suppressed immediately after publication), a work obviously inspired by the Count de Mirabeau's pioneer monograph, *Errotika Biblion* in 1783, in which, for the first time, the sexual history of mankind was attempted.

The illustration in question is a detail engraving given as Payne Knight's plate XI; and the full form of this sculptured group is later given as plate XXIV, showing its broken-off lower part (the man's penis and legs: restored), with an adjacent group in the same frieze showing a man with an impossibly long penis in intermammary coitus with a woman. This *Discourse on the Worship of Priapus* has been reprinted, with its illustrations, at least three times in the last century, including very recently, and the erotic frieze being considered may easily be consulted there. Payne Knight says of it, very pudibundly: "It contains several figures, in very high relief; the principal of which are a man and woman, in an attitude which I shall not venture to describe, but only observe that the action, which I have supposed to be a symbol of refreshment and invigoration, is mutually applied by both to their respective organs of generation . . ." This idea, that the

Hindu erotic sculptures are to be interpreted symbolically or mystically, is, incidentally, just as false as the similar whimsy or hoary fraud that the Biblical *Song of Songs,* which is a very clear and forthright Levantine epithalamium, or marriage-song, is to be interpreted in religious symbols as descriptive of the love of Jehovah for the Chosen People and the Church. (See the margins of any copy of the King James Bible.)

It has been objected, as to difficult postures such as the Hindu "cross-back" sixty-nine, that they are not really possible at all – or at least not to ordinary people – and are merely artistic exaggerations in Hindu temple-art of what were acrobatico-erotic fantasies in the first place, as evidenced by the inordinately long penis of the other male figure in the same frieze from the caverns of Elephanta. This is simply not true. Admitting that certain artistic conventions of exaggeration are present here, such as that of the over-long penis – a convention even more exaggerated in Japanese erotic art, and implying that the average penis in both nations is actually rather small – it is necessary to insist that the "cross-back" sixty-nine *is* possible, and that both it and all the other positions described here have been performed recently by living persons, none of them Hindus. The reader, if young and supple, has only to make the trial.

It is also of course a fact that the Hindu training of body & mind, in the discipline now known as Yoga, involves regularly assuming quite extraordinary positions (the *asana*), such as standing on the head with the legs deeply crossed, which may seem incompatible with sexual excitement. However, this is not always the case, nor are such positions at all impossible, and they are regularly done by hundreds if not thousands of persons, after a preliminary training – and this not only in India. I can well remember visiting the studio of a lady-artist in Paris, in 1954, to see her paintings, only to find her standing on her head stark-naked in the middle of her very large studio, poorly heated by a small coal-stove, meditating on the sky through a skylight window overhead.

She told me, without budging from her stance, that this was part of a course of occult training in which she was engaged, that she had been in this position for ten minutes before I arrived, and would probably continue for another twenty; and she invited me to "worship at her altar" (as she phrased it) by performing cunnilinctus on her, from *behind* – perhaps so as not to spoil her view – while she stood on her head. Owing to a previous engagement I declined with thanks, and am sorry now. Later she explained that she had cast my horoscope, in conjunction with her own, and that a horrible fate was in store for me, since the last person with the almost identical heavenly signs, the Roman orator Cicero, also born under Scorpio on November 2nd, had so infuriated the victim of his philippics, Mark Antony, that he was not only killed but his body was dug up after burial and a dagger driven through the tongue! This lady hoped to save me from such a fate by the "worship at her altar" referred to, which she sincerely believed had magical and protective powers, a belief shared by many primitives.

Without committing myself one way or the other as to the occult power of cunnilinctus – nor do I give a damn what happens to my tongue after my death (I have been asked to will it to the British Museum) – I will observe only that the standing-on-the-head position develops easily into an entirely new form of the vertical sixty-nine, and one which I do not believe appears even in Hindu erotic art. In this, the woman stands on her head with her legs crossed and out of the way, while the man kneels forward or sits upright *before* her to "worship at her altar," meanwhile so disposing his body as to allow her to worship reciprocally at his. This could also be reversed, the man doing the standing on his head, though I am not aware that this has been tried. Postures such as this involve an entirely different way of life from that common in the West, requiring, just to begin with, a very warm climate, though this can be approximated in a large, well-heated and well-carpeted parlor, or out-of-doors in high summer on the grass. Novices should also be warned that standing on the head often causes the blood to rush to that organ, with resultant dizziness, making any erotic activity in that position imprudent. A further discussion of Yoga positions for the sixty-nine is advertised in *The New Sexuality* (New York, 1968) signed Betty J. Cox, Ph.D., a work already discussed at the opening of the section on Fellation here, to which it may be added that the "*New*" sexuality referred to does not include anything on Yoga.

The matter of orgies, and of orgiastic and erotic spintrian chains ("daisy-chains") and other erotic permutations involving more participants than two, are very much not to our purpose here. They are in all cases erotically unnecessary to mature adults, despite the recent open propaganda for orgies, etc., among young people and young married couples in Europe and America, under the names of "wife-trading" and "swinging." Swingers are, in general, cold, mean egomaniacs, lost in their mental quirks, and never more obviously so than at the orgies they set up, which are also never pleasant for any of the people involved unless they have the matching perversions and quirks. Orgies are, at their psychological base, a fantasy form of infantile intrusion into, or disruption of, the sexual relations of the parents by the jealous or frightened infant: that is to say, by the adolescent or adult who was once such an infant, and who is now trying to set up the parallel situation again, but in a controlled way in which *he will win.* Namely, the orgy.

For this reason, the persons who frequent orgies, especially if habitually, are by no means simple, joyous folk, looking to add a new fillip to their failing marriages by variety of partners. This is simply their sound-track or sales-talk, for the benefit of recalcitrant spouses, something like "turning-on" other people to the drugs one is ashamed to be taking by oneself. Some are also, of course, sick perverts plainly looking for victims to be used in the sadistic orgies they prefer. But even at best, real orgiasts are almost always unconscious homosexuals or "bisexuals" – the mathematics of the orgy or daisy-chain usually requires this, as will be seen below. They are also invariably emotionally strangulated persons, frozen at the adolescent level in which they search endlessly for *group-permission* for the sexual acts they dare not enjoy with just one other person, for whom the forbidden tenderness and love might accidentally be felt. People do not fall in love at orgies. Those who go are those who know well that love is unconsciously forbidden to them. Proprietary jealousy is the highest emotion to which orgiasts seem able to rise.

No extended discussion of "spintries" or erotic human chains, etc., will or need therefore be made here. The subject has, in any case, been taken to the most extreme and compulsive limit of permutational development in the appendix of postures to the well-known *Manual of Classical Erotology* (1824) of the Fichtean philosopher, Friedrich Karl Forberg, and in a Swedish work, *Ju fler vi är tillsammans* ("The More the Merrier"), by a schoolteacher, Ragnar Aaslund, published in 1966 and intended frankly as a manual of group-sex. Some few technical points should, however, be made here, owing specifically to the close and even inevitable connection between erotic chains and the sixty-nine.

It is obvious, when the oragenital act is engaged in by only one partner, kneeling or lying at the other partner's feet, and when the "free" partner does not reciprocate by bending forward to complete the sixty-nine, that the mouth of the "free" partner is in fact free to engage sexually with some third person, if a third person is present. Such engagement may be only at the verbal level of *speaking* to the third person, as over the telephone meanwhile. (It is supposed to be particularly piquant for this to be the betrayed husband or wife – or the father of some father-fixated girl – who is thus brought into the orgy, as it were, all unknowing.) Or the third person, when present, may simply be kissed passionately. Usually, however, the "free" partner proceeds to engage with the third person in the oragenital act which, if he were to be engaging in it reciprocally with the first person, would form a classic sixty-nine. A chain is thus formed.

Orgiastic or erotic spintrian chains of this kind, whether of three people or of thirty, always permutationally *must* involve oragenital acts, since it is not possible for one man or one woman to engage at both ends genitally with two different people at the same time. This is the entire mathematical substructure of the erotic chain. The exception to the rule just proposed would be that of a chain composed solely of men in anal intercourse with each other, "*turpiter ligati*," as in the notorious painting by the seventeenth-century realist, Caravaggio, of thirty men forming such a chain.

Such chains must and do usually therefore involve a continuous alternation of oral and genital (or anal) intercourse by the participants. The final person – if the chain is long enough, and has been set up as a long curve or circle – engages ideally with the first person, to complete the circle, or otherwise remains free to answer the telephone. It is clear, topographically, that such chains are really only sixty-nines which have been "opened out," at the point of contact between the two original participants, to allow the joining on of other persons. Thus the sixty-nine can be "opened out" to include one other person, or in fact endless other persons, simply by arranging the participants in a more and more open circle. The difference is that in such a chain all the participants are *facing the same way* (rather than head-to-heels, as in the usual sixty-nine), and this irrespective of whether they are alternately face-up and face-down, or are all lying on their sides.

It should not be overlooked that in a spintry or chain composed of only three people, two must be of one sex, and one of the other; or else all three must be of the same sex. This is true of all chains comprising an odd number of participants, and only in chains of an even number of participants is it even theoretically possible to avoid homosexual "linkings" at some point, whether of two men with each other, or two women. In practical fact, however, when long chains are set up, involving everyone at such a party, homosexual and Lesbian linkings here and there are taken for granted, and are expected and desired by the unconsciously or unavowedly homosexual participants, who are there for just that reason.

The erotic foursome or *partie-carrée* allows a semblance of sexual normality still to be retained, even during a daisy-chain, since it can be and usually is so arranged that the two couples – often after a preliminary "swap" – form a chain or Maltese cross carefully alternating man & woman, so that no homosexual linking is anywhere required. Men who try to arrange matters so that there *is* a homosexual linking set up during a foursome, but only between the two women (the men engaging vaginally or anally at the "ends," but stopping to watch the women cunnilinguing each other), are generally unconscious homosexuals who lack the courage to engage in the same homosexual acts themselves. They are, as it were, doing it *through* the bodies of their wives, and the same is true of the homosexual urges of most orgiasts.

In the earliest work publicly suggesting the *partie-carrée* ("*partouze*," in French slang) for young married couples or lovers who are already jaded with each other's sexual offering and who presumably need variety as an aphrodisiac, *Interlude Charnel*, published in the 1940's under the pseudonym "Robert Sermaise," the men incite their wives to mutual oragenital acts, after making them drunk, and then engage in similar acts themselves. Such husbands are, of course, simply married homosexuals, with their wives as "*bitches' blinds*." Most married men who frequent orgies are of this type, and not always under the standard disguise of unconsciousness.

A final word before leaving the subject. Both the sixty-nine and the erotic chains which develop out of it, as just indicated, are difficult to describe verbally. One hardly expects some self-elected *arbiter elegantiarum* telling everyone what to do, like a square-dance caller, though this is sometimes what happens. More usually, people just add themselves on casually at the open ends, like dogs surrounding a salt bitch. Erotic chains are always either circles (or "opened out" sixty-nines), radial patterns, or straightaway lines. Figure-eight forms are also sometimes accidentally arrived at, stemming from a single female participant in the centre engaging three or more men at once: this is actually a radial pattern which has linked its ends to form two circles.

If considered topographically, rather than erotically, the problem in such sexual acts becomes essentially one of depiction or symbolization, and this must always have been true. Such symbols crop up in unexpected places, especially in folklore and antiquity, and may be considered to be allusions to erotic scenes and orgies of the type celebrated on the Greek figured vases – orgies which have existed for centuries and millennia, usually under quasi-religious pretexts. Allusions to the sixty-nine (itself a mathematical symbol, to be sure), and to orgiastic circles and chains of the kind that all religious heretics, devil-worshippers, and "witches" have regularly been accused of through the ages, will be found in folklore and religion only in the symbolic or expurgatory shorthand of such ancient signs as the Chinese Yang & Yin, the astrological sign of Cancer the Crab (Pisces the Fish are also sometimes similarly depicted, head-to-tail), the Greek triskelion, and the gammadion-cross or swastika. All of these are believed to involve allusions to such sexual acts, the last in particular to the possession in common of one woman simultaneously by many men, which there is every reason to believe was an ancient matriarchal ritual of worship. It has also been stated that the classic Greek "fret" design, of an endless line curving and recurving on itself – usually with squared angles – involves a similar allusion to an erotic spintry or chain composed solely of men. I believe this to be an error, and that the standard derivation of the fret design from the waves of the sea is the only correct one.

Relevant also is perhaps the interesting puzzle-figure known in Oriental and Levantine folk-art as far west as Persia, in which two little human figures – sometimes given as ceramic sculptured cherubs, since both are male – are shown *sitting on each other* in the position of stacked chairs, one being upside-down. The puzzle element then derives from two further similar figures which are then added, parallel but opposite to the first two, and crouching rather than sitting, in such a way that one can then cover or take away any two of the figures, either vertically or horizontally, without changing the connected position of the remaining two. A form of this is illustrated in Dr. Jurgis Baltrusaitis' remarkable *Le Moyen Age Fantastique* (1955).

This is clearly an adaptation to human bodies of the topographical idea of the Yang & Yin figure, which is in any case understood in China to represent the male & female "principles of nature," but here in a more complicated or doubled way, thus implying an erotic foursome or orgy, whether "right-handed" or "left-handed": *i.e.* with one's own spouse as partner, or with the spouse of the guest. It is also similar to the ancient Greek triskelion – here actually a tetraskelion or gammadion (swastika) – which was sometimes shown likewise not just as three curves radiating from one centre, but as three running legs joined at the groin. (In a simpler form of the puzzle, each figure is shown merely as bent forward in the middle, and supporting a similar figure on its back with legs outstretched. When doubled, to four figures, this does not make a double Yang & Yin, or tetraskelion, but only a Maltese or Templar's cross.)

Though there is ostensibly nothing erotic about these puzzle-figures, they are a very obvious charade of mutual pedication, or pedication in a ring or daisy-chain; but with the element of simultaneity and mutuality which is typical, in erotic acts, only of the sixty-nine. The puzzle-figure position might matchingly be referred to as a "ninety-six." The mental game or urge to set up orgiastic chains in this way, using erotic figures and combinations, has been amusingly shown in Ove Brusendorff and Poul Henningsen's *Love's Picture Book* (Copenhagen, 1959 *ff.*), with various combinations of two or more figures *6* and *9*, to which might also be added the letter-forms of *b*'s and *d*'s and *p*'s and *q*'s, to give all the necessary "turns." The little stick-figures thus created are much like the schematic representations of chemical formulæ.

Before considering, now, the evident and important psychological elements involved in the sixty-nine, a further word will not be out of place concerning the difficult subject of anilinctus. This very common action, in which almost all mammals except human beings engage, in the everyday process of cleaning their young, is reserved by human beings as an erotic act, or, rather, an act of erotic submission. Few normal persons would ever dream of asking another person to engage in anilinctus upon them, even in their most erotic transports. The anus is too persistently considered as being "dirty" – though it is usually cleaned more often than the face, in any given day – for the licking or sucking of it to be a caress that one person can reasonably ask of another, in the sense that no one would hesitate to ask for a kiss upon the face or mouth. Freud reserves one of his most sardonic passages for the paradox into which this can be developed, that it is essentially just as much a "perversion" of normal sexual goals – if these must be directed strictly to the genitals – to join together the top ends of the digestive tract, in kissing, as it would be to join together the bottom ends, not to mention one with the other! This is intended as a ponderous and typically Germanic joke, of course, yet there is a good deal in its paradox to think about. (*General Introduction to Psychoanalysis*, 21st Lecture.)

In practice, anilinctus is always offered by the oral partner, and never demanded by the other. A person who would or does *demand* anilinctus is clearly sadistic, and may be assumed to have anal-sadistic fantasies, while the demanded anilinctus is being performed, of defæcation on the other person, as the ultimate oral defilement. This fantasy appears often in sadistic literature. In the same way, persons particularly attracted to performing anilinctus must be considered to be acting out profound masochistic urges to be physically dirtied and socially hurt or debased. This is not infrequently disguised as "the most complete expression of adoration" for a loved woman, and other transparent nonsense.

Obvious scatophagous impulses, under similar disguises, are also expressed by the masochistic lover, in the form of drinking a toast of her bath-water in the belovèd woman's shoe, or of champagne which has been poured over her body, to trickle down and be drunk at her crotch. Not all men who do this are masochists, but the development of cunnilinctus, *as a submissive act*, is easy to observe here. In the original form of such toasts – called "Flapdragons" in the century of the Elizabethan gallants – what was drunk by the mad lover was plainly the contents of the woman's chamber-pot, later modified to a burning candle-end, raisin, or brandy-sop (the modern children's game of "bobbing for apples"), or anything disgusting, as in Hamlet's competing with Laertes at Ophelia's grave: "*Wilt drink up vessels? Eat a crocodile? I'll do't.*" (First Quarto only, V.i.300.) See further, on this psychologically very interesting folk-custom, my collection of essays, *The Horn Book: Studies in Erotic Folklore* (1964) pages 443–5, where it is considered in the context of erotic ordeals and initiations.

The technical consideration of anilinctus has been ventured in very few manuals of sex technique. See the extended discussion of anilingual techniques in the "Practical Treatise" in the chapter on Fellation, preceding. In English, only *The Gay Girl's Guide* and *The New Sexuality*, very recently, do more than mention the subject antiseptically, and the first of these loses itself in an absurd philological discussion of the presumed difference in meaning between two spellings of the relevant slang term, "rimming" (and "reaming"). The usual brief and romantic catch-all remarks in standard sex-manuals, to the effect that "Kisses on *any* part of a beloved woman's body cannot be considered abnormal," are by no means intended to include anilinctus, and are only covert references to cunnilinctus – thought sufficiently daring. Only the modern French work, *Les 32 Positions* ("Mexico," about 1958), signed "Docteur Pieli" but attributed to the surrealist poet,

Isidore Isou, has really gone into the subject at any length, and I cannot do better than to translate literally this evident specialist. (The passages quoted are from pages 37 and 65–66, here combined:)

"*The Rose-Petal.* Spread open the woman's legs, in any position, and press the buttocks well to each side, to allow the tongue to lick roughly over the anus. This is the simplest form, strictly for the sensation of the flat of the tongue on the sensitive anal tissues.

The Shoe. When the anus relaxes somewhat, press the tip of the tongue inward, and massage the inner surface of the anus (with a circular motion of the tongue, while massaging the outer surfaces with the fingers or thumbs).

The Funnel. Her buttocks being well spread, the woman draws or squeezes on the internal muscles of the anus, to press the tongue-tip in and out.

The Rose-Window. The buttocks being well spread and the muscles of the anus pressing hard, with the abdomen held tense, the anus opens like a rose. The everted inner surfaces of the anal opening appear, forming four tiny bumps or nipples, like a rose-window divided into sections. This is very exciting for the anilinguist, and offers a rare sensation for the woman. Also allows light biting of the anus.

Postillioning. 1. The anus is licked while simultaneously titillating the clitoris rapidly with one finger.

2. The anus is licked while driving the thumb (or the thumbs) in and out of the vagina.

3. The anus is postillioned with one finger while licking or sucking the clitoris and vulva.

4. The clitoris is sucked while the vagina and anus are postillioned together at the same time, with the thumb and forefinger respectively, pressing hard on the separating partition between them." (The thumb and forefinger need not

slip in and out, but shake the whole flesh of the perinæum back and forth in a powerfully exciting way.) This is called *The Bowling-Hold.*

As can be seen, Dr. Pieli/Isou does not concern himself at all with the possibility of wind being passed involuntarily, and embarrassingly, during the muscular pressure the woman is to exert in order to open out the anal tissues for the passage of the anilinguist's tongue-tip. This problem has already been noted, earlier, under Cunnilinctus, where there is also some further discussion of the *postillioning*, or anal digitation, here combined in various ways with anilinctus. It may be added that anilinctus is normally never engaged in alone, but always in combination with cunnilinctus or the sixty-nine – and in all the positions of which these are capable – and such other oragenital acts as the erotic progression of the mouth and tongue over the genital partner's entire torso or body, called "Around the World," as described earlier, under Fellation.

The principal psychological problem usually connected with oragenitalism, that of the dominance or subdominance of the partners, does not occur in connection with the sixty-nine, except as to the really irrelevant question of which partner is to lie on top. This is, in any case, best determined on the gallant basis of putting the heavier-weight partner – generally the man – on bottom, an arrangement even more important when the heavier-weight partner happens to be the woman! When the man is on bottom, the woman also does not have the sensation of being impaled and immobilized, or even choked, by the penis driven downward into her mouth by the whole weight of the man's body, while she is unable to communicate with him (except by wrestler's slaps on his buttocks or the small of his back, which he may mistake for caresses), to express her panic or her need for a moment of withdrawal. The position of the sixty-nine with the woman on top also allows the woman a great deal more freedom of action to caress the man's genitals with her mouth and hands. Such immobilization as that just noted, by the overlying body of the other partner, is also appreciably less when that partner is the lighter-weight woman, and when it is the man whose face and mouth are being pressed down on, from above, by the woman's pubis and vulva. This matter has been covered more fully, in the chapter on Cunnilinctus, in connection with positions in which the woman lies over the man, especially where she engages in the rhythmic "figure-eight" motions, back and forth, similar to posting while riding horseback, called in French "*La Diligence de Lyon*," and in English "*The Candy Bar*."

As to the rest, the author of the homosexual manual, *The Gay Girl's Guide*, expresses the matter very bluntly, from the point of view of homosexual men, who may very well have just met each other, and who are not in any love-relationship, though engaging in mutual fellation: "The chief advantage of 'sixty-nine' is the psychological one. Neither partner can be involved in a superiority-inferiority relationship implied when one has 'gone down on' the other. Furthermore, there can remain no anxiety as to whether, after one partner has been brought to an orgasm (oragenitally), he may proclaim himself unable to reciprocate.

"On the other hand, 'sixty-nine' has distinct disadvantages over other oral forms. Firstly, the position decreases each person's oral maneuverability. Secondly, the distraction at one end is likely to slow down, or for moments even side-track, his abilities at the other end. Thirdly, the tongue, which can play an important part . . . is of necessity on the upper side of the penis, where it is less likely to prove as satisfying as on the lower side, and with some people may even prove downright unpleasant."

Note that this author is carefully not committing himself as to which "end" the real pleasure or distraction is felt at, and which is simply being used to express one's "abilities." I have already quoted at the opening of the section on Cunnilinctus, as a proof of *the orality of oragenitalism*, the complaint often made as to the sixty-nine, that "what is being done to one distracts one from what one is doing." This specifies that it is the oral and not the genital "end" that is psychologically the important one during the sixty-nine. Or, at least, so it was to the person here quoted, who happened to be a man, referring to the sixty-nine with a woman. It should be observed that the opposite complaint is also sometimes made, specifically reversing the important and unimportant "ends," as by a woman referred to as "The Sexual Sophisticate" in *The Sexually Responsive Woman* by Drs. Phyllis and Eberhard Kronhausen (New York: Grove Press, 1964), to end their brief but excellent chapter 11, "Women and Oral Sex":

> The 69 position is in my book another of those that is for the young and athletic. To have cunnilingus and fellatio separately is always a pleasure, but when one attempts to do them simultaneously, it can become just plain hard work. If the woman is on top, she has to balance herself on her knees and one hand while holding the penis with the other. This makes vigorous movements difficult and tiring. I have found myself unable to enjoy what is happening to my body, as I am fully occupied performing fellatio and giving my partner pleasure.
>
> When the man is on top, I am able to lie back and relax, but I'm frustrated by not being able to freely move my head, which is necessary if one wants to do fellatio well. More threatening, of course, is that one loses control over how deep to let the penis penetrate

> into the mouth, since one cannot move one's head back freely, as is possible when one is on top. The main problem remains the same, whether I am on top or underneath in the 69 position: I simply cannot enjoy the man performing cunnilingus on me, and at the same time get ready for orgasm, if I have to simultaneously perform fellatio on him.

One has the feeling that, egoistic as she obviously is, so sophisticated a woman is not really getting the sexual partners she deserves — especially if she has to hold up their penises with her hand! That may explain why she apparently enjoyed the sixty-nine more when she was "young and athletic," when her partners were presumably younger and more virile too. Actually, the penis should be sufficiently erect, during either fellation or the sixty-nine, so that the woman need never touch it with her hands at all, unless she wishes to do so, after the first preliminaries, and often not even then. Unless, of course, the woman finds it necessary to fist the penis with her hand as a "sword-guard," as earlier described, to prevent too deep an entry into her mouth. Note how the Kronhausens' "Sexual Sophisticate" expresses fear of losing control over this depth of entry, which she considers particularly "threatening," and is anxious to be able to "move (her) head back freely." Many neurotic women feel this fear even during vaginal intercourse, especially those who would have preferred to be born men, and who are expressing in this way their unconscious animosity against both the penis — which they can never possess — and against men. In any case, if it is ever actually necessary for either partner to masturbate the shaft of the penis manually, during fellation performed only on the glans, in order to bring the man to orgasm, then fellation is not really being correctly performed. Sophistication is good, but authentic passion is better.

Oragenitalism has long been the orphan art in sexual technique. It is passed by almost in complete silence in the most detailed manual in English, Dr. John Eichenlaub's *The Marriage Art* (New York, 1961), and little more is to be learned in popular items of even more promising title, such as Vyvyan Howarth's *Secret Techniques of Erotic Delight*. The largest and most important work on coital posture ever written, Dr. Josef Weckerle's *Goldene Buch der Liebe* (Vienna, 1907), which gives no less than 531 postures for vaginal intercourse – the world's record – does not mention oragenitalism at all. More recent manuals, while attempting to give oragenitalism space, are still obviously less than comfortable with it. The most extraordinary example of this confusion is in the first publicly-issued manual of sex technique ever written in French – and even this pretends to be a translation – *Pratique Sexuelle* (Paris: Georges Fall, 1968), announced as "translated from the English" of a non-existent "Thomas Glynn," and possibly the work of the publisher.

This is a very detailed but extraordinarily cold and inhuman work, referring to men and women throughout only in circle-&-arrow symbols, and obviously intended to prepare human sex-life for the computerizing machine, to the degree that this was not done already by the Kinsey Report two decades before. The consensus among the embarrassed French reviewers is that *Pratique Sexuelle* is intended as a joke or leg-pull, but I doubt this. The author, who writes like a Swiss or French-German, is terribly hung up on *cleanliness*. Here is his final wisdom as to "Fellation (kissing the ♂ genital)," page 46: "When the ♀ feels the semen mounting in the urethra of the ♂ she stiffens her tongue and presses it against the meatus to receive the jet. Without this precaution, the pressure of the ejaculation – which can erupt with great force in the young, to as high as 12 inches and sometimes